CLANDESTINE WARFARE

▼ US Eighth Airforce parachute supply containers to the French *Maquis* resistance forces. One of many daylight drops made in the late summer of 1944.

CLANDESTINE WARFARE

Weapons and Equipment of the SOE and OSS

James D. Ladd, Keith Melton and Captain Peter Mason

BLANDFORD PRESS
London New York Sydney

First published in Great Britain in 1988 by Blandford Press, Artillery House, Artillery Row, London SW1P 1RT.

Distributed in the USA by Sterling Publishing Co. Inc., 2 Park Avenue, New York, NY 10016.

Distributed in Australia by Capricorn Link (Australia) Pty. Ltd., P.O. Box 665, Lane Cove, New South Wales 2066, Australia.

British Library Cataloguing in Publication Data:
Ladd, James D.
Clandestine warfare: weapons and equipment of the SOE and OSS.
1. World War 2. Army operations by Great Britain. Army. Special Operations Executive.
2. World War 2. Espionage by United States. Office of Strategic Services, 1941–1945
I. Title   II. Melton, H. Keith   III. Mason, Captain Peter
940.54'86'73

ISBN 0–7137–1822–6

The illustrations in this book have been collected from many sources, and vary in quality owing to the variety of circumstances under which they were taken and preserved. As a result, certain of the illustrations are not of the standard to be expected from the best of today's equipment, materials and techniques. They are nevertheless included for their inherent information value, to provide an authentic visual coverage of the subject.

Book designed by DAG Publications Ltd; typeset by Ronset Typesetters Ltd; camerawork by E&M Graphics, North Fambridge, Essex; printed and bound in Great Britain by the Bath Press, Avon.

CONTENTS

ACKNOWLEDGEMENTS

The authors wish to thank the many people who have provided documents, weapons and artefacts forming the collection on which much of this book's information is based. They also thank Mr T. Charman, Mr Arnold Ross and Miss Hilda Bamber for their assistance on various matters, Mrs M. L. Tasker for her assistance with detailed research, Mrs E. B. Clegg for preparing the typescript and the illustrators, Miss H. Snell and Mr R. Woodside, for the preparation of maps and diagrams.

General acknowledgement is made to the following for permission to reproduce photographs included on the following pages: Benton Films, p.66 (both photographs); Dr John Brunner, p.125; Alan Dewar (*Camp X* journal), p.69 (three photographs); John Drummond, p.43 (photograph of Claus Helberg); Willis George, p.80; Commander George L. Graveson, p.64; C. Clayton Hutton, p.106; The Imperial War Museum (London), p.29 (Lt Trepel), p.43 (Norsk Hydro), p.84, p.92 (both photographs of events near Cuneo), p.102; Bob Koch, p.92 (stack of containers); Pierre Lorraine, p.85 (both photographs); John Minnery, p.38 (penetrometer), p.138 (cut-away diagram); W. Stanley Moss, p.74; Jim Phillips, p.94 (three photographs); Jerry Richards (FBI laboratory), p.81 (Zapp cabinet); RN Submarine Museum, p.131 (Welman's recovery); Bruce Roberts, p.83 (Lysander); US Army, p.47, p.75 (both photographs).

All other illustrations are from items in the authors' collection. Use has been made of certain photographs that are of unknown provenance and are believed not to be the subject of claimed copyright. If a copyright is claimed in any of them, the authors will be pleased to correspond with the claimant and to make any arrangement which may prove appropriate. Details of all sources of information and photographs are available from the authors.

Fig. I Co-ordination between these agencies' agents in the field and Allied military units, depended more on the goodwill and sense of junior officers—in uniform or as agents—than on formal regulations.

In existence in 1939 and expanded in 1940s		**MID**	Military Intelligence Division of the General Staff, formed in 1880s.
British			
SIS	Secret (or Special Intelligence Service, formed in 1909 and continues in 1980s. Usually described as having two branches: MI 5 for counter-intelligence security; and MI 6 for gathering intelligence.	**FBI**	Federal Bureau of Investigation formed in 1908, responsible for national security and counter-intelligence on the American continent.
NID	Naval Intelligence Department.	**SIS**	Signal Intelligence Service, financed by the State Department.
MI	Military Intelligence, a branch of the War Office.	**RI**	Radio Intelligence Service of MID for interception of wireless signals.
AI	Air Intelligence, a branch of the Air Ministry.	**Agencies formed between 1939 and 1945**	
GC & CS	Government Code and Cipher School, established in 1919.	**British**	
Y Service	For radio interception from 1928 with various titles but as Y Service from 1943.	SOE	Special Operations Executive, formed in July 1940 as a secret military service to promote subversive warfare.
American		MI 9	A section of SIS which facilitated escape and evasion, Treasury funds approved 21 December 1939.
NIB	Naval Intelligence Branch of the US Navy.		

INTRODUCTION

THE secrets described in this book explain how men and women of the American Office of Strategic Services (OSS) and of the British Special Operations Executive (SOE) were able to carry out undercover operations during World War II. There are also references where appropriate to the work of agents in other Allied secret agencies. Yet before this war neither the American nor the British governments approved of spying, since 'gentlemen', as Secretary of State Henry Stimson once remarked, 'do not read each other's mail'. Certainly they would never have entertained the manner of sabotage, fire raising and encouragement to revolt, which became the job of OSS and SOE agents working in occupied countries. There the Germans, Italians and Japanese, the Axis powers, had well organized police and other security forces with their networks of informers ever ready to trap an undercover agent.

Disentangling the truth of such undercover operations has been clouded since 1945, as there has been not only the necessary secrecy to protect those agents who survived but also some fictional red-herrings (see Appendix 3.1). Other complexities arose during the operations of the agencies shown in the simplified diagrams (see Figs I-III), as their responsibilities overlapped. This resulted in, for example, American signals intelligence breaking a code, only to find this changed soon afterwards; a change made because another agency's operators in Spain had stolen a German embassy's code book, photographed it, but left the embassy safe open after returning it.

The chapters show the great bravery of the OSS and SOE agents, most of those who were caught being put to death. Only by great care and much cunning were others able to survive, as the book explains, using techniques and equipment of remarkable ingenuity as can be seen in the illustrations. (The authors would be pleased to hear from individuals with similar devices.)

The majority of these photographs are of items in the comprehensive collection of weapons, special devices and other equipment, owned by the authors. These items have been brought together over the past forty years. They constitute the largest collection of its type in the world, which is unique. The explosive devices, concealed knives, and special equipment was used for sabotage, for the collection of intelligence or to arm guerrilla forces. However, to follow the detailed histories of every agent who used the equipment would probably require as many years of research as there were agents. We have not attempted therefore, to tell the entire histories of SOE and OSS but have shown examples of the ways in which they operated.

J. D. Ladd, Topsham, Exeter, UK
H. K. Melton, Box 5755, Bossier City, LA 71171, USA
P. Mason

MI 19	For interrogation of prisoners and refugees, work carried out by MI 9 before December 1941.

American

OSS	Office of Strategic Services formed on 13 June 1942 for the collection of intelligence and the promotion of subversive warfare.
MIS	Military Intelligence Service set up to control MID's field agents from 1942.
MIS-X	The branch of MIS set up to facilitate escape and evasion.
MIS-Y	The branch of MIS set up to interrogate captured enemy forces and others.

Australia

AIB	Allied Intelligence Bureau formed in June-July 1942 with Australian, American and British personnel for intelligence and subversive operations in the Pacific.

Allied Governments in Exile

These politicians and their military staffs set up secret services including the French **BCRA.** Their agents often worked with the help of **SOE** and **OSS** but remained independent of these organizations.

Co-ordination

Co-ordination between these agencies' agents in the field and Allied military units depended more on the goodwill and sense of junior officers – in uniform or as agents – than on formal regulations. The above summary of the principal organizations excludes command links, etc, to keep it simple, as a piece for reference. Such details will be found in the text and specifically in the appendices.

Fig. II In this simplified organization chart, the Country Sections provided the links between agents in the field and SOE staff. An organizer, his courier and his radio operator worked to a staff officer in their Country Section. In the case of F Section this numbered 40 personnel by 1944 with 400 agents in the field. Several Sections might be grouped, with the majors in command of each Section reporting to a Regional Controller (see Appendix 3.2). There were also Specialist Branches which provided facilities for the Country Sections.

DEVELOPMENT OF THE SPECIAL OPERATIONS EXECUTIVE
Agencies from which personnel transferred on the formation of SOE

SIS' Section D
Formed in March 1938 to study the theory of sabotage etc, with a few agents in the field by September 1939.

War Office's GS (R)
Became MI R (the title used throughout this text) in the spring of 1939. Its small staff worked on aspects of clandestine warfare.

EH
branch of the Foreign Office. Set up in 1938 to study propaganda.

SOE
Formed as from 19 July 1940 with its Director responsible to the Minister for Economic Warfare but with no other links to his Ministry.

'Council'
(An informal body of senior staff and specific junior officers who met when required)

Operations

Facilities
For weapons, transport, etc but no centralised administration

Propaganda
Until August 1941 when this section became the Political Warfare Executive and no longer part of SOE. From time to time, SOE helped PWE agents.

Reorganised by March 1944 (See Appendix 3.2)
Council
Formalised from late in 1941

Operations

Special Operations Mediterranean HQ at Bari, Italy from April 1944

India Mission

Special Operations Australia

Mission in Washington

Finance
Intelligence and Security
Signals
Weapons Research
Training

Country Sections and numbered Forces included:

AMF	SOE agents working in France from Algiers
DF	SOE's escape section for north-west Europe
EU/P	for co-ordination with Poles outside Poland the majority of whom were in France
F	SOE recruited agents working in France from UK
R/F	For co-operation with Free French agents of General de Gaulle
N	SOE recruited and Free Dutch Force's agents working in the Netherlands
T	SOE recruited and Free Belgian Forces *et al* working in Belgium and Luxembourg

X	SOE Section for Germany
Force 133	In Cairo
Force 136	In SEAC command (south-east Asia)
Force 137	In Australia
Force 139	In Poland and Czechoslovakia
Force 266	In Yugoslavia and Albania

Cover names for SOE included:
Inter-Services Research Bureau (the name on the door of the Baker Street office); Inter-Service Signals Unit (ISSU); AI 10; NID (Q); and Joint Technical Board

Fig. III These two simplified organization charts illustrate the expansion of OSS between January 1943 and June 1945. The collection of secret intelligence and similar work was carried out by a separate branch of OSS throughout its existence. Strategic Services Operations were controlled through another branch with responsibilities for subversive activities (see Appendix 3.4).

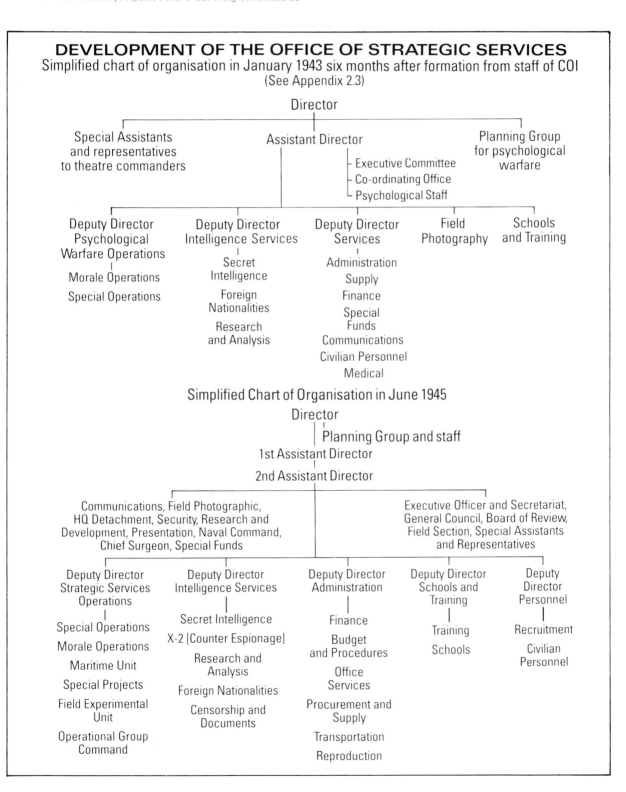

DEVELOPMENT OF THE OFFICE OF STRATEGIC SERVICES
Simplified chart of organisation in January 1943 six months after formation from staff of COI
(See Appendix 2.3)

Director

Special Assistants and representatives to theatre commanders

Assistant Director
- Executive Committee
- Co-ordinating Office
- Psychological Staff

Planning Group for psychological warfare

Deputy Director Psychological Warfare Operations
Morale Operations
Special Operations

Deputy Director Intelligence Services
Secret Intelligence
Foreign Nationalities
Research and Analysis

Deputy Director Services
Administration
Supply
Finance
Special Funds
Communications
Civilian Personnel
Medical

Field Photography

Schools and Training

Simplified Chart of Organisation in June 1945

Director
Planning Group and staff
1st Assistant Director
2nd Assistant Director

Communications, Field Photographic, HQ Detachment, Security, Research and Development, Presentation, Naval Command, Chief Surgeon, Special Funds

Executive Officer and Secretariat, General Council, Board of Review, Field Section, Special Assistants and Representatives

Deputy Director Strategic Services Operations
Special Operations
Morale Operations
Maritime Unit
Special Projects
Field Experimental Unit
Operational Group Command

Deputy Director Intelligence Services
Secret Intelligence
X-2 [Counter Espionage]
Research and Analysis
Foreign Nationalities
Censorship and Documents

Deputy Director Administration
Finance
Budget and Procedures
Office Services
Procurement and Supply
Transportation
Reproduction

Deputy Director Schools and Training
Training
Schools

Deputy Director Personnel
Recruitment
Civilian Personnel

1
SABOTAGE

DIM lights threw weak shadows across the giant cartwheel of tracks inside the roundhouse of Troyes' railway yards. Here engines were parked in the summer of 1943 on the spokes of the cartwheel, with a turntable at its hub. 'Germain' and five Frenchmen slipped into this engine shed. The French were over bold in their youth for they had not been on such a raid before. Even as they approached the roundhouse on the night of 3/4 July they had been obliged to walk brazenly past two sentries, stepping out in single file as if going on night shift as it was past curfew time. Their boldness had deterred any challenge. Later when they heard some shouting from a nearby siding they had ignored it, passing the German guard house which fortunately appeared deserted. Now in the roundhouse, the British officer code-named 'Germain' crawled into the pit under a couple of engines on the nearest spoke of track. He felt his way forward towards the steam cylinders which drove the big wheels of the nearest engine, glancing up between the front bogey-wheels to see two German guards. Their conversation echoed around the high roof mingling with the hiss of steam from a nearby generator. Some of his companions drew their pistols but Ben Cowburn, 'Germain', would have no precipitate action; they were in the roundhouse to sabotage railway engines, particularly those for long-haul freight traffic which was vital to the Germans that early summer. This included trains which travelled 150km north-west from Troyes to Paris, and those going south to the Mediterranean carrying military supplies brought to these marshalling yards from Germany.

Ben felt for the place to put his explosive charges on the cylinder ends near the stuffing boxes, where the piston-rods emerge to drive the wheels. Being the professional that he was, Cowburn made sure that he and his team would damage similar parts on each engine. This would prevent any subsequent cannibalizing of good parts to make some engines run. He guided the hands of each Frenchman in turn to the spot where charges should be placed. The men pressed round him, grimy already from the coal dust, oil and soot in the pit. He left two of his men to place their charges on this and one or two other engines on the spoke. Two others crawled to the next pit before fixing their charges, while Ben and the calm young Senée took another sector. There were some dozen engines in the roundhouse but as it was 100m in diameter they were relatively far apart. The men therefore had to work quickly in the 20 minutes that they had allowed before they must be clear

of the targets. These were recently built locos used to haul express freight trains and Ben found a couple more in a nearby siding. Other engines had to be left undamaged as the team had to leave before they could place all the charges in their haversacks. Tempting as these other targets must have been, Cowburn wanted everyone clear of the area before the charges on their one-hour delay fuses went off.

The team came out of the railway yard and were making their separate ways from a back-road level crossing towards the city, when the first explosion boomed their success. Instantly, or so Ben Cowburn felt, a powerful German motorcycle came down the road. He heard other vehicles moving near the railway, as if a search was underway for the saboteurs. This was no time to be in the open, therefore Ben and Senée took to the fields. The British officer ran easily in his gym shoes, the trainers of the time, and the Frenchman—having taken off his boots to be able to walk quietly around the railway shed—ran as best he could, heading for a small farmhouse. They were stopped dead by an invisible wall, like the characters in a cartoon film, as Cowburn described it. A moment of heartbeating doubt—were they trapped? The answer in retrospect is not surprising but at the time must have been a shock: they had dashed full tilt into chicken-wire surrounding the farmer's hen coop. They felt their way around it, before deciding that the German activity was not coming in their direction and they walked home.

This roundhouse rumble was a most successful piece of sabotage although described by Ben as 'a small bang'. Thirteen engines had been damaged yet all the saboteurs escaped without attracting suspicion, in part because the Germans found one charge which had not exploded. (The man who placed it no doubt forgot to break the ridge setting the acid to flow in the time-pencil fuse, a not uncommon error.) The charge was made '. . . strictly in accordance with the British pattern . . .' therefore the Germans reasoned: it could not have been placed by any of the workers they had arrested; and these Frenchmen were released. One of the many rumours at the time in Troyes suggested the job had been done by British army engineers parachuted to the scene and taken home by an aircraft which had landed on some field.

Cowburn's success owed much to his habit of '. . . taking 10 times the necessary precautions . . .' to avoid capture, even if these made him appear absurdly cautious. He made four successful missions to France as an agent of SOE's F (French) Section, the first in September 1941. In Troyes on his third trip he revitalized 'Tinker' as this network or circuit of agents and sub-agents (local people) had been inoperative for some months. As its leader he was sometimes known by its code name, although at other times he used his personal code name, 'Germain'. In the early summer of 1943 when he went to Troyes he made contact with Dr Mahée who had a comfortable home, tastefully furnished with a spinet displayed in one corner of the lounge. Like so many who led the Resistance, the doctor faced a sharp contrast between his daily life as a leading citizen and his undercover work, for he was the leader of a large organization in Troyes. He was also in contact with General de Gaulle's Free French intelligence bureau in London; but he knew nothing and did not ask details of Cowburn's circuit, which was divided into two 'firms' each group working unbeknown to the other. The doctor was willing to help Ben and introduced him to a railway official, and helped the British officer in other ways, for the doctor was told of the intended sabotage in the roundhouse.

At that time 50,000 people lived in the city with the usual numbers of gossipers and a few informers, one of whom was to take an interest in Cowburn's house. It was suppposed to be empty and up for sale, but behind the empty windows was a veritable arms depot. It

reeked of the smell of almonds given off by one type of plastic explosive used by Cowburn to make up explosive charges. Stored there were also incendiary pots which by 1943 came in several varieties as explained later, but were incriminating evidence if found by the Gestapo. There were Sten guns, pistols and other goodies of the saboteur's trade, if not the *sabots* (clogs) which disgruntled eighteenth century French workmen threw into machinery—hence the origin of the word sabotage. All Cowburn's stores came in by parachute, dropped to so-called dropping zones (DZs) and carried to the house or occasionally brought by car, only three of his most trusted assistants knowing where the arms depot was. They also helped to distribute prepared charges for jobs. Then they might call on foot to collect a 'one-night outfit' of explosive charge and heavy automatic pistol. The charge might be used by a Frenchman to cut an electric power line or derail a train. Such caution in limiting the sub-agents who knew the house, proved justified when Dr Mahée warned Ben that

▼ The general principles of explosive charges involved firing a detonator with either a slow or other type of fuse. The detaonator exploded a primer to set off the main charge, although on occasion a knot of instantaneous fuse was sufficient to set off charges of plastic explosive. Bickford No. 11 safety (slow) black powder fuse burnt at the rate of one foot in 35 to 40 seconds but more quickly when used under water. Cordtex burnt at the rate of 200 *miles* a second and was therefore virtually instantaneous, as was the American Primacord.

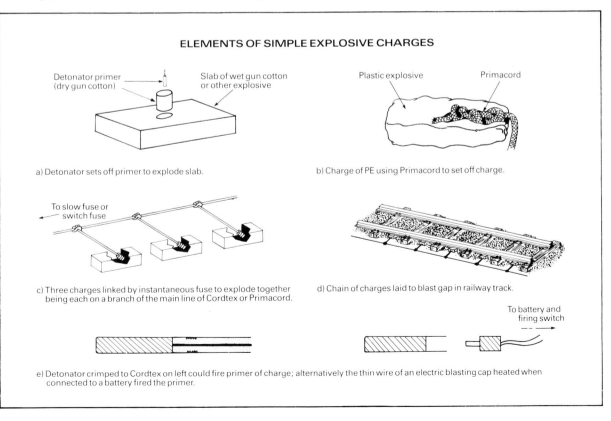

ELEMENTS OF SIMPLE EXPLOSIVE CHARGES

Detonator primer (dry gun cotton)

Slab of wet gun cotton or other explosive

Plastic explosive

Primacord

a) Detonator sets off primer to explode slab.

b) Charge of PE using Primacord to set off charge.

To slow fuse or switch fuse

c) Three charges linked by instantaneous fuse to explode together being each on a branch of the main line of Cordtex or Primacord.

d) Chain of charges laid to blast gap in railway track.

To battery and firing switch

e) Detonator crimped to Cordtex on left could fire primer of charge; alternatively the thin wire of an electric blasting cap heated when connected to a battery fired the primer.

the French circuit might be compromised. Nevertheless, Germain went with one of the railway officials to reconnoitre the railway sidings. Posing as a visiting manager of a team that was to play the Troyes railway football team, he saw the pitch; and—what could seem more natural among railwaymen?—he was shown the roundhouse. This reconnaissance gave him a chance to plan how he might enter the site with three helpers, but he was not certain of the layout of the machinery of the locos to be sabotaged. Therefore he made a second visit a few nights later. Padding softly through the back streets of the city dressed in blue overalls and wearing gym shoes, he arrived at the level crossing brightly lit on this occasion. After waiting for some engineers going on night shift, he crossed into the railway yard with them. Unless he also had incriminating explosives, he did not carry a gun, relying on strong nerves and false identity papers to get him past any identity checks. On this occasion he was not challenged, spending an hour in one of the pits of the roundhouse checking the precise positions of the cylinders and stuffing boxes under one of the new engines. Several of the guards passed close to where he worked but if they noticed him they must have mistaken him for a maintenance engineer.

Mahée found him five volunteers, two more than Cowburn wanted but the doctor thought that these young Frenchmen would benefit from watching Ben work. They would also learn much from his lessons in secrecy. For instance he never brought a team together without making sure that there was little or no chance of them being compromised. The doctor was less fortunate since he worked with those who volunteered their services, often as the highly-esteemed friend of someone already in the circuit. Such friends turned out on several occasions to be double agents and one probably joined the doctor's circuit. The Germans certainly knew which houses to surround, taking the novel precaution in the way that they made a series of reconnaissances one morning. As they motored about Troyes that day, they made a pretence at having an exercise for car drivers while the men under instruction—the security forces who would arrest the French agents—took a good look at the many houses to be raided. That night they arrested the doctor and many others.

Despite this set-back Cowburn realised that the doctor had not told any details of the plan, the five volunteers were still free and neither of Cowburn's firms had been penetrated. However one of his contacts reported that the Germans were expecting an attempt to sabotage engines in the roundhouse. Cowburn explained this to his five volunteers but they accepted the added risk with shrugs of Gallic indifference to the tortures of the Gestapo. Therefore Ben arranged a meeting in the classroom of one volunteer who was a

school master. There the British officer used the blackboard to explain the layout of the roundhouse and the approaches to it with an entrance through a gap in the wall made when an engine overshot the tracks. They were shown how to fuse the charges, and set the pencil time fuses. Each man was given a small rucksack with half a dozen charges, a pistol, some cigarettes and chocolate ('comforts' issued in the way the Royal Navy used to issue rum). The meeting concluded with a final check on the timing for the raid which would be made on the next moonless night.

Cowburn forgot to clean the blackboard of its obvious details; any child would know this was a picture of the railway yard, but the schoolmaster's wife had wiped the board clean before any of his class arrived. This was a stroke of luck, the first of several which contributed to the success of this operation, for no matter how carefully plans are made, every sabotage raid needs an element of good fortune to succeed. On another

▼ These time-pencil fuses enabled a saboteur to leave an explosive or incendiary charge set to go off after a delay of ten to 30 minutes or longer with an appropriate fuse. The box of OSS time-pencils pictured here were buried in France in 1944 and unearthed in 1982. The pencil fuse measured five inches long and a quarter-inch in diameter. The relatively soft metal surrounding the ampule of corrosive liquid was crushed to activate the acid which ate through the wire holding the striker against its spring. The coloured tag on the safety strip indicated the period of delay in temperatures of about 25°C: black for 10 minutes; red for 19; white for one hour and 19 minutes; green for three hours and 10 minutes; yellow for six hours and 30 minutes; and blue for 14 hours and 30 minutes.

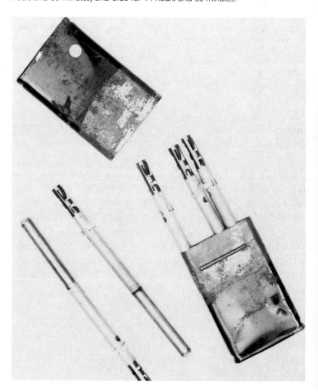

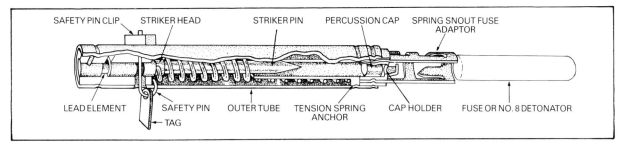

SAFETY PIN CLIP · STRIKER HEAD · STRIKER PIN · PERCUSSION CAP · SPRING SNOUT FUSE ADAPTOR

LEAD ELEMENT · SAFETY PIN · OUTER TUBE · TENSION SPRING ANCHOR · CAP HOLDER · FUSE OR NO. 8 DETONATOR · TAG

▲ The L-delay fuse worked on the principle of a spring stretching tellurium lead which has the property of stretching uniformly until it breaks. The lead-break was provided by a short rod, grooved in its centre to form a neck of reduced diameter. One end was fixed to the casing and the other pegged into the striker head. The extended end of the tension spring fitted into a slot in the striker head which was surrounded by a brass collar that could slide easily in the housing tube or cover. The other end of the spring was anchored as shown. Once the lead broke then the spring contracted and drove the firing pin into the percussion cap. Once the safety pin was removed the tension of the spring was set to break the led in the period indicated on the tag of the safety pin. A margin of plus or minus 30 per cent had to be allowed on timings but over long periods the delay was often precise, although it varied with the temperature. For example a one-hour delay at 65°F became a half-hour delay at temperatures over 85°F. A delay of 3 days at 65°F became six days at 45°F, and one of 28 days became 10 days at 95°F. These examples are from the ten different delay-periods available with No. 9 Mark I L-delay fuse.

occasion, for example, two agents were caught on their way to a meeting because their false identity papers were made out in the same handwriting. Yet they claimed to be from different towns 100km apart, where each said his identity papers had been made out. Cowburn's volunteers were not challenged as several of the guards were busy examining a derailed truck on one siding. Others, as we have seen, let them go by. The truck, around which there was some shouting heard by the saboteurs, had accidentally come off the rails. Yet the Germans decided this was a minor piece of sabotage by those who had escaped their comprehensive sweep of the resistance workers in Troyes. These arrests had made the Germans over confident or at least more relaxed in their duties.

Such good luck did not last for Cowburn, yet his cool head in adversity got him out of trouble, even if he sweated at the dangers he ran when moving his precious stores from the house. This had been watched by a nosy neighbour who reported that a car was to be seen outside an apparently empty house on some strange business. The report was intercepted by a patriotic French police officer, who on looking up its registration number found that he knew the owner's father-in-law. Cowburn was told and a new hiding place found for the arms and explosives in a cheerful carpenter's workshop.

Moving them there was a dangerous business yet Cowburn, fortified with a litre of wine, made the journeys himself. Had he asked others to make them, this might have led to their being recognized. If he was seen he might vanish back to England but the French-

men who helped him must live in Troyes probably for the rest of the war. Yet the carpenter, George Avelines, accepted the explosives, guns and incendiary pots knowing that the Germans might already be watching this removal. He just smiled his acceptance of such risk. Pierre, the car owner, joined him to keep watch as Ben began moving what he called 'our beastly supplies' on a small cart towed behind his bicycle. On returning to the house with this cart, Ben put a dozen grenades, two Stens, two pistols and loaded magazines near a first floor window. He would not be captured easily, although he resisted the temptation to keep looking out of the window into the street, to see if German security police were about to storm the building. He sweated as much from the stress of such fears as from the physical effort in moving the stores.

He made a number of trips, perhaps a dozen; each time as he returned to the carpenter's workshop George or Pierre would signal if the street was clear. At last there was only a single load left at the old depot and Cowburn searched the building before he brought this away. Had there been a single round or a scrap of grease-proof wrapping from a block of plastic explosive, 'PE' as it was known, this would have compromised the house owner and anyone else who the Germans might associate with it. The smell of almonds he hoped would disperse on the breeze after he had opened the windows. The breeze and Cowburn had done a thorough job by the time the original report was passed to the Germans, for they found nothing amiss in the empty house. The neighbour's report was therefore put down to one of the many denunciations made at that time without foundation if not without malice.

Cowburn, an oil technician from Lancashire, survived the war, for, as he said himself, he took precautions. Some of his techniques for distributing men and 'beastly supplies' owed much to his *rapport* with local people. He travelled a number of times in the space beneath a railway engine's tender above its wheels. He replaced—as others did—the charcoal-burning mechanism of lorries, using the empty generator cylinder as a secret compartment while the truck was running on petrol. A final touch in this last deception was to have chemically-made smoke wafting from the cylinder as if it came from burning charcoal.

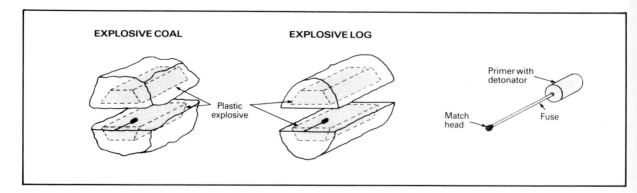

THE history of Allied sabotage raids of World War II goes back to the work of a section under the control of the Foreign Office—this Section D later became a part of SOE. In 1938 the section worked from a few shabby rooms in the St Ermin's Hotel near Caxton Hall in London. Its head, the tall distinguished Royal Engineer Major (later Major General) Lawrence Grand, was not allowed at that time to put any agents in the field. His Section nevertheless worked on plans for possible sabotage, technicians of the section working to improve designs for the pencil fuses and many devices. These included explosive coal, later followed by explosive cow-pats, mule dung and ultimately with explosive elephant dung when the war spread to south-east Asia. Explosive horse dung 'apples' were provided by 1943 in cylinders of five, spaced with wood-wool, the top 'apple' containing a concealed detonator. These would be piled in the hope that an enemy vehicle might run over the detonator on a road in Albania or elsewhere in central Europe. Such devices took a more complex form with OSS' tyre bursters but on the other hand some sabotage ideas were extremely simple. For example, a lighted cigarette with the unlit end jammed in a partly-filled match box, could be a useful incendiary device. A factory worker could throw it into a pile of rubbish just before he or she went home, then the cigarette acted as a slow fuse to ignite the matches and rubbish after the worker had left the building.

In March 1939 Grand was allowed to send agents into central Europe, some of whom were mining engineers working for the firm owned by Charles Beatty. He paid them and provided jobs which were a cover for their secret work, although it did not remain a secret for long. Their tunnels in the Yugoslav cliffs of the Iron Gorge narrows on the Danube, were discovered by the local police, before the great quantity of explosive required to cause a landslide could be positioned. This plan was masterminded by the owner of a shipping company, Julius Hannan, who also headed Section D's Balkan operations. Had the operation closed the river by blocking a section of this 200m-wide gorge, then the Germans would have been forced to find other means of shipping oil and grain across central Europe. Other attempts were made with a concrete-filled blockship provided through the Jewish organization running escape lines from Germany, but the ship was impounded by Yugoslav police before it could sail and its Section D crew perhaps lucky not to be interned. A plan to sabotage the Rumanian oilfields came to nothing because these were too well guarded by the summer of 1939. Nor did two disabled anti-Nazis manage to cut the telephone lines in the southern sectors of the Siegfried fortifications on the Franco-German border. On the fall of France, however, Section D left 10 dumps of sabotage stores spread at points along an arc running 240km north from Paris to the German border. Some of these explosives were used by resistance forces but there was no means of re-supplying the dumps, and therefore the two men left with each one were absorbed into the Allied organization of escape lines (see Chapter 8). Yet these small beginnings formed the vanguard of great networks of agents devoted to sabotage and ultimately to revolt on a wider scale. There were reasons, however, to restrict sabotage activities at times when guerrilla units were being trained in the locality. Otherwise the enemy might be provoked into searching for these men before they were properly organized and could evade the searching patrols.

In 1940 explosives were scarce and other means of sabotaging enemy vehicles and installations were perfected. For instance the British discovered that a handful of sand dropped into the axle of a French railway waggon, did not bring it to a grinding halt, but put in the correct part of the box, caused the axle to seize up. By 1943 an axle-seizing grease was provided by SOE with finely ground carborundum mixed into it. Indeed the abrasive mix could be provided also as a heavy oil and in a tin or grease-gun to suit the style of those in general use where the saboteur was working. In late May 1944, for example, the Second Panzer Division's rail transporter cars were in various sidings outside Montauban in southern France a couple of days or less from Normandy. Each transporter was under a pair of old French railway waggons to hide it from Allied air reconnaissance. Yet the empty cars were inadequately guarded despite such precautions, enabling two sub-agents of F section's 'Pimento' circuit to replace the axles' lubricant with doctored grease. Its carborundum later ground the transporters to a stop, as they were being shunted to assemble a train which was due to take the Division's armour to Normandy two days after the Allied invasion there. Replacing these rail transporters then took a frustrating week for the Division as the Allies enlarged their beach-head.

It was often claimed that a spoonful of sugar dropped into the petrol tank of a German truck would make it immobile, but this did not prove effective. However, demerara treacle dissolved in the right proportions of petrol could seize an engine. More effective still was the Caccolube, or OSS' 'Firefly', a small three-inch incendiary which could be palmed into a gasoline tank or storage container. The 'Firefly's' self-contained time delay was set for two to seven hours, after which it exploded, rupturing the tank and usually causing a fire. A less obvious but more frustrating sabotage from the point of view of the enemy's supply officers, was the jumbling of waggon destination dockets and cards in a railway siding office. Trains were then made up with the wrong waggons, perhaps sending urgently required

▼ All manner of hiding places were devised for explosives which were distributed to sub-agents, here two four-ounce cartridges in their waxed paper wrappings are hidden in a loaf of bread. The wrappers bear the manufacturer's imprint—Imperial Chemical Industries Ltd—with stencilled 'PE' and a number that might identify the production batch or factory.

tank tracks to Marseilles when they should have gone to a Panzer unit in Normandy. Or a saboteur with a knowledge of machine tools could slip the wrong sized cog in a chain of gears to jam them. Such knowledge also helped the man wielding a sledge hammer, for not only were the cast iron bases of many 1940s machine tools easily broken by heavy blows, but one machine in a shop of 10 might be the only one that was irreplaceable in the short term. Or one electric supply switch board could be more important than its neighbours, and if you only had a few seconds to wield that hammer you wanted to do worthwhile damage. Most agents had contacts among plant foremen and other engineers who provided this know-how and if the agent used the knowledge wisely, the broken machine or fused electric circuit appeared to be an accident of mischance. An 'accident' described by the French in the 1940s as *insaisissable*—that which cannot be 'scooped'—for the Germans could not readily trace its cause nor the saboteur who caused the mishap. After 1942 a common practice in major operations was to spread around Allied parachute regiments' badges, like brash calling cards that suggested some outside hands, not those of local people, had fired the petrol store or destroyed a vital piece of machinery.

The co-ordination of research into sabotage and associated devices, fell to SOE's head of scientific research. He inherited Section D's weapons research team which worked as Section XII with Section XI for radio research. Both were located in a one-time private hotel, the Frythe in the north London suburb of Welwyn Garden City. This officer in 1941 was the resourceful D. M. Newitt, a famous chemical engineer who had started his career in a Scottish explosives factory. He moved the purely manufacturing part of 'XII' to premises at Stevenage some way north of Welwyn, while developments of all manner of devices from fuses to one-man submarines continued at this Welwyn Experimental Laboratory (hence Welpen, Welbike and other inventions with the 'Wel' prefix). Similar research was carried out by an offshoot of M1 R known as M1 Rc which never became part of SOE although working closely with its staff, and enjoying the patronage of the Prime Minister from which came the name 'Churchill's Toy Shop'. It was headed by Millis (later Sir Millis) Jefferis, an explosives expert who wrote among other publications 'How to use High Explosive' a companion pamphlet to Gubbins' booklets of 1938/39 on guerrilla warfare. Jefferis spent the war conceiving explosive devices for use by regular as well as clandestine forces, with a team that was moved from the dangers of air raids on London to The Firs, a large house in Whitchurch, Oxfordshire. There experiments were carried out away from the supervision of the Army's Ordnance Board with its rigid safety rules.

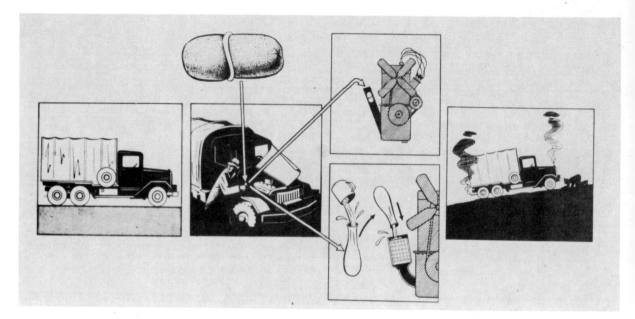

▲ The thin-rubber prophylatic sheath of a Caccolube contained 'a gritty chemical compound that damages any type of internal combustion engine'. This cartoon was published for OSS agents and resistance forces in January 1945, showing how the 'sac' might be used. It could be dropped into the oil intake of an engine. If this had baffles, the sac's content could have any liquid added to make a slurry which might be poured into the intake. The Caccolube was about two and a half inches long and weighed two ounces, with the extra length of sheath twisted and folded to retain the content. This, after 30 to 50 minutes in a vehicle's engine, damaged the cylinder walls, pistons and bearing journals beyond repair. The heat of the engine during this running time 'deteriorated the rubber sac' leaving the contents free to circulate with the flow of lubricating oil.

The Firs' team produced a rival to the pencil fuse: the L (lead) delay fuse. This worked on the mechanical action of a spring which after a pre-set time stretched a thin rod of lead to breaking point in order to trigger an explosive charge. Each batch of lead had to be tested for its breaking strain before being put into fuses. Short lengths of lead were then cut to give a length and thickness appropriate for accurate delays of an hour to three weeks, the safety pin holding the mechanism being tagged with a label coloured to indicate the pre-set delay. This might vary, however, according to the temperature, being tagged for use on a summer's day in Europe at 18°C. Agents therefore carried a table showing the time conversions for use in different temperatures. Nevertheless, the accuracy with which the L-fuse delay could be set, made it useful in a limpet or a clam. This a saboteur might want to explode at the time enemy staff might be in a booby-trapped conference room, or a ship might have sailed to deep water. The chemicals of the time-pencil fuse could also be affected by temperature, taking twice as long as the indicated time when used in freezing conditions. Therefore agents often used two time-pencils for one charge, to ensure that it exploded before the enemy found it.

Other fuse switches were a press-to-fire mechanism used often in cutting railway tracks as a train depressed the rail a fraction, and pull switches. The latter were used more extensively by uniformed troops laying trip-wires to mines than in sabotage. SOE's anti-personnel 'ground switch' mechanism had similar uses at times, when guerrillas placed several of these to protect paths approaching their secret base. Then the unwary might trigger one off to explode between his legs and it was therefore known as the 'castrator'. The release switch, held under a crate of wine bottles perhaps, would fly open when some looter lifted the box, unintentionally exploding a booby-trap charge. Although this tactic was used more often by retreating armies than by agents, release switches were included in the items dropped to guerrillas with the suggestion that they might be used under a cooking pan or other item in enemy billets. The most ingenious fuse switch worked by the expansion of bellows on a fall in atmospheric pressure and could be set to explode a rubber tube filled with PE at heights of 2,000 or 4,000m. Its inventors no doubt had in mind its use under a pilot's seat in a plane carrying VIPs who after the explosion would be killed when the plane crashed. There is no record of the device ever being used operationally by SOE, but in a reference to Russian saboteurs' work in Estonia there is a suggestion that 'three aeroplanes . . . have blown up mysteriously in the air'. These could have been sabotaged by time-delayed charges or charges set off by atmospheric fuses. Most planes could relatively easily be destroyed on the ground by slapping a charge of PE with a short time fuse, on a propeller boss. The time delay had to be short or the enemy would remove the charges if they were seen by sentries. The British SAS troops used such a charge for sabotage involving an incendiary element sending a sheet of flame to ignite the aircraft's fuel as well as shatter its engine cowling and propeller. This so-called Lewes bomb, however, does not appear to have been used by SOE.

During 1943 the Research and Development Division of OSS devised the SSR-204 radio-controlled switch. This could be left to fire a sabotage charge, or light a guiding flare for incoming aircraft which transmitted the appropriate signal any time within 72 hours of the switch being set. It might also be used to activate a homing beacon or similar signal beams for Allied aircraft equipped to trigger the switch.

The explosive used in many of these charges for all manner of sabotage was PE, a plastic explosive invented in the late 1930s by researchers at the Royal Arsenal at Woolwich, two of whose experts were sent to Section D to suggest ways in which their discovery might be used. The ways proved legion because this plasticine-like substance could be moulded to pack the angle of a bridge girder, the coupling on a powerhouse generator, or as we have seen with 'Tinker's' team, the stuffing box exterior

▼ These various types of switch-fuses and igniters were used to set off explosive charges by the release of pressure or by its application or when a tripwire was pulled. The spring-hinged box-like switch (top left) opened when a weight was lifted, releasing a firing spring that drove a firing pin (striker) into the percussion cap that fired a detonator. The type-A pressure switch (top centre) was used to react to the 40 lb to 50 lb pressure as a railway train passed over a line. The antenna—a two and a half inch steel rod—could be adjusted by its screw threads to ensure a firm fit against the under side of a rail. When this was depressed the lid of the fuse was forced down against strong springs of the sear mechanism, this sear moved upwards to release the striker on its firing spring. Top right is the pull switch, a tug of three pounds on the trip-line ring was sufficient to release the striker. The device had two safety pins: the first near the ring was removed once the tripwire had been attached. If the striker then flew forward because the wire was too taut, the pin struck the second safety pin. If all was correctly set up, then the second safety pin slipped easily from its position protecting the percussion cap. Bottom left is a similar pull-type switch known as the A-2. The large matches (bottom centre) could be used in even a strong wind to light a slow fuse. The release type A-2 switch (bottom right) had a hinged lid. Its lip could be secured to the base's lip by a pressure of one pound, but greater pressure was needed to hold down the upper part of the lid. Once this pressure was applied, the restraining binding was removed from the lips. When subsequently the lid was freed, the sear moved upwards releasing the striker spring (see diagram). The small size of these fuse-switches made them easy to conceal. The A-3 pressure switch measured 1¼ x 2¾ x ¾ inches with one and an eighth of an inch extension known as the Spring Snout (into which a detonator would be fitted). The pull-switches were about four and three-eighths inches long (including the Snout). The release-type A2 switch was 3⅜ x ⅝ x ⅝ inches and weighed two ounces.

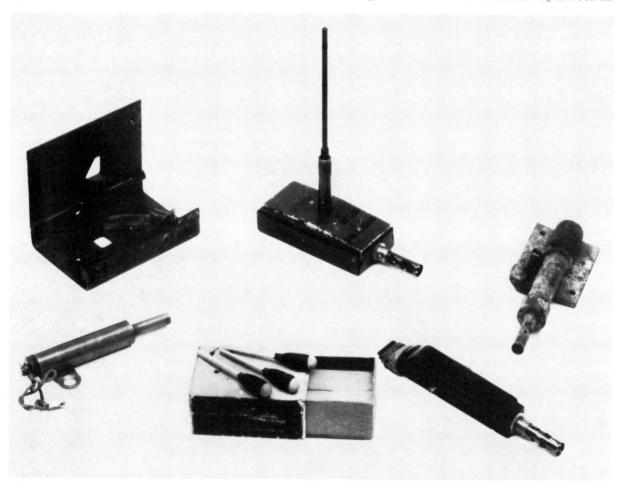

of a locomotive. A few ounces would cut the leg of an electric pylon, the control valve of an overland fuel pipeline or bring down palm trees to block a jungle road. A heavier charge of a kilo of PE gave a very respectable landslip in a cutting to block the escape of a vehicle convoy ambushed further down the road. Yet this explosive was safe to handle being unaffected by bumps when in transit or when hit by shell fragments, because it needed a detonator or its equivalent well buried in its dough-like charge before it would explode. Then the explosion was powerful enough not to need tamping with a packing of clay, unless the blast was required to be concentrated in a particular direction. It was very effective under water which tamped the charge of PE in limpet mines (see Chapter 10), cutting a large hole in the side of the ship to which the 'limpet' clung by its magnets.

Noble 808, one of the earliest varieties of PE, smelt of almonds as it did in Tinker's house, but other types of PE (see Appendix 3.5) did not smell, and looked not unlike butter. All types could be safely cut with a knife, although at low temperatures this was like cutting butter from a refrigerator, because the plasticizing material used to prevent the explosive from crystallizing, could itself become less than normally pliable if the explosive was being used at low temperatures.

PE-2A and the American C-4 were considered the most powerful explosives used in sabotage work, but they were not always readily available or, as suitable for say blasting embankments, as explosives stolen from local quarries or mines. Then one of the commercial explosives like dynamite might be used. The difficulty with these explosives was that whoever handled them required more than a passing knowledge of their characteristics (see Appendix 3.5). For example, the dry gun cotton's dirty white fibrous slabs each six by three by one-and-a-half inches weighed 19oz when in prime condition, but three of these were water which might dry out. Then the slab was an unstable flaky explosive unsafe to use, not that such dangers were always heeded.

Another explosive 'pressed into service' was Polar Ammon (PA), a form of gelignite. This could separate into its constituents of unstable nitroglycerine and the stabiliser of Fuller's Earth or a similar base material, if stored where the temperature was relatively warm and there was no ventilation. As happened with a tin supplied to Pete Mason: a one-foot square, black-painted Smith's potato crisp tin that held 20lb of gelignite securely sealed by the taped lid. When he opened it, the 'gelly' wrappers were floating in nitroglycerine with the base material sunk to the bottom of the tin. Nevertheless Pete used the lot as there was no way to divide out the measured quantity which he required. 'It made a lovely bang,' he recalls,

▲ Stanley Lovell of OSS and the National Defense Research Committee, seen here with two of the many devices he developed for OSS. In his right hand is a 'Beano' grenade, in his left the .22-cal HDM semi-automatic pistol with its supressor (silencer).

▼ The 'Beano' grenade was originally intended to be the size of a baseball but this proved too small to be effective. It was eventually designed to weigh 12 ounces three-quarters of which were the weight of the fragmentation case and its explosive charge. It had the usual safety pin and a type of fuse originated by the British which made the grenade 'live' only after it was thrown. This feature was intended to enable the thrower to carry safely a 'Beano' after taking out its primary safety pin. Once the grenade was thrown a so-called 'butterfly cap' was caught in the air stream of the grenade's flight, pulling the cap and its attached nylon string. After travelling 10 feet, the cap pulled out a second safety pin which allowed a pair of metal balls to drive the firing pin into the detonator no matter at what angle the grenade hit an obstruction. Practical difficulties with this butterfly cap lead to delays in production during the winter of 1944-45, see main text.

'even if it was more than I needed'. A risk perhaps, yet who in his youth at the explosives game has not been tempted to take such chances when in a hurry. Perhaps he crimped a detonator to a length of fuse by using his teeth, as somebody else always seemed to have the crimping pliers. Such liberties were not to be taken with major charges of commercial explosives. These came to be used by sub-agents who were miners, or for other reasons had professional knowledge of explosives. Nor could these explosives be easily used in hand-thrown charges like grenades.

Both British and American agents made extensive use of conventional grenades and had a few of their own invention. One of these was the Gammon grenade invented at The Firs. This No. 82 grenade to give it its official title, had a black cloth bag which could be filled with a kilogram of PE. The black bakelite case of its fuse mechanism had a cap which screwed over the fuse to hold a half metre of tape wound around the mechanism. You took off the cap and when the '82' was thrown a small piece of lead fixed to the tape pulled it clear, detaching the safety pin (a stiff piece of wire) to make the fuse 'live'. It then only needed to hit the ground or some obstruction, at any angle, for the weak spring holding a small but heavy ball-bearing to strike the firing pin and the detonator exploded the '82'. When intended for use against troops in an ambush, the '82'

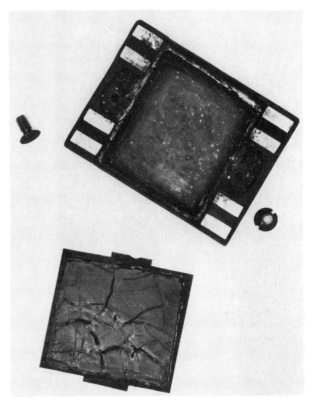

◀ ▲ The Clam was a small plastic box filled with about half a pound of plastic explosive. Its four strong magnets at each corner could hold it to the metal dashboard of a vehicle or to its petrol tank. It might also be used to destroy electric motors on machine tools or for similar sabotage. It was designed for use with two time-pencil fuses. The empty case weighed 13 ounces and was 6 x 2¾ x 1⅜ inches in size. Supplied in pairs, the magnets of the second one were protected by keepers if one of the pair was used.

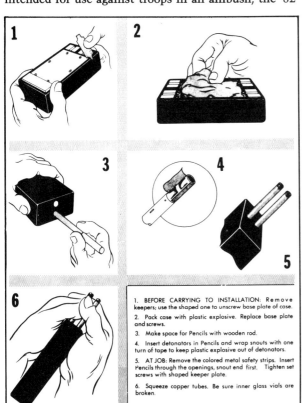

1. BEFORE CARRYING TO INSTALLATION: Remove keepers; use the shaped one to unscrew base plate of case.

2. Pack case with plastic explosive. Replace base plate and screws.

3. Make space for Pencils with wooden rod.

4. Insert detonators in Pencils and wrap snouts with one turn of tape to keep plastic explosive out of detonators.

5. AT JOB: Remove the colored metal safety strips. Insert Pencils through the openings, snout end first. Tighten set screws with shaped keeper plate.

6. Squeeze copper tubes. Be sure inner glass vials are broken.

might be packed with nails and other lethal bits of metal around the PE, creating a shrapnel effect when it exploded. The Clam was another device packed with explosive, held to metal objects by magnets to damage if not destroy, say, an electric motor. It only measured 5¾×2¾×1½ inches, being conveniently disguised within the covers of a book after the pages had been removed or cut, to conceal it when possibly fitted with an L-delay fuse. The Clam and the PE-packed limpet were both invented by Jefferis.

PE was stuffed into the bodies of dead rats, which could be left in the corner of a factory for some unsuspecting person to shovel into the nearest furnace. Nine are claimed by one source to have been used to good effect in the furnaces of Belgian factories, before the Germans discovered some in a crashed British aircraft. This could account for the Germans' reluctance to dispose of any dead rats in the usual way, cumulatively wasting considerably more production time in slave factories than the repair of a few steam boilers required. Another use for these explosive

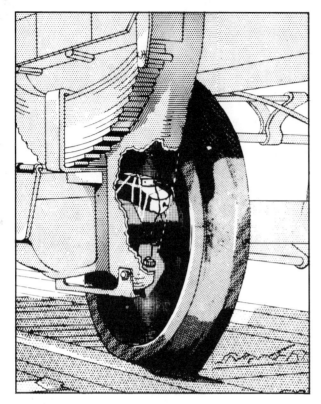

▲ Railway trucks could be derailed in tunnels by using the Mole. This fired a charge of plastic explosive when the sudden darkness of entering a tunnel affected its photo-cell. (This was not however affected by the slow change of day to night.) By exploding the charge on a waggon's front wheel and with a linked second charge to cut the coupling, 'a complete wreck' was assured. Both charges could be linked to one Mole, but its photo-cell unit had to be positioned where it 'saw' a well lighted part of the railway track. The cell was held in position by magnets, its two wires being connected to an electrically fired detonator. The device had been designed to be 'unnoticeable under European-type railroad cars'—to quote an OSS manual.

▲ The OSS pocket incendiary device (top) was a flat black celluloid case filled with a 'jelled petroleum fuel'. Two special time-pencil fuses were attached to the case, and were designed to ignite the fuel after an appropriate delay from ten minutes to 14½ hours according to which of six types of fuse was used. The lower illustration is of a British pocket incendiary fired by a time-delay fuse which had to be crushed to release its corrosive fluid. The OSS Mark I pocket incendiary measured 5¼ x 3 x ⅞ inches. It produced the best results when laid flat in a vehicle cab, under fuel drums or beneath combustible materials.

rodents was to leave the bodies in bunker coal to be loaded on ships or hidden in the loco coal stocks of railway yards. On other occasions French children dropped them into the tenders of engines passing under a bridge, for the fireman to shovel into his fire box under the boiler. No doubt the French crews of these engines knew what the result would be, for many railway workers actively contributed to the Resistance.

All these grenades and explosive charges could be adapted for particular purposes: the detonator might be fired by a pressure switch; by a time delay fuse; or by the flame of an ignited fuse. This last could be No. 11 safety fuse of black powder in a black waterproof cover, the powder burning at two feet in a minute, give or take seven seconds. At other times this safety fuse might be connected to Cordtex or Primacord instant fuse burning at 200 *milles* a second, its white covered lengths linked to several charges, with the result that they all went off

virtually at the same time. The saboteur setting such charges crimped each Cordtex end into its detonator, bunching the free ends together after paring them to give good contact with a piece of time fuse. With this joint taped securely and the time fuse cut to the length required, the agent was given time to be clear of the charges but not long enough for them to be disconnected by an alert sentry.

No record has been traced of SOE using such pieces of military engineers' hardware as the 'bee hive' charges used to blast a 2½-inch hole for two feet six inches into reinforced concrete, before filling this with the main charge. However, 'beehives' were available apparently to SOE in the Far East. In general SOE and OSS went in for less extensive demolitions, like those resulting from the fires created by small incendiary devices no larger than a pocket diary. A wooden rod covered a slot down one side of this 'diary', being removed to expose the pencil fuse which could be set by running a coin down prongs so that it always fell with a three-inch steel spike pointing upwards to puncture a car tyre or embed itself in the heavier low-pressure tyres of trucks. Either vehicle then came to a halt to be ambushed, for this type of road block like any other—an induced landslip filling the road with earth, or whatever—was as often as possible covered by armed men. They might also cut down telegraph poles to prevent any warnings being passed from one garrison post to the next along the road, the poles being easily sliced through by a few turns of Cordtex. This could also cut down small trees, but gun-cotton slabs were more suitable for felling larger ones. An avenue of felled poplars across a road could, however, cause only brief delays to military vehicles which could drive across the roadside fields.

O SS were able to make use of SOE's research and on occasions used the Executive's equipment but they developed explosive and other sabotage devices through the National Defence Research Committee's Division 19 (D19) after March 1942. OSS also gave development and production contracts to a wide range of specialist manufacturers for some of this special equipment. Much of it was similar to SOE's in time-delay pencils, AC delay fuses, incendiary and other devices. Some, however, may appear more complex than the SOE equivalent but in general terms was as serviceable if perhaps produced more lavishly. The Mark 3 time delay clock shows the technological detail of such devices: it weighed 11oz (300gm) being $2\frac{3}{4} \times 2\frac{1}{2} \times 1\frac{1}{2}$ inches ($7 \times 6 \times 4$ cm) with a glass-covered luminous dial and the normal external time-setting knobs, winder and a safety switch. Its near silent mechanism could be stopped or started by rotating a knurled knob to run with much greater accuracy than any chemical delay fuses, for 15 minutes to $11\frac{3}{4}$ hours. This precision was obtained because the mechanism was self-compensating for changes in temperature, even when used under 20 feet of water to trigger a limpet mine.

Reference has been made to the Caccolube, with its ingenious mixture of ingredients, but the difficulties of developing special if relatively simple weapons are shown by the history of the Beano. This was conceived as a fragmentation grenade the size of a baseball, familiar to most American soldiers and which interested OSS as an easily thrown grenade which would explode on impact with its target. D19 considered the project 'with the support of SOE representatives' from England, who gave the Americans access to the British 'Allways' fuse. This was fitted to the Gammon and the No. 69 Bakelite grenades to explode these grenades regardless of the angle at which they hit a target. Experimental work on the Beano in

▲ The caltrop tyre spike of three inches in diameter was used against road vehicles and on airfield runways. The design on the left was produced for OSS, its four prongs always ensuring that one was upright. The Christmas-tree design (centre) was dropped by US Air Force aircraft onto enemy airfields. The experimental design (on right) was hollow with the intention of deflating self-sealing tyres. A small explosive tyre burster was available from OSS and supplied with notes on how to disguise it as mule droppings or a stone.

the slot, breaking the fuse's ridge. The colour of the rod indicated the fuse's time delay with red for 30 minutes to blue for 24 hours. The pocket incendiary then burnt fiercely for a minute, long enough to ignite a truck's fuel tank or a radio cabin. Larger fires could be started by Newitt's incendiary block from the Frythe: this brick of highly combustible material gave off a supply of oxygen to feed the fire. It could then take hold even if tucked under a pile of blankets which might smother less persistent fires in a store room. The Firs team also produced their one-kilogram firepot which was filled with thermite (a mixture of aluminium powder and metal oxide). It burnt with an intense heat that could penetrate three millimetres of mild steel plate to ignite petrol in jerry cans or burn through the cables in a telephone junction box.

Less spectacular but in many ways as effective were the scaled down medieval caltrops once used to stop horses. The USAAF dropped one version from the air in Italy. SOE's caltrop, like the American design, had four

September 1944 showed that if it was a 5½-ounce baseball, it would be too light to cause any worthwhile damage. The weight was therefore increased to 12 ounces with OSS approval. The following month Eastman Kodak, the camera manufacturers, were given an order for 300 development Beanos which could be tested with various fuses, followed by 2,000 early in 1944 for range tests. By May the USMC and other units reported that their tests were satisfactory, the Beano—officially named the T-12—was therefore ordered in quantity with 825,000 equal to 15 per cent of all American grenades to be produced in 1944. At this time D19 and Kodak also worked on different versions of the Beano including a white phosphorous smoke grenade.

The First Allied Airborne Army had used over 2,700 T-12s by June 1944 but at least two troopers had been killed and 45 injured by premature explosions of the grenades; others were duds. The problems apparently came mainly from the designs of fuses which were intended to arm the T-12 in flight ready for it to explode on hitting the target. These troubles were not cured until Kodak, working with the Ordnance Department's experts, modified this fuse and the grenade body was redesigned as the Ordnance's T-13 and its derivatives, which as small fragmentation grenades came into production towards the end of the war.

We will see more of OSS and SOE's use of conventional and unconventional weapons in later chapters, but a word of warning is necessary about the value or lack of it in deterring the enemy. Itching powder, for example, supplied by SOE to some sub-agents in the 'Tinker' circuit, was put in shirts being sent to U-boat crews. This probably caused the wearers no more than a passing irritation among the many others when living in a boat. Yet this bit of sabotage did much for the morale of those who doctored the shirts, judging by the number of times that the tale has been retold. Indeed sabotage from the destruction of heavy water in Norway, to the old lady in the Paris Metro who tripped up German officers with her umbrella, often did nearly as much to boost Allies' morale as it did in damaging the Axis war effort. One hopes that Dr Mahée as he suffered in Troyes prison before his execution, was in some way compensated for all his bravery when—and if—he heard of the 13 explosions of 'Tinker's' charges that put as many locomotives out of use for a period.

▼ These two illustrations are from a German police publication of May 1944 *Englische Sabotageanweisungen* ('English Sabotage Methods'). The top illustration shows a method of creating an anti-personnel mine using a fragmentation grenade. Its safety handle is released when the grenade is pulled from the can by a tripwire. The lower picture shows 'fireplates' distributed among crops and haystacks. These had phosphorous patches which had been covered with airtight seals. Once the seals were removed the phosphorous ignited setting fire to a liquid held between two celluloid plates. The plates were of two sizes: two or four inches square. Other illustrations in this booklet included various forms of charges held in place by large U-shaped magnets. There is an illustration of the H-capsule with its potassium chlorate and sugar mix weighted by buckshot. When these ⅝ inch capsules were left in a bottle containing sulphuric acid, they gave a brief hot flame some two hours after immersion. Several pictures show the installation and use of a *Wurfbombe* (Thrown Bomb) that could be launched from a device fixed to a tree or similar upright structure.

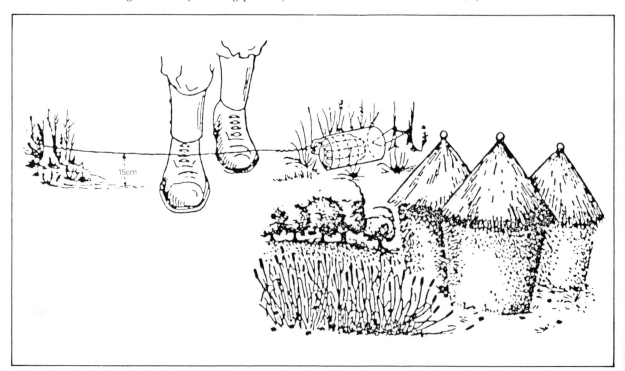

2
ASSASSINATIONS AND ELIMINATIONS

SABOTAGING equipment, ambushing military personnel along with other forms of death and destruction became a routine—if not exactly a daily one—for many OSS and SOE agents. Yet they were rarely involved in political assassinations. In the last week of February 1944, however, agents throughout occupied Europe set out to assassinate as many senior Gestapo and other security police officers as possible. But few of them were killed in this Operation 'Rat Week'. As a general rule assassinations were not pre-planned but Axis officers and security troops were killed on many occasions when they cornered an agent. One even snatched the pistol from the corporal of his execution squad and killed several before he was shot.

The plot to assassinate Hitler lies outside our story although unbeknown to SOE the plotters used some captured SOE explosives. Hitler escaped with only minor injuries and had he been killed there are serious doubts as to whether the war would have come to an abrupt end. Indeed, as Professor M. R. D. Foot has pointed out, '. . . modern history shows the utter futility of assassination as a political weapon . . .' This view was held by Winston Churchill who discouraged such ventures, although several were considered. In one case SOE Cairo's staff without advising London of their intentions, sent a Macedonian terrorist to kill Hitler. The man reportedly got drunk in Vienna and was caught. The only assassination of World War II which had some lasting effect was the death of the Polish leader General Sikorski, which has been attributed to Russian intelligence working on information from their English spy, Kim Philby. This view suggests that the General's plane crashed after an explosive device had been planted on it during its overnight stop at Gibraltar, although this crash is believed in many informed quarters to have been an accident.

The SS general, Reinhard Heydrich was the only major political figure known to have been assassinated in Europe. At 37 he was appointed Imperial Governor of Bohemia and Moravia (part of modern Czechoslovakia) and already had an unpleasant record of subversive successes. These included the forging of papers shown to Stalin which led to half the Russian officer corps being put to death in the 1930s; and organizing the deception that 'Poles have invaded Germany'. An SS major and 55 troopers had made preparations in August 1939 when posing as geologists, gathering more than intelligence along the border, for they acquired Polish uniforms, four Polish machine-guns and some rifles.

These were used to equip the 'raiders', all former inmates of concentration camps, in Polish army uniforms. They were then injected with lethal Skophedal and spread out to be shot near a German frontier post. Their bodies were shown to newspaper reporters after the Germans had manufactured this excuse for counter-action, crossing the Polish border next day at 0445 hours on 1 September 1939. Such evil powers of organization were put to different use by the new governor in September 1941 and within a short time 750 Germans were able to control 350,000 Czech civil servants. Other Czechs received inducements of better rations and holidays in hotels in exchange for harder work; while the rich who had used these holiday resorts before the war, were—Heydrich claimed—to be destroyed. Ploys which, with other political finesse, led to a serious risk that the Czechs might join the Germans in 'fighting communism'. If they did this there would be as many as 20 extra divisions on the Russian front. Dr Eduard Beneš approved the plan by the head of his secret service in exile to have the Governor assassinated.

General Frantisek Moravec had headed the Czech secret service for a number of years and ran one of the most efficient clandestine agencies of that time. But the provinces Heydrich ruled had been annexed by Germany in March 1939, depriving Moravec's agents of many contacts. Nevertheless Moravec with the help of SOE arranged the training of Lieutenants Jan Kubis and Joseph Gabčik as an assassination squad. Kubis, a 27-year-old regular Army officer had already worked in a Czech resistance organization during 1939 before leaving for England. A sturdy man in build and nature, he had a Moravian farmer's powerful hands and forearms. His great friend Gabčik was a locksmith, cheerful and volatile in the Slav tradition. Both were in training with the Czech commandos, making them physically fit and they had shown the great perseverance needed to fulfil their mission, code-named 'Anthropoid'.

They dropped by parachute as did several other Czech teams, from a Halifax bomber on a frosty night in December 1941. Gabčik sprained his foot in landing as he hit the ice-hard ground. This was not however where they expected to be, near a forest 20 miles north of Prague. Therefore they hid their parachutes near a gardener's hut not burying them as they had been taught, and also cached some of their equipment casually under seed boxes in the hut. Such casualness—one Czech team left a note by their equipment: 'please do not report this to the Germans'—stemmed as it did in France and no doubt elsewhere, from the belief that everyone was as committed to the Allied cause as were the agents. In reality local people were to prove in some cases distinctly hostile to the two assassins. Indeed they were lucky that no unfriendly locals picked them up that first night, for each had an identically tailored suit quite unlike those worn in central Europe. (A book could probably be written on such errors, for Burtons', the 50-shilling tailors had not been adequately briefed: they supplied British wartime utility suits, the trousers having no turn-ups. Yet in these years many people in occupied Europe wore well-preserved old suits of a heavy tweed cloth, with baggy trousers. Agents were also given top coats with raglan sleeves that were not generally worn in central Europe. Station X overcame such difficulties in dressing OSS and some SOE agents. Its staff accumulated a master wardrobe of European clothing, suitcases and personal effects from refugees reaching America.) Other giveaways to Gabčik and Kubis' recent origin were the corned beef not 'continental' sausage in their rations; English cigarettes; and weapons with British markings. These guns had not been cleaned of all identity as were the so-called sterile weapons sometimes issued later in the war.

As they were 140km from their intended landing, they were again lucky to be seen as they dropped, by members of the *Sokol* cultural movement. Its gymnastic clubs cloaked much of the resistance forces' activities. These patriots spirited away the two agents from the country-house garden near Pilsen, safely to Prague. There they lived with a railway worker named Moravec—no relation to the General—whose wife Marie was in her fifties. Her eldest son was flying with the RAF but the youngest, the 20-year-old Ata lived at home working as a courier for *Sokol*. Another courier was the young and pretty widow, Anna Malinovia who became a close friend of Kubis, during the six months he and Gabčik were in Prague.

A second team dropped on the same night from the Halifax, with the intention of setting up radio communications with London. After various adventures they achieved this in January 1942, and for the next few months passed information from *Sokol* through their radio hidden in a quarry's engine shed known as broadcasting station *Libuse*. The Germans never found the station but knew that this team had landed because a farmer passed the Germans a parachute which he had unearthed, being no doubt a Sudeten Czech of German origin. After radio contact was established a third team—Lieutenant Adolph Opalka, Sergeant-Major Čurda and their radio operator—were parachuted in but took a foolish risk in visiting their homes before going to the contact's

address which they had been given. The fourth and final team from England involved in this mission were dropped in the puppet republic of Slovakia, far from where they should have landed in central Moravia. They had a brush with a border patrol, two of whom were killed by the team leader, Lieutenant Oldrich Pecel, after they had taken his identity card. His photograph was recognized in the local police station by a man who had known him some years earlier and it was soon on 'wanted' posters. His family were threatened and fearful of capture he lived in the forest until months later. Then he was tricked into surrender and killed while in prison.

His sergeant, Arnost Miks, was a bold man with a boxer's physique and a tendency to see matters in black-and-white terms. He eventually made contact with *Sokol* and took his 20-year-old radio operator, Corporal Gerik to Prague. There by February all the teams were in touch through Jan Hajsky, a schoolmaster in the Resistance who had contact with one of its local leaders known as *Jindra*. A key figure in the local Resistance with contacts in several circuits of subversive activity, he also was a schoolmaster. Yet his pale round face, unkempt moustache and nicotined fingers might have suggested a less commanding character. He, like many others in the Resistance was not keen on Heydrich's assassination, but Miks brought orders reinforcing the exiled Government's wish for the Governor to be killed.

Not long after he arrived in Prague, the sergeant went with another agent to recover a radio set cached in a forest. They were intercepted by a police patrol and in the gun battle which followed Miks was badly wounded in the legs. He then urged his companion to escape, which he did. The sergeant, now alone and surrounded, shot himself rather than be captured, for he knew a great deal about the 'Anthropoid' mission. When he did not return to the hotel in which he and the young Gerik were staying the youngster lost heart. He asked the local barber for help and was told to give himself up. This he did. *Jindra's* men, finding that the young radio operator had left the hotel were concerned that he might have told all.

Meanwhile Kubis and Gabčik had obtained false medical certificates which excused them from normal work, so they were able to spend most of the day investigating Heydrich's route from home to work. He arrived there about 0945 hours each morning in his chauffeur-driven Mercedes, having travelled the 25km from his castle home in about 30 minutes. Some 10km from the city the car had to slow as it rounded a hairpin bend, where twin tram tracks curved down a hill to the river bridge. Sometimes the three-car trams on this route passed on the bend, which could have obscured the assassins' view at the vital moment when the car came close, but this was a chance Kubis decided to take.

On the morning of 27 May 1942, a beautiful early summer's day, Heydrich was late leaving home. Therefore he sent the guards in their car ahead of him rather than keep them waiting to escort the green Mercedes as they usually did. Yet Oberscharführer Klein who was his personal bodyguard would prove nearly sufficient match for the assassins. The governor also had plenty of courage, at one time flying a fighter aircraft on the Eastern front. The Mercedes' late approach was signalled by mirror flashes from an agent 600m from the hairpin bend, repeated by Lieutenant Valcik nearer the assassins, who saw the car at 1030 just as a tram was coming up the hill. Gabčik stepped into the middle of the road, dropped his mackintosh to take aim with the sten gun hidden beneath it. Kubis saw the car begin to brake but there was no sound of firing as it passed him and he flung a grenade. This exploded on the side of the car near the back wheel, flinging two uniform jackets high in the air. Black smoke followed as the car came to a juddering halt, Heydrich and his chauffeur jumping out, pistols drawn. The tram, some left side windows shattered by the explosion, had by now stopped.

Kubis ran for his bicycle as a second tram rounded the bend. The passengers from the first tram were already crowding the road, but they parted for Kubis as he brandished his pistol. Reaching his bike, he pushed it clear of the crowd. A Czech policeman moved to stop him but Kubis was too quick. He fired a shot as he jumped onto the bicycle before pedalling hell-for-leather down the hill. A woman scrubbing her door step saw him as he fled and flung her bucket into his front wheel. Yet he managed to stay on the bike, although riding it was also difficult because a grenade splinter had gashed his right eye-brow and blood oozed into his eye. A second woman pushed in front of him, but bracing his left shoulder he sent her flying. He heard shots and braver souls from the tram were running after him, a confusion of shouted alarms which grew fainter as he gathered speed near the bottom of the hill. His momentum then carried him over the bridge into a deserted main road from where he was able to reach a safe house.

Gabčik had been less fortunate after realizing that his gun was jammed. He flung it down and made for his bicycle as the crowd grew at the top of the hill. Heydrich was firing at him. Then he realized that his only escape lay in running back up the hill beyond the two trams, even if he had to pass through the edge of the crowd and leave his cycle propped on the pavement edge. At this moment the chauffeur Klein rejoined his master after chasing Kubis but hesitated to leave Heydrich who was injured. This gave Gabčik the chance to run for cover up the hill. He was 100m ahead of Klein before the German took up the pursuit, but by cutting across the corner of

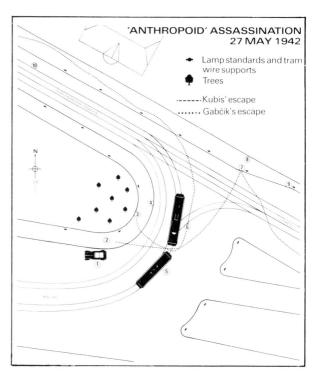

'ANTHROPOID' ASSASSINATION
27 MAY 1942

Lamp standards and tram wire supports
Trees
------ Kubis' escape
.... Gabčik's escape

▲ This sketch map is based on material provided for a police report on the assassination of SS General Heydrich in the suburbs of Prague. 1 Heydrich's car; 2 Kubis' position when throwing grenade; 3 mackintosh abandoned; 4 Sten gun dropped by Gabčik; 5 first street car (possibly linked as a double car to 6); 7 lamp standard against which Kubis propped his bicycle; 8 cloth cap left by Kubis; 9 Gabčik's bicycle found against lamp standard; and 10 direction of butcher's shop (not on map).

the road, he got within 30m of Gabčik before the Czech could escape. He then turned and fired twice at the German before rushing on up the hill, past a carter who held his hands high although his horse shied at the commotion. Near the top of the hill the Czech dodged up a side road into a butcher's shop. If this had a backdoor Gabčik got no chance to use it, for the butcher called the attention of the passers-by including the German. He and the Czech exchanged shots, the German being wounded in the thigh and ankle before the Czech ran off. He was followed by the carter and the butcher but they soon gave up the chase. Gabčik was far ahead of any pursuers when he reached the main road parallel to that of the ambush. There a tram driver saw the Czech was running and obligingly slowed to let him jump on the street car. This took him to the city centre where he waited a while to be sure that he was not being followed. Then he took another tram to his safe house in the Liboslava district. He arrived to hear a news flash being repeated on the radio, offering ten-million crowns for the assassins' capture.

Meanwhile Kubis, his eye bathed and bandaged, made his way to a second safe house where he borrowed his host's overalls, dressing as a railwayman. He could mingle unnoticed with the workers going home that evening and was able to reach the Moravec's. There he learnt that Mrs Moravec's bicycle—the one Gabčik had propped on the curb—was pictured in the evening papers, as was the cap which Kubis had borrowed without realising the dangers for its owner. Anyone with information on these items or the assassins must, the papers said, and the radio kept repeating, go to the police. If they did not and were later caught, not only the culprits but all the members of their families would be shot.

German reprisals and searches began although the agents of 'Anthropoid' were successfully—if sometimes only just in the nick of time—moved from one safe house to another, avoiding the searchers. Young Gerik, however, was in police custody giving them names, addresses and the location of hidden radio sets, because—he told them—he had only acted as an agent in order to return to Czechoslovakia. The Gestapo paid him, sending him to his home village where he boasted of his experiences, although he probably did not say that he had been taken to identify Miks' body.

Heydrich died eight days after the ambush, splinters of steel, horse hair and other bits of the back seat driven deep into his lower back. Blood poisoning had completed what the grenade had failed to do. News of his death and the reprisals reached Sergeant Major Čurda hiding on his mother's farm that May. Over 2,000 people—more would die later—were executed, among them were Pechal's father, mother and two brothers, Miks' two brothers and no doubt others known to Čurda. He was frightened into going to the police and perhaps tempted by the reward which was now twenty million crowns, worth perhaps several million US dollars at that time. Čurda told of the Moravecs about three weeks after the assassination.

The Gestapo burst into the Moravecs' flat, marshalled the family against the sitting room wall and began questioning them. Marie Moravec persuaded her guards to let her use the upstairs lavatory, where she swallowed her lethal (L) pill carried in a medallion on a chain around her neck. As the sound of the flush brought an officer running up the stairs, she fell out of the lavatory door—'a heart attack' her husband is reported to have said. Her son Ata was broken at the Gestapo headquarters, before he gave information on the schoolmaster Hajsky, who died by his L-pill when the Gestapo came to arrest him. There were more revelations because the young courier had been told by his mother that the next day he was to go into hiding in a church on Resslova street.

For some days Father Petrek had given the agents sanctuary in the vaults of his eighteenth century Orthodox church. Its crypt had only an air shaft en-

trance from the street, and access through steps normally covered by a stone slab in the church floor. In the early morning of 18 June Kubis, Opalka, from the second team that had parachuted in five months earlier, and another agent named Jaroslav, were keeping watch in the silent church, when they heard the footsteps of SS men beginning their search. Kubis and Jaroslav are believed to have been on a balcony, Opalka probably in the nave, as they opened fire. The SS retreated in some confusion, hastened by a grenade. The defenders even attacked these troops as they re-assembled outside the church, sending two quick bursts of fire among them from a window. The siege continued for two hours under harsh arc lights which the Germans rigged to light the scene as they prepared for a resolute attack through the church door. This time there were riflemen on ladders against outside walls, who fired through windows into the balcony, pinning down all three agents as the attack developed. One was killed in this fire and the other two shot themselves to avoid capture. Their bodies were then identified by Ata Moravec and Čurda who had been brought to the church.

The priest resisted blows to make him tell if any other agents were in the church, but the Germans found the stone slab to the crypt stairs. The first SS man to go down the steps was then met with Sten and pistol shots from Valcik, Gabčik and two other agents, Bublik and Hruby. All were positioned behind the buttress walls lining the crypt which provided good cover from the Germans' fire. The Germans persuaded the priest to call on the agents to surrender but they answered that they knew no priest. About this time the Germans also organised the local fire brigade with a smoke machine used in practises, pumping its smoke down the air vent to the vault. Tear gas had been tried but the canisters were shot away almost as soon as they were lodged in the air shaft. Water hoses had also been dropped through its opening but were lacerated by Sten fire, nevertheless water steadily flooded the crypt floor. Yet the level was rising too slowly for the German police officer,

▲ The lethal L-pill of Zyankalium might be carried in a signet ring. Here the right-hand thread of the ring makes it unusual as jewellers use left-hand threads. The L-pill killed in five seconds when swallowed to avoid torture and possibly revealing the names of other agents.

Superintendent Panwitz, in charge of the siege. He twice had men lowered clear of the steps through the stone floor entrance, only to see the leading men shot. SS engineers then blasted a wider entrance enabling some 30 troops to attack in several waves down the steps, firing their Schmeissers to cover this movement. Their first attempts were again repulsed until the agents ran out of ammunition. As the SS regrouped for another assault, four single shots reverberated through the building. The defenders had shot themselves.

Anna Malinovia, the young widow who had befriended Kubis was taken into custody and gassed at Mauthausen. A doctor who had attended Kubis by disguising himself in a tram conductor's uniform, a woman eye specialist who had treated the agent's wound, the mother and sister of the youth whose cap had been left at the ambush, the little girl who had been sent to wheel Gabčik's bicycle from the curb where he had left it, all were killed or died later in concentration camps. These were some of the many in the eventual total of 5,000 Czechs who perished in German retributions, repressions which led to the elimination of active resistance for some years. In 1944 when the resistance forces attempted a revolt some Czechs, perhaps from those of German origin, helped the security police, one betraying OSS Groups in the Tatra Mountains.

The price of political assassination had been high. In one of the dead agents' pockets was a note mentioning the villages of Lidice and Ležáky. Men, women and children of both villages were put to death and their homes completely destroyed, the sites being ploughed to remove the least sign of their existence. Yet such overreaction led to almost all Czechs of German extraction being forced to leave the northern provinces after the war. Then also Čurda was traced and executed for his treachery, young Gerik also probably died soon after, if not before the end of the war in the general purge of collaborators.

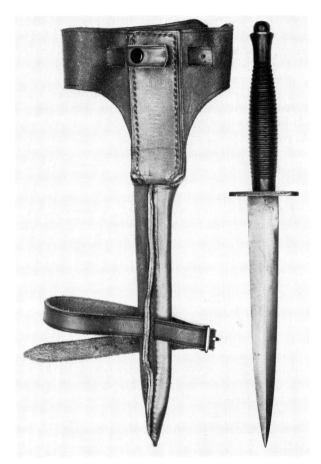

▲ This Commando knife, known also as the Fairbairn/Sykes (F/S) knife, was made in several patterns. Illustrated is a 'Mark 3' version with the sharpened edges running to the oval cross-guard. The knife was used by commandos and available for SOE personnel, some of whom used an arm scabbard (on left) which was strapped beneath the sleeve of the wearer's jacket. The first F/S knives were made in the Shanghai police workshops when Fairbairn was helped by Captain S. S. Yeaton USMC in about 1938. The first 500 produced by Wilkinson Sword for the British army, had a ricasso top to the blade. This squared top was moved in later designs in order to simplify the hand finishing of the seven-inch blade. About 250,000 were produced including several varieties sold to the general public.

A N individual sentry met his death in much less spectacular circumstances. He might be knifed, shot with a silenced pistol or killed by an agent using his bare hands. The first of those methods of killing was— and is—by no means as simple as it might appear, for as John Minnery has written in the privately published book *How to Kill* '. . . one thing that must be considered . . . is the issue of blood—there is a terrific amount gushed about in any throat-cutting operation . . .' The agent using a knife had therefore to keep his victim's mouth closed and be prepared for the last gasps of his victim which were unlikely to be silenced even if the dying man's first cry was stifled. The dead man's bowels and bladder also let go at this time, so the agent had to be prepared for this and telltale stains on his clothes. At best the agent's jacket was put on one side before he tackled the sentry, then it could later hide bloodstains on a shirt. Folding knives and single-edged knives of agents were not entirely suitable for such kills. These blades did not make large enough wounds, but both the Fairbairn/Sykes Commando fighting knife and the OSS stiletto were designed for such work. Their razor sharp blades slid easily into a vulnerable part of the body, when the mouth and nose of a sentry was grasped firmly to prevent him calling out. Knife thrusts at the kidneys or lower body could be less effective, even with a sharp commando knife. For even this strong blade did not easily penetrate a German greatcoat worn over a tunic, shirt and vest. On the other hand any deep cut slashed on the exposed cheek or the backs of the victim's hands, could cause such a loss of blood that he could pass out in seconds, if he did not die.

Other knives—or 'blades' as they are known to the cognoscenti—were available to OSS, SOE and other agents. Most of these could be concealed in the agent's clothing, whereas the Commando knife or a stiletto was not easily hidden, even though they might be carried in an arm sheath worn beneath the sleeve of a suit jacket. Less bulky for concealment was the 'Nail' and similar special knives. One type of these could be withdrawn from its concealed sheath by using the fore and second fingers. Another, the 'Bodkin' had a seven-inch, nail-like blade fixed to a metal ball which fitted into the palm of the hand. Several 'Bodkins' were used experimentally by commandos in training at the swimming baths in Hove, Sussex. Possibly these knives were intended for use by swimmers, should they be captured when their working knife with its heavy blade would be taken from them.

Both SOE and OSS provided a wide selection of lapel knives, see Appendix 3.6. The thin, three-inch leather sheath was sewn under the lining behind a lapel. This was usually the left one near the top breast pocket of a suit. From this lapel the agent might slip out this knife as he was supposedly reaching for his identity papers. The sheath might be sewn in the large pocket for maps in a commando's battledress trousers, others were fastened on a man's trouser braces (suspenders). From wherever the blade was drawn, it remained concealed in the agent's palm as he faced, say the guard of a road block. He might then slash the guard's face or the back of his hand. Such a cut, across the veins on the back of the hand, was sufficient to give you time to take a dozen running strides down an alley, perhaps, or over a hedge into the darkness to escape immediate arrest. A single-edged razor blade could be used in similar fashion and might be less incriminating if found when a searcher was looking for messages, perhaps hidden behind a lapel, since the lapel knife was as incriminating as any gun. These small knives certainly gave agents some

reassurance but any knife, small or large, is only as effective as the determination of its user. Even the trained knife fighter, knowing where to strike and how to toss his blade from hand to hand as he approaches an enemy aware of his attack, needs this killer instinct. He also needs agility and the knowledge to strike upwards, not downwards. On some occasions the knife had to be left in the victim as there was insufficient time to twist and jerk it free of the wound, therefore OSS provided knives without any manufacturers' markings. Such 'sterile' knives could not be traced to their OSS or even American origins. Other types of knives are described in later chapters as they were designed for special purposes or for use in the jungles of Asia.

An alternative means of killing sentries, double-agents or any others an agent needed to eliminate, was the garrotte. Originally British Commandos, if not SOE, used simple cheese cutting wires. These had a piece of wire (sharp edged in some cases) with a wooden toggle at each end and were used by grocers to slice cheese blocks into portions for customers. The agent used them to cut his enemy's throat, creeping up behind him to slip the wire over his head and heave the two toggle or metal rod ends cross-wise to tighten the loop, which in strong hands could almost decapitate the victim. The usual method was to cross the hands while holding the garrotte vertically as an extended loop, then by pivoting the hands forward this loop could be slipped over a sentry's helmet and down around his neck. You then tightened the loop while putting one knee firmly in the victim's lower back to force him forward. A more effective method was to hold one end of the garrotte in the left hand while also grabbing the sentry's collar or shoulder straps, before passing the other hand and toggle end over his head. As the wire came down around his neck, the agent turned back to back with the sentry, crossing the wire in doing so. Then as the agent humped his back, the sentry's feet left the ground as the killing wire sliced into his throat.

SOE developed garrottes and these may on occasion have been used by OSS, as they were by the USMC in the Pacific. There were also a selection of coshes,

▼ The scabbard for F/S knives issued to OSS personnel had a metal mounting made by the Ecko Company. This was stamped by a tool that produced four slots similar to those in a kitchen spatula. The scabbard therefore became known as the 'pancake flapper'.

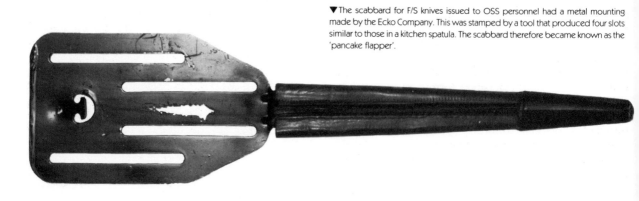

▲ Commandos trained to use their knives in the manner shown against vulnerable arteries at the side of the neck. Alternatively various slashes could be made against an enemy's stomach with an upwards motion of the knife. Lieut. C. Trepel of the Free French Forces serving in 10 (I-A) Cdo demonstrates the use of his knife. He was later killed during a reconnaissance on the Dutch coast in February 1944.

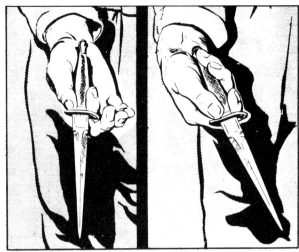

▲ When approaching an enemy aware he is to be attacked, the fighting knife was held lightly between the thumb and next finger with the handle lying between 'the fatty tissues of [the] palm'—to quote an instruction manual.

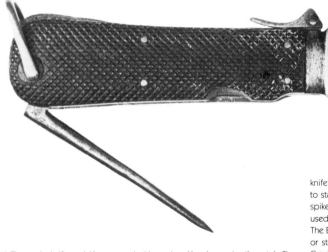

▲ The gravity knife could be opened with one hand by depressing the catch. The first 500 of these were made for SOE and other Special Forces in 1944, by George Ibberson & Co. The design closely resembled the German 'Flight Utility Knife', the *Fallschirmjägermesser* or Paratrooper's knife, originally issued to German aircrews. The British knife had a checkered grip (replacing the wooden grip of the German knife), an easily opened spike but no maker's markings. The blade could be used to stab an enemy in the neck when he was surprised from behind, this and the spike also provided useful tools for men living in the open. The blade might be used on occasion to cut parachute rigging lines when these were caught in trees. The Bexoid synthetic material of the grip proved ideal, enabling the user to slash or stab with this knife which was ten inches long when the blade was open. Gravity provided the means, so to speak of allowing the blade to drop open or fall back into the knife body, when the catch was released. After the first batch was produced subsequent batches carried the maker's name and markings. Ibberson and the Joseph Rodgers Co., both of Sheffield, Yorkshire, produced between 120,000 and 150,000 of these knives.

amongst which is the combined dagger-cosh-garrotte known as the 'Peskett'. The steel-bodied Mark 1 with a phosphate finish was issued to the special Home Guard units trained in 1940 to be left behind enemy lines if England was invaded. These were also issued to some Dutchmen of 10 (Inter-Allied) Commando. A subsequent pattern had a nickel-plated brass body. BCRA purchased about 100 of these but no reports have been traced of their use in action.

Many different forms of cosh were used in World War II. The simplest was a sand-filled sock, easily filled after walking through a road check at which a 'Peskett' would have been found in any thorough body search. Some 'hanging' straps used by standing passengers in London's underground trains were acquired by British service personnel if not by SOE. These knobs-on-springs may have been used by interrogators as they look more fearsome than the police truncheon wielded to frighten the man being questioned. But as with knives, the interrogator or the agent using a cosh had to know precisely where to hit his victim. Also important was the strength of the blow, especially if the agent only wished to knock out a French policeman or a Thai guard.

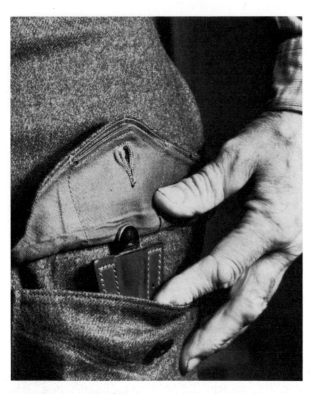

▲ One method of concealing the slim small 'thumb' knife was to sow its scabbard in the map pocket of battledress trousers. There it might be overlooked when a man was searched hastily after capture.

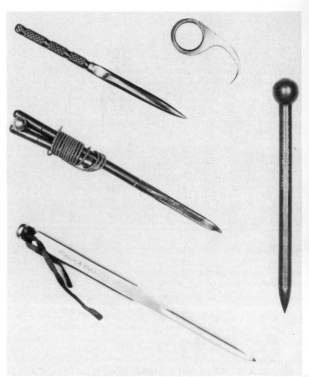

▲ These are examples of various forms of knives that could be concealed in the clothing or about the person. Top centre is the 'tyre-slasher' which could be concealed behind the buckle of a service gaiter. Other slashers were carried in a leather case or pivotted behind a coin, all were used with a downward motion to lacerate an enemy's face or upwards to slash the tyres of police vehicles. Top left is a Mappin and Webb five-inch brochette with both edges sharpened and shaped handle for a firm grip. Centre left is one of ten knives made for BCRA with blade tips that could carry poison and with a garrotte attached. The Mappin and Webb 'nail' knife (bottom left) like the 'bodkin' dagger (on the right) could be used with the base resting in the palm of the hand for a stabbing thrust of great force. There were many varieties of these so-called 'nail' and 'hat-pin' daggers. The Mappin 'nail' had a triangular cross-section, was about seven inches long. It had a thong or cord attached to its hilt-top by which the user might pull this blade from its hiding place in his clothing. The BCRA knife was drilled to take poison. Its user released this by breaking the tip's synthetic seal on a rough surface, before using the knife.

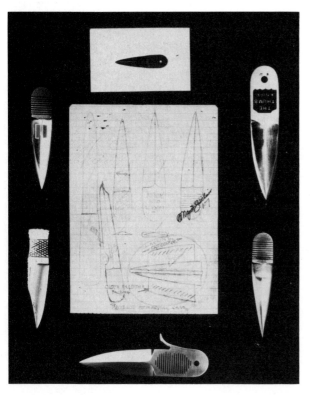

◀ The sketches above were made at a meeting on 22 December 1942 between a Major Sinclair of SOE and the jewellers Mappin and Webb of London. They set out the basic design for a lapel knife that was like a 'double edged sharpened nail file'. The chosen design—as 'ticked' in the sketches—had a thin diamond cross-section was $3^{1}/_{8}$ inches long and $^{5}/_{8}$ inches wide. The knife was to be 'blue' finished to avoid a shiny surface and have a milled thumb grip. Many subsequent variations were made, but apparently they always appeared too large and shiny for SOE's procurement officer. Mappins therefore gave him the ultra-small black knife as a joke, see top of illustration. Several blades were made possibly for other presentations or personal knives. The blade top left has the red, white and blue French emblem enamelled on it. The bottom left item is in the form of a skeandhu and was sold in Scottish tailors. The bottom item has 'the hand of Fatima' (of unknown origin in this case) protruding above the blade. Top right is a Wilkinson Sword thumb knife, razor sharp and marked 'WD' for War Department. It is $4^{1}/_{4}$ inches long. Bottom right is one of the first Mappin and Webb blades, without the hole for a thong loop which was added to later types.

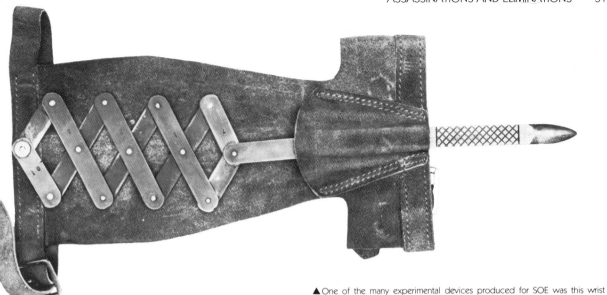

▲ One of the many experimental devices produced for SOE was this wrist extension for a five inch blade. The leather sleeve was strapped inside the forearm from where the user might extend the knife on its folding metal arm. There is no record of this device being produced in quantity, perhaps because the prototype proved too bulky under a jacket sleeve.

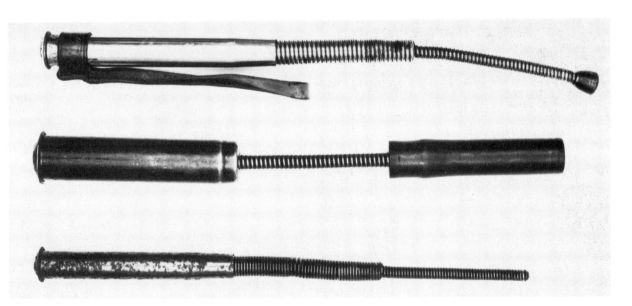

▲ Spring loaded coshes enabled the user to conceal this weapon up a sleeve, the weighted end extending only when the swing of the user's arm extended the spring. A right-handed man threw his weight forward onto his left foot, as he swung the cosh at an enemy's temple below his helmet. The OSS cosh (at top) was held around the wrist by a cord that was loose enough to be easily slipped from the hand. The German 'Sipo' (*Sicherheitsdienst*) cosh (second from top) had similar features to the OSS cosh, but the SD's rubber truncheon (third from top) was designed to cause injuries that were not lethal. The SD also had a miniature cosh (bottom) which could be easily concealed on the person. The OSS spring cosh telescoped into its seven-inch handle but measured 16 inches when fully extended as both concentric springs came out of the handle. This was of tubular steel covered in leather with a metal loop for the thong. Its total weight was 10 ounces.

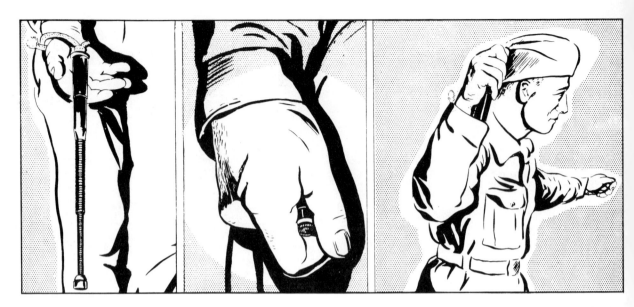

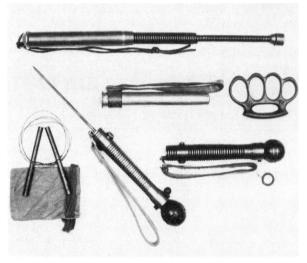

▲ This series of weapons for close-quarters combat illustrate several features of SOE and OSS equipment. The garrotte (bottom left) was issued in a small cloth bag coloured 'olive, drab'. The metal handles are stamped 'WD' and the throat-cutting wire coiled for stowage in the bag. The Peskett close combat weapon had a dagger (extended in centre illustration) that could be retracted into its handle. This example has been stamped with the cross of Loraine, the symbol of the Free French forces. The folded Peskett (on right) has the ring used to pull a garrotte from its spool inside the handle, the weighted ball end was used as a cosh. The knuckle-dusters (top right) are made of a low grade metal and not the usual brass. They carry a stamped marking 'BC 41' and are probably not an item regularly issued but sold possibly as a 'British Commando 1941' item. Top centre is a folded 'Sipo' cosh for comparison with the Allied weapons. The McLagen-Peskett was seven inches long when the blade—a spike blade, according to the patented particulars—was in the body. This in the Mark I was of ribbed steel with a release latch for the 5½-inch blade. The blackened body's knob could be rotated to wind the garrotte wire onto its spool. This wire was of square section being a patented salmon fishing trace sold as 'Paternoster' wire. The Peskett was sold commercially by Cogswell and Harrison of London and although only 100 were produced for SOE and BCRA, the quantity sold commercially is not known. The Peskett's leather sheath had tabs for sewing to clothing.

In using knives, garrottes or coshes, the agent had to get close to his or her victim, at times needing a silent approach or at others, the brazen boldness which put an enemy off his guard. Major Fairbairn contended that the '. . . knife was a woman's weapon . . .' since she could more easily get very close to the man she needed to kill. More often, however, the ladies needed the certainty of a bullet to kill their enemy. Yet, as Ben Cowburn has written, any hand gun, '. . . fired by the average person . . . would merely be a useless noise at a range of more than a dozen yards . . .'. Therefore Fairbairn taught agents and others how to hold a hand gun, so that it was much easier to aim than by using the 'extended arm' stance which had been used in military pistol shooting. Instead the pistol was held in both hands and aimed with the arms bent at the elbows. Women favoured the Webley '32' as it could be easily cocked by sliding back the mechanism, its outside hammer also apparently appealing to the ladies. This and other small pistols could be fitted with silencers, or 'suppressors' as they are called by weapon experts. Different suppressors are known to have been fitted to a few of SOE's 1910 Mausers, 1937 Czech automatics and Italian Berettas. They were also fitted to OSS hand guns like the HDM (High Standard Model D Military) a .22-inch pistol.

SOE had Webley Scott .22-inch target pistols fitted with silencers for accurate shots that might be needed in assassinating a double-agent or security police official, before the weapons researchers at Welwyn produced the Welrod Mark 1. This single-shot weapon was the most silent weapon of World War II as not only was it silenced but its low velocity bullet made no tell-tale 'crack' when fired. The Mark II A had a magazine feed for about five rounds but the muzzle velocity of ordinary bullets which it could fire produced a distinc-

The .22-cal HDM silenced pistol (top) was designed for close range shots, and could not be heard above traffic noises or might be mistaken for a door closing 'or other activities of everyday life'. It was produced for use by OSS personnel in a closed room or to eliminate a sentry. The Webley Scott 6.35mm pistol with its suppressor (second from top) was used by an SOE agent in France. It has the chilling inscription on its silencer 'mort aux Boches' (death to Germans). The Colt Commando 38-cal pistol (third from top) was one of 1,000 shipped by Colt to OSS on 28 September 1943. Subsequently it was used by C. W. (Maggie) Magill in Greece, who filed rough checkering on part of the gun to prevent it 'slipping in combat'. The Webley Scott 7.65mm pistol (bottom left) belonged to a British policeman before World Warr II, he later carried it in France when working for SOE. Bottom right is a German Walther 7.65mm 'PPK' pistol, one of a number captured during the war. This one was chosen from OSS' stocks of enemy weapons by a member of the American Special Forces while in Europe. The silenced .22 automatic was 14 inches in length, weighed 2 lb 12 oz and could not be used without its supressor. This had a wire mesh lining that needed frequent replacement. The clip of 'long-rifle high-speed ammunition' could take ten rounds.

tive crack. Its suppressor had also to be specially ventilated to dissipate energy, using rubber baffles 'for total efficiency'. The result was that gases continued to hiss faintly from the gun after firing. There was also some danger of setting the holster or your trousers alight with the powder and rubber fragments that smouldered after firing. There was a special holster for a Welrod but the gun might also be carried in two parts. These were hung on loops inside the trouser legs where they might not be detected if an agent was casually frisked.

Any pistol found on an agent during a security check was bound to lead to his or her interrogation and probably to subsequent execution. Therefore some weapon was needed that might not be immediately recognised as a fire-arm and which could also provide a means for agents to commit suicide if they did not have access to an L-pill. Welwyn produced the Welpen, designed to fire a .22-inch bullet and look like a fountain pen. Only a hundred were made at Welwyn before the more generally deceptive Enpen was produced by the British ordnance factory at Enfield. Its .22-inch round was built into the pen-like body of the weapon. This had a mechanism made of such high quality components that the spring powering the bolt was effective in one which was fired at a practice target 40 years after this Enpen was made. The device was also much closer than the Welpen in appearance to a cheap pen. One agent carried two or three of these in preference to a pistol, as they did not attract attention, and a frontier guard was unlikely to consider such ordinary looking pens worth stealing.

The Enpen might be fired like OSS' Stinger, or the Welpen when pulled from the breast pocket to shoot an interrogator. Alternatively, '. . . if you were being led by the arm or even handcuffed, you could place this pen-gun backhanded against your captor . . .', firing it close to his body. Then its blast was muffled by his clothing and unlikely to attract the attention of other guards in the next rooms.

Another single-shot device was the Wel-Woodbine, ¼ inch in diameter and three inches long, firing a specially hardened 4.5mm projectile from a one-inch barrel. The device could be rolled in a cigarette paper, (although not necessarily that of the popular Woodbine brand in the 1940s). There was a recess in the barrel mouth designed to take a little plug of tobacco pasted in place before it was charred. This suggested that the Wel-Woodbine had been stubbed out and therefore when offered a packet of cigarettes, the intended victim took one of the others leaving the agent to 'finish' the once-lit Wel-Woodbine. He then bit its cork-plugged end with some piece of theatrical business perhaps spitting it out, as the safety-pin came out with the cork. All the agent then needed to do was to touch the small trigger protruding through the paper, firing the device with his thumb nail. The shot could wound the interrogator or if the agent turned the weapon to fire into his own mouth, it would kill him. It could be reloaded if you survived its first use! The tiny breach was then taken out by removing the cross-pins which held it. After loading, the trigger mechanism was made safe by replacing the pin attached to a new piece of cork.

All these small devices could be as dangerous to the firer as to the enemy, so they were held as you would hold a dart with fingers along one side, and the thumb at

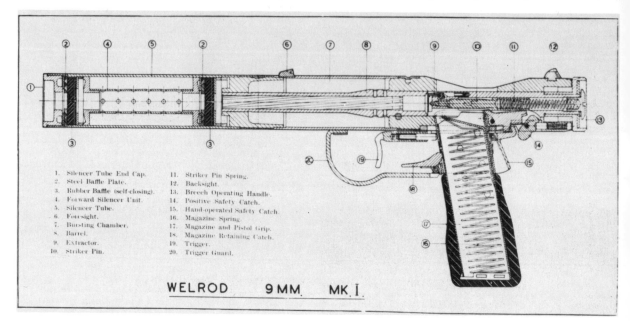

1. Silencer Tube End Cap.
2. Steel Baffle Plate.
3. Rubber Baffle (self-closing).
4. Forward Silencer Unit.
5. Silencer Tube.
6. Foresight.
7. Bursting Chamber.
8. Barrel.
9. Extractor.
10. Striker Pin.
11. Striker Pin Spring.
12. Backsight.
13. Breech Operating Handle.
14. Positive Safety Catch.
15. Hand-operated Safety Catch.
16. Magazine Spring.
17. Magazine and Pistol Grip.
18. Magazine Retaining Catch.
19. Trigger.
20. Trigger Guard.

WELROD   9 MM.   MK. I

▲ The Welrod 9mm Mark I was a single-shot pistol with a supressor shown here as illustrated in an American secret technical review of May 1944. Its general purposes were to provide aimed shots at 15 to 30m, or when fired without the silencer it was a single-shot pistol. It could be fired by untrained sub-agents when pressed against an enemy's body. An earlier model fired a 7.65mm round with a low muzzle velocity that avoided the usual crack of a high-speed bullet. The gun fired any type of parabellum 9mm ammunition with accuracy. The firer steadied the barrel with thumb and fore finger of one hand while applying steady pressure to the trigger with the other hand. Five or six rounds were carried in the pistol grip and loaded individually by pulling the 'breech opening handle.' There were two safety catches: a positive catch locked the bolt; and a second behind the grip was depressed to arm the weapon. It weighed 3 lb 6½ oz, and was 14½ inches long (including the supressor). The fixed sights were accurate at 15 yards, the firer having the back-sight six inches from his eye when standing to take an aimed shot. The Welrod did not come into general production until 1945. A 'Mark IIA' was also designed with a magazine feed.

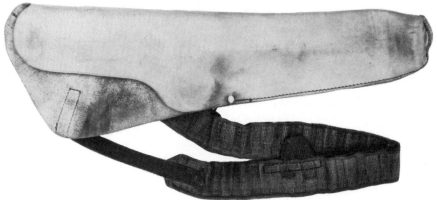

The shoulder holster for the Welrod pistol was made by Mappin and Webb. ▲

▶ This series of small single-shot 'pens' and other easily concealed weapons were for close-quarter shots. At the top is a training aid which showed the elements of an Enpen. This single-shot .22-inch gun was produced in quantity by the British Ordnance factory at Enfield and available to agents from late in 1944. It could not be reloaded but a training version was made (second from top) which fired reloadable blank cartridges, simulating some of the effects of firing a production Enpen. It was supplied in a leather case with blank cartridges, an ejector rod and a tool to cock the gun. An experimental example of the Welpen (third from top) was used by SOE in evaluation tests after which the Enpen was selected. Some pen-like weapons fired tear gas as did the .38-inch gun (fourth from top) supplied to both SOE and OSS. A 'Mark II' version of the Enpen (fifth from top) was developed which could be re-used. Its barrel unscrewed to allow a fresh round of ammunition to be inserted. A sophisticated weapon that was supplied in a leather pouch, it compares starkly with the OSS Stinger (bottom). This was intended for use by an agent who might fire it into the face of an interrogator or use it to commit suicide. It might also be used by a guerrilla when pressed against his victim in a crowd. A throw away weapon once fired, its single .22-inch bullet could be as dangerous for the firer as for his enemy when the Stinger was misused. The Stinger weighed 1/3 oz being only 3½ inches long. The cartridge was built into the weapon during manufacture. It was fired by raising the lever along the body and then this was pressed back to its original poisition. Design difficulties—see Appendix 3.8—delayed production until the summer of 1944. The Enpen proved more reliable, with its bolt held by two ball-bearings which when displaced by a two-inch long rod, moved apart to engage in small holes in the pen's body. To cock the weapon and fire it, the pocket-clip was moved back three-quarters of an inch. This moved the rod from between the bearings, allowing them to move together and free the bolt which flew forward on its spring. The official instructions for this 'Auxiliary firing device, hand-held Enpen Mk I' warned that the user should allow the pen to move freely in the hand as 'owing to its small size and quite a smart recoil, it may not be grasped firmly'.

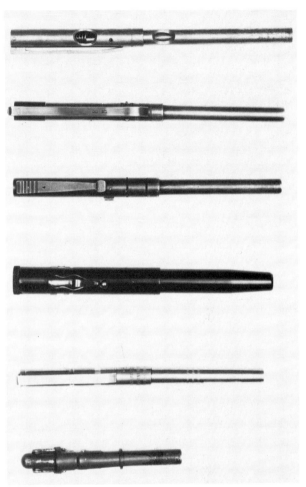

▲ A .22-cal single-shot device made by Welwyn Laboratories for OSS. It resembled a pipe with a bayonet twist mechanism 'suitable for mass production by USA factories'—to quote the legend on the display.

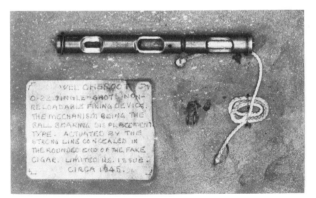

▲ This Wel Cheroot fired a single .22-inch bullet and was not reloadable. About four and a half inches long, the 'cheroot' had a mechanism that was activated by pulling a strong line hidden in the rounded end of the cigar. This released the ball-bearing which held the firing pin. A limited number were issued to OSS in about 1945.

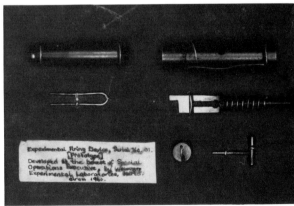

▲ This display board illustrates the components of the Welpen. This single shot weapon assembled to look not unlike a fountain pen of the 1940s but was never produced in any quantity. The weapon illustrated has the serial number 01, and was designed to fire a single .22-inch bullet. The legend on the display board reads 'Experimental firing device, Serial 01 [prototype] developed at the behest of Special Operations Executive, by Welwyn Experimental Laboratories, Herts. circa 1941'. The board was one of a series made up by the laboratory at the end of the war.

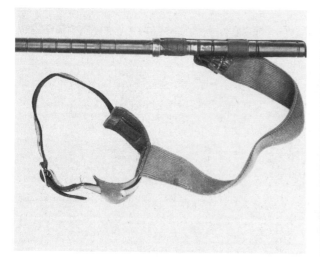

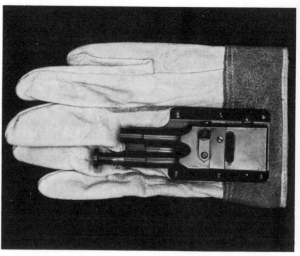

▲This Wel Wand was a non-reloadable single shot device that fired a bullet probably of .22-cal. It is approximately a foot long including its supressor. The weapon hung by its elastic inside the forearm with the leather band fixed around the shoulder and beneath the arm pit. All the weapon was concealed beneath a jacket sleeve or other clothing. Once pulled down into the palm it could be fired when pressed against the victim, the device then slipping out of sight as its elastic pulled it up the sleeve. The firing mechanism was similar but larger than that used to fire an Enpen.

▲The US Navy's glove pistol or 'fist gun' was designed for the wearer to go about his normal activities but with a weapon instantly available. The Mark II shown here fired a single .38 inch bullet. The plunger cocked the weapon when it was pushed against an assailant and then fired the gun, in one motion. After being fired the gun could be used as a form of knuckle duster. S. M. Haight patented the Mark I which fired a 410 shotgun 'shell'. US Naval Intelligence modified this design as the Mark II which weighed only a few ounces.

the other side or below it. The thumb nail could then trigger a Wel-Woodbine or raise the pen-like pocket clip of the other devices to fire them. Care, indeed great care, was needed to hold such devices to the side of the head clear of the face when firing them, as they recoiled so violently they could become a missile going the opposite way to the bullet.

US Naval intelligence had a 'fist gun' which fired a single shot from the back of the wearer's gloved hand if he was attacked, say, by a mob in a market. This, like the Winchester sniper's rifle, was not in the main stream of SOE or OSS weapons but were usually available from associated agencies if the Special Forces required them. Special Forces in American terms implies clandestine agencies but to the British it meant Commando and SAS uniformed forces, rather than SOE or SIS. This distinction was more a matter of word than fact for in the guerrilla wars of the 1940s both uniformed and Secret Special Forces had a good deal in common

when training. All, for example, learnt something of the use of enemy weapons which SOE, OSS and SIS, had available for operations. There were also no doubt special guns which could be fired from suit cases by the agent carrying one of these, or similar lethal toys. One of the most effective 'specials', produced in such quantity that it cannot now be regarded as a special weapon, was the 'Liberator', a .45-in pistol supplied in great quantities to guerrilla forces. It was to be used for the single shot which killed an enemy soldier in order that his weapons could be stolen for the Resistance forces. This very cheap gun was assembled with such secrecy in 1942 that factories producing components for the gun were given blueprints with misleading titles—the striker/firing pin being called a 'control rod', the trigger guard a 'spanner' and so on. The assembly was called a Flare Projector to mislead the inquisitive, although there was an infra-red signal flare that could be fired from it. but its original purpose as set out in a proposal

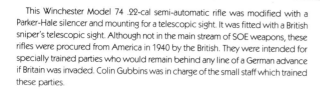

This Winchester Model 74 .22-cal semi-automatic rifle was modified with a Parker-Hale silencer and mounting for a telescopic sight. It was fitted with a British sniper's telescopic sight. Although not in the main stream of SOE weapons, these rifles were procured from America in 1940 by the British. They were intended for specially trained parties who would remain behind any line of a German advance if Britain was invaded. Colin Gubbins was in charge of the small staff which trained these parties.

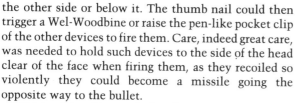

▲ The 'Liberator' hand gun was widely distributed to guerrillas, as it was intended to shoot an enemy whose weapons could then be captured. Known to many as the 'Woolworth' gun when these stores sold nothing costing more than six pence or a dime, Filipino guerrillas called it the 'Kangaroo' gun. Many were shipped to the Philippines in Australian submarines but few were distributed in Europe. By the autumn of 1942 one million Liberators had been manufactured by General Motors at a cost of $1.72 per gun. The gun fired .45-cal single rounds, with 10 rounds of this ball ammunition in the handle. It weighed 1 lb 7 oz with the 10 rounds and was six inches long. Spent cartridge cases were pushed by a wooden rod through the breech retainer after firing. The barrel was of seamless tube, the body of pressed metal, yet one Liberator withstood eight shots being fired before it became dangerous to use. Its official designation was the 'FP .45'.

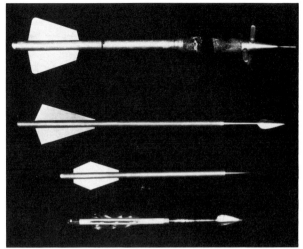

▲ A series of darts were developed by OSS for use in the Penetrometer project. This was intended to produce a silent, flashless weapon using a form of crossbow. Several different sizes of bow were used experimentally by both OSS and SOE. The large incendiary dart (top) was fired from 'Big Joe' as was the anti-personnel dart (second from top). The 'William Tell' dart (third from top) and the still smaller dart for 'Little Joe' (bottom) were effective at 80 yards. The largest Penetrometer, 'Joe Louis' weighed 35 lb and was intended to fire grenades. 'Big Joe' type-5 weighed 9.4 lb, fired its darts an effective 150 yards, its 'estimated killing range'. Its darts penetrated three-quarters of an inch into fir plywood when fired at six feet, which suggests that a vital part of the human target might have to be hit at 150 yards. 'Little Joe' fired a 24-gram dart up to 700 yards using a 160-pound pull on its elastic.

from the joint Psychological Warfare Committee and dated 20 March 1942 was to provide arms for civilians in occupied countries as a boost to their morale. Although the committee realised that the Germans or Nazi sympathizers might find four of every five dropped, the psychological effect would be startling. The committee suggested that a radio broadcast might say, '250,000 revolvers (sic) are being dropped'. Then if the Germans found only 100,000, 'the knowledge that 150,000 guns were missing ... would have a direct effect upon German morale'. The Committee therefore proposed that, '... the United States and Britain undertake at once to manufacture and distribute from five to ten million very small, inexpensive, heavy calibre pistols ...' One million had been made by the end of 1942 but few were distributed in Europe for reasons which are not clear. These may have been political rather than military as many exiled governments were wary by late 1943 that their return home after the defeat of Germany might be met by civil war.

These weapons all fired conventional jacketed bullets which met the requirements of the Geneva Convention on warfare. This had specifically barred the use of the plain lead bullet which could—as a dum-dum round—splay out to inflict needlessly damaging wounds. The initial production of Stingers however, incorporated a

commercial .22-inch lead bullet used on firing ranges. These early Stingers were therefore distributed to guerrillas in South-East Asia. They no doubt had as much difficulty in deciding which was the lethal end of this device, as did the instructor who shot himself while demonstrating how the Stinger worked.

THE possibilities for the use of bows as silent strike weapons were explored by two Commando officers, Lieutenant Colonel Jack Churchill and the Danish Major Anders Lassen. The Major probably, but certainly a commando, killed a German sentry with an arrow during a raid on Sark in the Channel Islands on 3/4 October 1942. Both he and the Colonel later carried bows and arrows during raids in the Aegean and Adriatic but apparently with no significant results. OSS used darts against dogs as explained below but not against humans, nor was the ingenious dart pen intended for MI 9's escape lines ever issued, although it was tested by BCRA who sent a few to Paris. It worked on the same principle as an air rifle. Perhaps the German seeing such a dart, a flighted wooden gramophone needle, might have believed he had been poisoned. Certainly there are reports of poison being available to BCRA but its use on dart-tips was no doubt impractical.

A much larger air-powered weapon was cheaply produced with a phosphate finish to fire a ¾-inch hollow bullet which had a hyperdermic needle point behind which was sealed a tranquillizing drug in liquid form. This would be injected into a dog when the bullet hit its target, and a lead pellet broke the syringe seal. The drug put the dog to sleep rather than killing it, for a dead dog was a sure sign that intruders were about while a sick one needed all its handler's attention after it did not answer his call. The air-gun could be reloaded by pressing the now extended barrel back towards the butt. OSS used arrows for similar purposes in experiments on taking out guard dogs in the China-Burma-India theatre.

More conventional means of drugging dogs were powders, one of which SOE agents nicknamed 'Bob Martins' after a well known conditioning powder and another which OSS called 'Hush Puppy'. Either powder sprinkled on a piece of strong-smelling meat or fish, could be thrown to dogs in a wired compound or the dog-run between a pair of perimeter fences.

OSS also had Dog Drag equipment which was a cloth bag containing an ampoule of 'persistent aromatic fluid'. The ampoule could be broken by a thumb screw after removing the safety-catch. Then the liquid soaked into a wick in the drag (cloth bag) which was pulled on a length of cord to leave a trail which would confuse

▲ The 'Big Joe' Penetrometer required a force of 300 lb to stretch its elastic. But this type-6, lighter than the type-5, fired three to four darts a minute. These each weighed 44 grams and at six feet could penetrate 16 inches into horse meat. The type-6 'Big Joe' was 5 x 28 x 15 inches when opened but folded to 5 x 24 x 3½ inches. It weighed 5.8 lb.

▼ The tear gas gun (top) was available to both SOE and OSS who distributed a number of these among French resistance forces. The gun fired a .38-inch ampoule of gas which might cause sufficient confusion in a crowded room, to enable an agent to escape arrest. SOE's air powered dart pen (bottom) was designed by Clayton Hutton of MI 9. It fired the hard-wood gramophone needle which had been adapted to take the flights used on air gun metal darts. Hutton's intention was that this gun should be fired into the face of a soldier or policeman challenging the agent. This would cause a distraction that enabled the agent to evade capture. The gas gun could be reloaded by unscrewing the body of the gun to insert a new ampoule and charge. The dart gun was re-charged by depressing the extended part of the gun (at the right on the bottom picture). Correspondence from BCRA dated 18 October 1943 states that the Bureau could use 2,000 to 3,000 of this 'psychological weapon'.

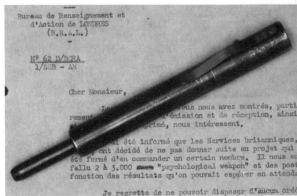

▲ The only known example of the SOE dart pen lying across a letter from Colonel Passy expressing regret that he cannot get sufficient of these.

▼ Lieutenant Colonel W. E. Fairbairn's skills in close-combat, pistol shooting and associated martial arts had a major impact on the training methods of Special Forces. He was one of the designers of the commando fighting knife, established the commando methods of unarmed combat, trained SOE agents and later was an instructor at Camp X. There he trained OSS personnel during the last years of the war.

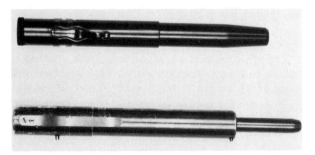

trained tracker dogs. As this scent lasted some time, the Dog Drag was intended to protect foot-paths leading to concealed stores or similar hides which might be visited regularly.

Equally smelly but used for quite different purposes, was MI 9's teargas pen. This was supplied to some personnel running escape lines and might, like the lapel knife, distract an enemy long enough for this agent to make an escape.

M OST agents when confronted by an unexpected policeman or in Europe by a member of the German *Feldgendarmerie* (military police), might not have a knife or gun to hand. He or she would then have to rely on their bare hands and whatever they might grab to break free. At other times a sentry might be attacked in this way, the agent wearing brass knuckle dusters in anticipation of a brawl. With these he could hit the man on either side of the neck, or—if the sentry wore only light clothing—he might be punched in the kidneys. As he fell a few sharp kicks would lay him out if not kill him, a ruthless but vital approach to hand-to-hand fighting. Such methods Major Fairbairn had taught first to Commandos, then SOE agents and during the last two years of the war when he was a lieutenant colonel and instructor for OSS at Camp X. He had devised throws, chopping blows and nerve-deadening hand holds from a mixture of ju-jitsu, other marshal arts and his own practical experience in the Shanghai police during the 1930s. He also taught the principles by which you win such fights in the mind rather than by physical techniques: being totally ruthless from the start, no tentative jabs as a boxer might make in measuring his opponent's strength. Yet going straight for the kill does require supreme self-confidence, a habit of mind which he most successfully taught to his pupils. They therefore left this part of the training course willing to tackle anyone, however tall or strong he might appear.

Harry Rée, a schoolmaster before the war, whom F Section sent to organize the 'Stockbroker' circuit in 1943, had many successes. In one of these he blackmailed the French director of a factory working for the Germans, into sabotaging its output or facing the destruction of this Peugeot factory by Allied bombing. Rée was betrayed and a German military police patrol came to his supposedly 'safe' house. One of them found Rée in the kitchen but he fought to resist arrest, striking out with a bottle of brandy as the kitchen crockery crashed around them in a fist fight. Unable to remember any details of Fairbairn's teaching, Rée nevertheless showed the determination to win this fight even if he could not gouge out his opponent's eyes. Rée managed to get out of the back door but was shot several times as

he ran. One bullet penetrated his lung and another grazed his heart, four more caused less serious wounds, nevertheless he reached a river nearby. He leaped or fell into its strong current, swam to the far bank and crawled 6km from there through woods and across fields to reach a doctor. The wounds were so serious that only sheer determination had kept him alive. He later recovered sufficiently to escape across the Pyrenees in November 1943 after nine months in France—a remarkable feat of courage by a man who hated war and later became a Professor of Education.

There are a number of such epics of survival against great odds, in the histories of SOE and OSS. Others certainly went unrecorded because the agent died before he finally reached safety. Jan Baalsrud did survive, although as a Norwegian Commando in his early twenties he was sent by the Free Norwegians in March 1943 on an SOE supported mission. Its four agents were caught by a German patrol when they landed and all but Jan were killed or captured. He managed to reach a gully and climb through its soft snow, before four Germans could capture him. His pistol iced up but at the third attempt he shot the patrol leader who had not realized that Jan was armed. This enabled him to escape further up the hill although he had lost one boot and a toe from his right foot, shot off in a rattle of German bullets and the heavier crunch of ship's shells. He was hunted, swam fiords, and was helped by farmers on the Lofoten Islands before he crossed to the mainland. There originally he and the other agents were to set up a training course for the Norwegian Resistance later to attack the German airfield at Bardufoss. In the event Jan's feet became frost bitten, he endured four days lost in the Lyngen Alps early in April. Three weeks later and closer to the frontier with Finland, he was hidden by a Norwegian family and friends after they found him blind from the snow's glare. They took him food when they could between blizzards which buried him in a sleeping bag on the open mountain for a week. During May these friends made three attempts to get him across the Finnish border on a sledge. They finally succeeded towards the end of the month when some Lapps took him across on a sledge pulled by reindeer in the middle of a great herd of reindeer. A German patrol tried but failed to intercept them on this leg of his escape as the deer crossed a frozen lake. During the next week the Lapps took him across north-east Finland to reach Sweden on 1 June.

As soon as he was in hospital under the care of the Red Cross, he began drafting a report on his mission. Such were the men of the Linge Company of Norwegian Commandos who served in 10 (Inter-Allied) Commando, sometimes working on missions supported by SOE and at other times landing with British Commandos for military style raids.

3

THE INTER-ALLIED COMMANDO ANI

THE training of commandos and of the OGs fitted them for clandestine work with little specialized training. This we have seen with the two Czechs of 'Anthropoid' and Jan Baalsrud in Norway although in military operations commandos almost invariably fought in uniform as did men of the British Special Air Service (SAS). The exception was blurred in that 10 (Inter-Allied) Commando with its sub-units drawn from several Allied armies, provided men who from time to time served as agents of their countries' secret services. Their operations were usually supported by SOE who provided special weapons, specific training for such missions and access to the military intelligence on which plans were based. We will unravel in Chapter 5 some of the complexities of such organization in explaining how both SOE and OSS administered their operations, but in 1942 '10(I-A)' trained with Company Linge. In this company were the most able of the Norwegian commandos like Jan Baalsrud, and their raids were almost as often involved with clandestine work as with purely military operations.

Norway had been overrun in May 1940 by German mountain troops whose initial operations were prepared in great secrecy and brushed aside Norway's neutrality. Seven ships sailed ostensibly to pick up cargoes of fish from Norway's northern port of Narvik, from Trondheim and Stavanger. Hidden in the holds were troops who, after the ships had been moored alongside the quays, surprised the local police and soldiers by seizing these ports in the early hours of Tuesday 9 April 1940. Other German forces landed in Oslo and within six weeks—after the Germans had launched Panzer divisions across Holland, Belgium and northern France—Norway was occupied and a puppet government established by the Germans.

So far as is known no British Secret Intelligence Service (SIS) agents (who could speak Norwegian) were in Norway at that time. And not even a British military mission was in Norway before April of that year, because the Norwegians had wished to maintain absolute neutrality. But Section D had Gerard Holdsworth secretly looking for possible future contacts, should Norway be invaded. He had orders, however, to leave when Norway was invaded because he did not speak Norwegian. At this time nevertheless a remarkable report came through the British naval attaché from an anonymous scientist. It included references to glider bombs, 80cm rockets with gyrostabilizers, a radio beam to guide aircraft and many

more innovations. All this seemed too good intelligence to be true. Had not SIS sent misleading technicalities to the Germans through a double-agent Johnny Owens? The fact that his German controller put off a meeting that April, because—he said—'. . . a major offensive is pending . . .', was ignored by British intelligence along with other pointers to possible German activity in Scandinavia. Among these was heavy signals traffic from the German ship *Widar* in Oslo fjord, intercepted but not analysed by the British, whether they decoded it or not.

Colin Gubbins was commanding at this time a number of independent companies, forerunners of the commandos, and Malcolm Munthe, son of the author, was sent by Military Intelligence Research (MI R) as their liaison officer in Norway. Wounded, he was captured but later escaped as did several hundred Norwegians who came to Britain to join the Norwegian forces of their exiled government. Many of them escaped by sea, which would become a two-way highway with a regular service to Norway from the Shetland Islands that was later known as the 'Shetland Bus', a service run jointly by SOE and the Norwegian military. Such activities, however, did not have the unquestioned support of exiled politicians in London as they feared heavy reprisals against local people. This fear was heightened when two Norwegians were caught in possession of explosives after landing in April 1942 to attack aircraft at Stavanger. They died, but in a gun battle killed the head of the SD in Bergen and another officer, reason enough by the Nazi creed to take retribution with the execution of 18 civilians.

Despite such understandable concern by the Norwegian Government in London, there was one target in the south-western province of Telemark which was of such importance that its destruction could decide the outcome of the war. This was the Norsk Hydro Company's factory at Vermork where heavy-water was manufactured. Difficult to process, this liquid required vast quantities of electricity to create small quantities of a fluid that could be used in making atom bombs, as it absorbs neutrons, in the way graphite is used in some processes.

The British special agent Bill Stephenson—of whom more later—visited the plant in 1939. He knew that it was largely owned by I.G. Farben the giant German chemical group of companies who manufactured industrial chemicals and other materials for the German war effort. By February 1942 Farben planned to expand production of this heavy water to 4,500kg a year, sufficient for the possible development of a neutron bomb when used in conjunction with Uranium 235. This was known to Professor Tronstad, who had passed details of the process to Bill Stephenson, as were many more of such technicalities, when Tronstad again contacted the British SIS while still in Norway. The Germans learned of his contacts and a double-agent warned him to leave. Escaping to England he was later appointed head of the Norwegian clandestine forces, Section IV of their High Command.

Combined Operations Headquarters (who controlled the commandos at that time) and SOE, both considered what might be done to destroy this plant. Their first opportunity to evolve a realistic plan came with the arrival in England of Einar Skinnarland from Rjukan. He had taken a holiday from his job supervising construction work of the Mös lake dam, 12km west of Vermork. During this 'holiday' he sailed to Scotland with some companions and his potential value as an agent was realized after his interrogation at an MI 9 reception centre for escapees. SOE gave him a short course in clandestine activities before he was parachuted back to Telemark within 11 days of leaving Rjukan. There he renewed his friendship with several workers in the nearby heavy-water plant, sending reports by courier to London while continuing his civilian job.

In September the days became shorter and among the plans considered by SOE was one suggested by the Norwegian Jomar Brun. With the longer hours of darkness a plane might fly to Telemark, land on a frozen lake and fly out with the stocks of heavy-water, without attracting too much attention from German aircraft. However the ice on the lakes was apparently not yet frozen solidly enough to withstand the weight of such a landing. Dr Brun who had designed the Norsk Hydro plant sent other reports, some on 35mm film hidden in tubes of toothpaste. He also put small quantities of castor oil in the vats, not knowing that others were adding cod liver oil to the process on Stephenson's instruction. Both these additives caused excessive frothing which slowed the process but did not prevent stocks of heavy-water being built up. More drastic action was required but bombing was at that time considered to be out of the question as the factory lay on the edge of a steep-sided valley and would be difficult to hit from the air.

Combined Operations came up with a plan to land 34

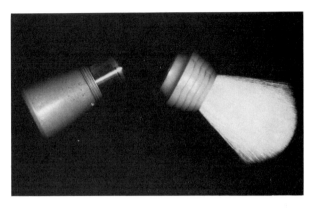

▲ The hollow chamber in this shaving brush could be used to hide photographic film or clandestine messages.

engineers of 9 (Airborne) Field Company of the Royal Engineers in two Horsa gliders towed by Halifaxes. But 'Jack' Wilson saw that this scheme had serious drawbacks. He headed the Scandinavian Country Section of SOE, after serving as its first director of training. Always calm, patient and accurate in the detail of his work, Wilson had been an officer in the Indian police and a leading figure in the Boy Scout movement. (He wrote *Scouting Round the World*, Blandford 1959.) He realized the difficulties for glider pilots caught in the air currents over the Hardanger Plateau north of Vermork, even if they could spot the landing strip through the clouds which hung over these Telemark mountains. Nevertheless the British War Cabinet decided that the flight must be attempted.

An advance party led by the tall Sub-Lieutenant Jens A. Poulsson with Sergeants Claus Helberg and Arne Kjelstrup both from Rjuken, and Knut Haugland a former Merchant Navy radio officer, parachuted onto the plateau on 18 October 1942. They landed 'blind'— that is, without any reception party to meet them—but were able after many privations to clear a landing strip for the gliders due in mid-November, and set up a Eureka homing beacon. On one attempt this did not work, however, because of a breakdown in an aircraft's Rebecca radar transmitter. The aircraft failed to reach the landing zone on their third attempt because both gliders and a Halifax iced up in the severe cold over the mountains. All three then crashed and the 20 survivors were shot or put to death by doctors in the hospital treating the injured. After this failure, the destruction of the Norsk Hydro plant became solely an SOE responsibility.

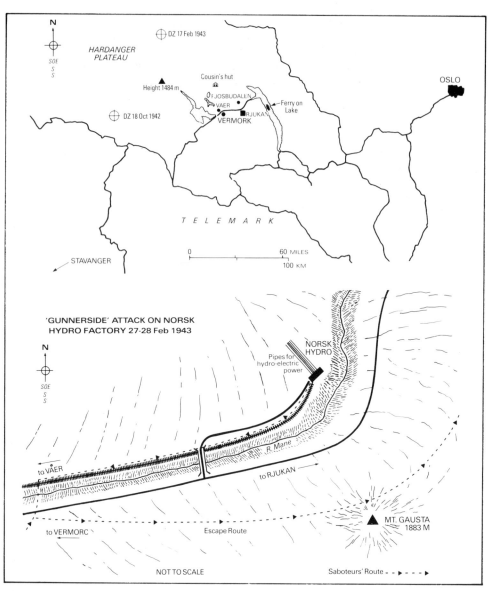

◄Vermork was in Telemark (see map at top). Its Norsk Hydro factory was attacked by Norwegian saboteurs who had been trained by SOE. The final stages of their approach to the factory and their escape route are shown on the lower map.

That winter of 1942-43 SOE were mainly concerned in Norway with the training of men for the local Milorg (Military Organization) of resistance forces. The Executive ran for example 11 courses in guerrilla warfare, sabotage and close combat in one region alone. But Poulsson's team lost their main contact in Milorg when Skinnarland's brother was arrested along with others seized by the Germans, although later Skinnarland would visit them in the cabin—built originally by Poulsson's cousin—30km north of Rjuken. Meanwhile they survived on oats, supplemented by reindeer moss and little else as persistent fogs prevented any hunting. Five weeks passed before Poulsson shot a reindeer after a difficult stalk. He was an experienced hunter, knowing such tricks as keeping a patch of

flannel behind his wristwatch where it was handy when his binoculars needed cleaning. The liver and kidney of this deer provided the vital vitamins the men needed to cure not only hunger but also sickness caused by malnutrition. Reindeer meat then became the staple diet as herds migrated north across the plateau, before a second team parachuted into the mountains in the early hours of 17 February. They landed 50km from 'cousin's hut' which they reached after several days, surviving a severe blizzard. The physical endurance of all these Norwegians almost surpasses belief but they were not the only ones to endure such hardship. On their journey they met a black market dealer in reindeer meat, 50km north of his home town Uvdal. He was given a curt welcome but agreed to act as a guide in locating

▲ The Norsk Hydro factory on the edge of the steep-sided valley near Vermork. Here in 1943 the Germans were supervising the manufacture of heavy water, a process requiring large amounts of electricity which was available here from hydro-electric generators. The heavy water might have been used in the manufacture of atomic bombs.

▼ Claus Helberg, the radio operator landed on 18 October 1942 with an advance party, remained on the Hardanger Plateau with this team to be joined in February by a second team of saboteurs. Here he is transmitting on one of SOE's Type B Mark II 'suitcase' radios.

'cousin's hut' for which he was rewarded with 100 Crowns, rations and some chocolate.

The leader of this second team was a regular army lieutenant, Joachim Rönneberg, who was to command the operation now code named 'Gunnerside'. Rönneberg had selected his team for their good sense, quick thinking and physical fitness rather than brawn, traits that would make ideal agents in any operation. The morning that he explained the details of the plan to Poulsson and his men, Skinnarland was visiting 'cousin's hut' as he did on occasion, bringing cooked meats and more important titbits: news of events in Vermork. Later that day he and a radio operator began a journey to the high peaks in the west of the plateau near S k)rbu, from where they could more easily keep in radio contact with London. The others were divided into two teams: Rönneberg and three sergeants would form the demolition party; his second-in-command, Lieutenant Knut Haukelid, with Poulsson and three sergeants would provide the back-up. The demolition team had been trained with particular secrecy at an SOE camp where all other training had been stopped. They therefore had been able to practise their tasks on a mock-up of the 18 high-concentration cells. These were the vats in which the electrolitic final stage of heavy-water production was carried out in the semi-basement of the Norse Hydro building.

The seven-storey building stood on the northern lip of a ravine 200m deep, through which the river M)ne flowed eastwards emptying into rivers that reached the Skaggerak. Power for the plant came from seven reservoirs on a hill to its north, down which water was carried in three giant pipes to the hydro-electric generators. These were in a power house separated from the main building by an asphalted yard. Approaches from the north were covered by German machine-gun posts on the roofs of the reservoirs' valve sheds, mines and barbed wire. A road to the south crossed a narrow suspension bridge 400m west of the site with two sentries guarding the bridge which could be flood-lit. Another approach was by a single-track railway running from the west on a line blasted out of the northern face of the ravine. It entered the factory site through a heavy iron gate in the high fence around the complex. This was the route the saboteurs would take, joining the railway line some 500m west of the suspension bridge, after dropping down the southern side of the ravine to cross the ice-covered river and climb to this railway.

More difficult than the approach would be to break into the building, but Rönneberg expected to be able to force open quietly either the steel door to the semi-basement or another door leading into the ground floor. There was also a third entry point, a duct carrying water pipes and power cables at ground level into the building. These ran along one side of the ceiling of the concentration room with its 18 cells, in the semi-basement. This lay out had been studied from plans of the site which also showed a small building where at least 25 Austrians of the duty guard were billeted 25m from the main building's north-east corner. The number of guards was known to have been recently increased and there were doubts as to whether the railway track might have been mined. The conditions on the north side of the ravine also gave Rönneberg some concern because it was steep and might be impossible to climb without mountaineering ropes.

Helberg volunteered to find the answers to these questions, having shaved off his beard and dressed in civilian clothes. He went down to the valley, met an old friend in Rjukan who worked for the Norsk Hydro and made his way to rendezvous with the others. They had moved to Fjosbudalen less than 5km from the plant. He arrived there a few hours before the others on Wednesday 24 February and could confirm that the railway was not mined, but he was uncertain about the north face of the ravine. He made a second recce next morning to find that there were gulleys in the north face which they might climb provided the ground remained frozen. A condition which could change if the warm *foehn* breeze should spring up, when not only would the gulleys be slippery with melting ice but the ice on the river might become too weak to cross.

On Saturday afternoon they were making a final

This diagram of an agent's jump suit illustrates its many pockets and special features.

check of their kit when four youngsters were seen making for a nearby cabin. These two couples were told to stay in the hut all next day, no explanations were given and none were requested although the saboteurs posed as holiday makers during their time on the plateau. Their rucksacks were packed that afternoon with sufficient food for the first part of the journey four of them would make to Sweden, once the concentration cells had been destroyed. Two of the demolition party also carried a pair of identical charges in case one of them failed to reach the concentration room, for their only weapon was one revolver apiece. The others carried grenades, Thompson sub machine guns and revolvers, total loads exceeding 50kg. Each man also had a compass and a map printed on Chinese silk showing their escape route. The challenge that night would be 'Piccadilly', the password, 'Leicester Square'.

Clouds hid the stars as they moved off at 2000 hours this Saturday night, skiing in good conditions across a frozen lake. They would loop westwards to cross the head of the valley before turning towards Vermork. When they reached the woods beyond the lake, they carried their skis, following Helberg through snowdrifts waist deep in places. Strong tree branches snagged against their packs in the dark and the going was not much easier when they reached the road beyond Vj er. Here, fresh snow covered the frozen ruts from an earlier thaw, but the weather in this region changes rapidly and they felt a warmer wind blowing down the valley. Several kilometres from the plant they could hear the throb of its generators before a sudden break in the clouds flooded the countryside in moonlight to show the high building on the northern lip of the ravine. They had barely time to look at the objective before they also saw lights of vehicles coming up the road. Jumping up the road-side bank they hung desperately to tree branches as two buses passed, but none of the passengers noticed them. They climbed down, moved on eastwards now, to reach a track beside some power lines, where they dropped their heavy rucksacks. They also stripped off their white camouflage outer jackets and trousers, restowing emergency rations in their battledress blouse pockets, checking their L-pills were still in a trouser pocket. Rönneberg and Sergeant Stromshein took the sets of charges from their rucksacks and put these in backpacks specially designed by SOE's experts. The others carried the spare magazines, grenades and revolver ammunition in the long pouches of their British web equipment. Haukelit also carried some tubes of chloroform in these to silence Norwegian workers if this proved necessary.

They left the track, recrossing the road before scrambling down into the ravine, a wet, unpleasant start to the operation as a thaw was setting in. Yet they hardly noticed the rivulets of ice water running down

were 62 teams mainly in Norway but with some in Denmark. That winter an OG unit was also formed as the Norwegian Special Operations Group (NORSO) with 100 all ranks drawn mainly from Americans of Norwegian origin who had been serving in France. They were commanded by 24-year-old Major William E. Colby, (after World War II he became a director of the CIA). He moved the group from London to rigorous training in Scotland. There they could enjoy the local whisky without attracting the military police whose nearest post was 80km south of the training area, near the Royal Castle of Balmoral. Here a stag was shot on one survival exercise but apparently without incurring the King's displeasure. After this training they were to be flown to Norway that January but the bad weather prevented any flying during the moon period.

This delay enabled an advance party of five under Captain Tom Salter to be sent through Sweden and to cross into Norway in February. They were to set up a reception committee for the main party of thirty-six, due to drop during a night when there was moonlight that month. In the advance party was NORSO's best radio operator and a Norwegian liaison officer to work with Milorg at a DZ north of Trondheim. Everything went according to plan on the ground, but bad weather forced the eight Liberators to abandon their flight. Their fuel supplies then became so low that they only reached the USAAF Harrington Air Base in Lincolnshire on the return flight by jettisoning the containers of OG equipment carried in their bomb bays. This probably led to the Norwegian press hearing of and reporting the flight which may have been the reason for the Germans reinforcing their garrison in the area of the DZ. An

▲ Four of the Norwegian speaking members of OSS who took part in operation 'Rype'. They cut the railway line running north from Oslo, delaying the movement of German troops in March-April 1945. They are Borge Langeland (on left), Cpl. Kai Johnsen, Major William E. Colby (later a Director of the CIA), and Sgt Matti Raivio who was born in Finland. Several of them are wearing the Special Forces' parachute wing badge, and Johnsen is also wearing parachute 'wings' on the right shoulder. The small badge above the left breast pockets of Colby and Raivio was a metal insignia worn by men of OSS' Operational Groups. Colby is also wearing the American flag shoulder flash, a readily recognized symbol of American forces when there were many men in uniforms that civilians could not easily identify as friend or foe. Colby wears his badges of rank on his shirt collar.

alternative had to be found for the flight in March, when Colby again led the 36 raiders aboard the eight black-painted Liberators which took off on Good Friday, 24 March. This was apparently as 'uneventful' as any 1,100km mission might be in the rough weather over the Norwegian mountains. It forced three planes to return before reaching DZ, a fourth flew 80km into Sweden before its five parachutists jumped. They were interned but OSS negotiated '. . . an arrangement with the [Swedish] secret police . . .' to quote OSS' War Report, and they were released.

About midnight Colby and 15 others landed without mishap at the DZ on the frozen Lake Jaevsjo surrounded by wooded country. At first there was no sign of the reception committee, before Colby moved through the mist towards a fire burning on a base of logs over the ice. Near it he challenged a tall figure who did not give the right reply to the password but—as Colby guessed—he was one of the Norwegian helpers. These included a farmer and a reindeer herdsman who led the OG to an isolated farm in the woods. Among these trees they cached some of their containers and used their camouflage parachutes as tents, hiding their camp from any holiday skiers who might pass that way. Other containers were scattered about the lake and not found until Easter Sunday. A delay which might have been disastrous earlier in the war but by 1945 there were few German planes flying reconnaissances. Nor did the German garrison 30km to the west in the Snaasa valley send out any patrols to check the purpose of Friday night's air activity. Colby therefore settled his men in the woods to await the return of the aircraft on another moonlit night with the rest of the OG. He listened with others to the personal messages broadcast on the BBC's Norwegian service. One of these would tell him by a coded phrase that the aircraft were due. None arrived despite attempts to reach the DZ on two or three successive nights. Then the joint SOE/OSS headquarters in London—the Special Forces HQ—radioed that two Liberators had crashed on the last attempt, killing the crews and 10 OG personnel. Colby was to proceed with operation 'Rype' without his full teams. (Rype is Norwegian for the ptarmigan which changes the colour of its feathers from brown in summer to snow white in winter.)

The two targets for 'Rype' were a bridge at Grana on the Northland Railway and another stretch of this line. At that time the railway was carrying a battalion of German troops each day from the northern front to the defence of their Fatherland. The bridge was six days' hard skiing and climbing through the mountains to the west of the OG's lakeside base, therefore Colby had to plan on taking sufficient rations for a couple of weeks from the supplies dropped by container. These had to feed his OG for the next month or more as there were no local foods available in these mountains. Each man now carried over 50lb while taking it in turns to manhandle their sledge carrying 60lb of explosives. They were helped by six local Norwegians including their guide. The weather continued to be very cold with fierce blizzards and the boulders on the mountain tracks had iced over to make climbing even more difficult. They skied where they could across frozen lakes and down the gentler slopes. They avoided any skiing accidents because Colby insisted, however undignified it might appear, that they should sit down on their skis if they went out of control. They made steady progress averaging over 25km a day until they reached the mountain ridge west of the bridge. There appears to have been no German air reconnaissance to spot their tracks as they approached, but by 1945 the Germans were short of aircraft and the fuel to fly the few which they had.

Colby took two men with him to cross the ridge and recce the bridge which he found to be strongly defended, no doubt because the Germans were expecting Milorg to attack it. Certainly there were too many guards for the OG to fight if they wanted to gain control of this bridge. Therefore Colby skied back over the ridge— skiing, learnt at High School in Vermont, proved invaluable if not over swift on this mission. On reaching the main party he looked on the map for a second target which surprisingly had not been decided earlier, and chose the five-metre Tangen Bridge some distance from Grana. The OG skied through that night arriving at dawn on Saturday 15 April on a mountain overlooking the section of the railway where they found that the bridge was unguarded. Scouts were sent out to warn by walkie-talkie radios, probably SSTR-3s, of the approach of any train from the north or south. A necessary precaution as Colby hoped to blow the bridge with a troop train on it but wanted to avoid injuring civilians in the scheduled passenger services on this line. No trains appeared as the OG waited and before any German patrols coming along the tracks might discover the raiders, the charges were blown. The Americans then scattered stars-and-stripes shoulder flashes near the bridge as calling cards which told that the raiders were regular forces, not a Milorg unit. This was a further attempt, as at Vermork, to prevent reprisals against local people. The raiders skied eastwards to suggest to any patrols finding their tracks that they were heading for the Swedish border. Benzedrine tablets kept them going for the men had not slept for more than cat naps in the previous 36 hours, and had slept out in their sleeping bags for over a week. Yet their guide '. . . with legs [seemingly] made of spring steel . . .' according to Colby, forged paths through soft snow, maintaining a pace which brought them to the border before any German searchparties. There the raiders turned north along the border and at last the main party could rest. Colby, however, his radio operator Borge Langeland and the redoubtable Herbert Helgesen, their Norwegian liaison officer, skied back with few rests until they reached the lake-side base. There they were able to radio reports after over a week of radio silence. When they reached the lake they had found the five men who had crossed from Sweden, and after the main party reached the lake they had a few days' rest. During this they checked their equipment before again setting off for the railway.

They reached it on the moonless night of 23 April after another hard ski-march. They divided into small teams to place charges along two and a half kilometres of track. Each team worked separately to a time table, but when Colby's team was discovered by a German patrol which fired a flare, this hurried the team's last checks on the charges. The Germans then began to fire at the Americans, one bullet flicking a pebble against Colby's forehead before he left the track to retrieve his skis. He would not let his men fire back with a Browning Automatic Rifle, for the sound of this BAR would reveal that they were not local saboteurs, and Colby did not want the Germans to begin a detailed search of the tracks. His teams therefore had just time to fire their 240 separate charges before they skied safely away into the mountains. Their operation at the bridge, and here on a long stretch of track helped to reduce the German rail movements to such an extent that reportedly only one more battalion could be moved south in the last few weeks of the War.

Colby's OG reached their base after another ski-march with almost no rest. They had followed a roundabout route which avoided enemy patrols, before a snowfall covered their ski tracks. Nevertheless a five-man German patrol found their base during the first week in May. In the resulting shoot-out one Norwegian was killed, as were all the Germans. No doubt other patrols would have followed them but the war in Europe came to an end in the next day or two. Colby had wanted to set up a redoubt with Milorg guerrillas on the Lierne mountain but this proposal was now being circulated among the many Allied staff officers who might be interested. They wished to avoid such a complication for fear of upsetting negotiations for the surrender of the German forces in Norway, and perhaps mindful of the disaster on the Vercors. While Colby waited for their decision, a patrol of his men found and buried the bodies from one of the Liberators which had attempted to drop men after the main landing, but otherwise the OG lay low until four days after VE-day. Then they were ordered to the Snaasa Valley where they took the surrender of a large garrison. Later that May they were back on the Northland Railway as passengers, disappointed to find that within a month this line and bridge had been fully repaired.

4
CODED COMMUNICATIONS

THE OGs by 1945 had sophisticated and efficient radio communications but these had taken several years to perfect. When SOE first operated, SIS provided the radio communications but after 1 June 1942 SOE had its own radio networks, operators and codes. In the field these operators were often nicknamed 'George' by their fellow agents in 1942, working from a safe house with a job that gave them cover for their clandestine activities. Typically, George would have a radio transceiver by that date which was known as type B Mark II which packed into three cases each 22.5×10×8cm and could operate on a range of frequencies (see Appendix 3.7) suitable for transmissions by day or night in northern Europe. Sets of this type had replaced the earlier sets which were in two parts: a receiver and a transmitter in plywood boxes together weighing 20kg and powered by a six-volt car battery. Although they were not easily moved around from house to house, the B MK IIs could be mistaken for pieces of hand luggage as the set was built in a suit case. Its separate six-volt car or wireless battery was a 'wet' accumulator of a type common at that time for powering home radios, but this had to be kept upright when charged. Otherwise its liquid content was spilled, as it was virtually a glass jar with two plates, generating electricity by electrolytic action in a solution of acid with distilled water. The Mark II* might also be operated off the main supply of town electricity.

▲ SOE's type A Mark III suitcase transceiver was the smallest of the conventional 'sets built in 1944. It was used for communications over distances of 500 miles or more, its receiver was particularly sensitive and could 'hold' to a frequency without varying the reception's quality. This set was built with miniaturized components and small American valves. At the centre of the set (to the right of the on-off switch) is the casing of a crystal plugged into the set. At the bottom righthand corner is the two-speed tuner on which the operator selected the frequency required by rotating the graduated drum-spool.

◄ The SOE transceiver type 3 Mark II was the suitcase radio generally known as the 'B2'. It operated from a mains electricity supply or from its batteries. It was in general use for long range communications from 1943 until the end of the war and no doubt used after then by some agencies. At the top left is the transmitting key, here resting on the box section that contained spare parts. A coil of aerial wire obscures the volt meter and the send-receive switch to its left. To its right are: first the meter selector; and beside it the P.A. grid tuner. The pair of knobs below and to the right of these are respectively: a waveband selector and the crystal selector. An emergency crystal could be inserted in the sockets above crystal selector. On the left of the centre section of the set (seen near the aerial coil) is the aerial matching dial with the anode tuner to its left. Bottom left of this section is the waveband selector for aerial trimming. The concentric coarse and fine tuning knobs (seen above the keyhole of the suitcase lock) could 'shift about three kilocycles from one side of the frequency to the other in the event of interference'. The righthand pair of knobs here controlled the BFO (for CW operation) and the volume on the headset. The righthand section housed various sockets used with special plugs to select the voltage that matched the mains supply, and on-off switches for power sources.

There are many stories from early in the war when agents were nearly caught—if they were not actually caught—moving this incriminating luggage through security checks at railway stations or elsewhere. Perhaps the most startling is that of the agent with two suitcases containing radios, who saw he was to be stopped at a ticket barrier. There everyone's luggage was being searched as they left the platform. He held the suitcases high over his head calling out in German to the soldiers opening baggage: 'Gestapo, Gestapo, we have found a clandestine radio!' They let him pass without question and he hurried to safety outside the station.

A second feature of these sets was the crystals which in some types could be plugged in, as we will see, to transmit on different frequencies. But George had a great deal more to concern him than whether his batteries were charged or if he had inserted the right crystal. In the early days he also spent hours encoding outgoing messages and decoding those which he had received. Our George probably lived in an apartment which was 'safe' because the Germans did not know of it, his neighbours accepting him for the park keeper which was his daytime job. (The ideal 'safe' house had a rear or second exit, and good views of the street or other approaches which the security police might use.) His 'niece' would come from college each day to prepare his tea and tidy his flat. His papers might explain that some old injury prevented his doing heavy work or there might be other medical reasons why he could not work in a factory. Whatever his cover, George would get home each evening to begin his work for SOE. He first checked that his accumulators were on charge, just in case the mains power failed as it sometimes did at the vital time he was due to broadcast. George would then go to the old pile of bills in his cupboard among which his 'niece' had left the messages to be sent that night. She was a courier for the senior agent who ran the circuit for which George provided the radio links to London. And she would have taken the decoded messages from last night's reception from London, although in an emergency George might seek out another courier to get urgent messages to his chief early in the morning.

He broke the words of each new message into five-letter blocks, the 'words' of signallers' language, then using a code (see Appendix 3.9) he worked from a grid of figures particular to his messages, this might be:

	1	2	3	4	5
1	C	O	M	E	N
2	V	I	T	S	U
3	R	L	A	B	H
4	D	F	G	J	K
5	P	Q	X	Y	Z

(W=X in this SOE grid to get 26 letters into a 5×5 grid)

He began to encode the first message with this Destelle code by putting the figures at the head of each column in place of the letters, and below these the corresponding figure to the left of each letter: (six men will go tonight to Paris) then becomes:

SIXME	NWILL	GOTON	IGHTT	OPARI
42334	53222	32325	23533	21312
22511	15233	41211	24322	15332

Now by reading the numbers horizontally in pairs as 42, 33, 42, 25, 11 below the first word, he read off the matching letters from the grid using the second number as the key to the vertical column, the letter 'F' which replaced the original 'S' and his first word became 'FAFUC'. A laborious job, needing care and rechecking in encoding perhaps 500 letters in half a dozen messages. The result, however, was coded messages which in the 1940s could not be decrypted—that is decoded without the grid—using mathematical analysis. This was in part because there was not the computer technology to work out millions of sums in perhaps half a day, which in 1942 would have taken several mathematicians months, if not years.

George was not supposed to send more than a hundred of his five-letter words in any one transmission, as he could tap out 500 letters in perhaps half an hour: he was trained in sending morse code at 20 to 25 letters a minute. With the Mark II set he would not normally need to plug in a crystal since several of these slices of quartz were fitted into his set. Each gave different wave lengths (frequencies) according to the thickness of quartz through which a high frequency current was passed. George could therefore select any of several frequencies by the turn of a switch, giving him the frequency which London had chosen for his transmissions and matching the specific crystals fitted in his set. These were usually for the 3 to 4 megacycle band (Mc/s) as the one most suited to night broadcasting in northern Europe. He also had at least a pair of loose crystals which were for emergencies: for daytime in the 6 Mc/s band more easily received than 3 Mc/s used at night.

Before he went on the air he would check the small square of 35mm film, hidden no doubt where it could not be easily found as it detailed the times on which he was to broadcast. He then put his pistol where he could reach it before setting his radio where he could comfortably use its key—on the kitchen table, perhaps— and he would be ready to come on the air at the time set by London. On cue he would begin to tap out his call sign—'tap out' is perhaps misleading as this key was designed to make no noise that might attract the attention of neighbours. He might in 1942 have some difficulty in hearing London's acknowledgement of his call sign. Not until 1943 did SOE's more powerful transmitters hold to their set frequency and be heard over the background 'mush' of atmospherics which had made earlier signals difficult to hear. Difficult or not, the signaller in SOE's communications centre (as it would be called in the 1980s) listened out on George's frequency at the agreed time, answering his call sign. If George did not transmit at that time the signaller at this home station would listen for only five minutes, as he or she had a busy schedule. The signaller would then move to another agent's frequency, coming back to George on his next scheduled time to broadcast, which might be 48 hours later. George could, however, always use his emergency frequency should any vital message have to be sent before then.

The schedules of transmitting times included day-time transmissions after the end of 1943 but the routine of transmitting messages was constant. George's hand sent messages continued to be recognized as being from his transmitter by the way he grouped dots or the length of his dashes, known in the trade as George's 'fist'. SOE were later to have electrically charted records of each operator's 'fist' which could be compared with messages received in London, in case a German used George's call sign after he had been captured. There were also means of knowing if an agent was transmitting under German control, perhaps being forced to transmit messages or be executed. A simple but by no means foolproof system of security checks was devised. In one of these George might send an 'M' as the fourth letters in the second and third words regardless of the correct coded letters. London would see these in the message and know that no German was controlling what George sent unless George had volunteered to give away his checks. Unfortunately the system failed on several occasions. In one case London sent an agent who was following the correct drill: 'You must not forget your security checks'—although he had a German pistol at his head. By 1944 agents had two security checks, one which he or she might reveal if caught and a second which could still be used when captured. Yet these did not always reveal that a set was being controlled by the enemy. On occasion a staff officer might decide there was only some oversight when he received a signal pad message endorsed 'bluff check present, true check omitted'. His decoders had noticed the deliberate error but there were invariably a number of mistakes in messages, because there were so many chances to make them. The first was in the encoding of the original. The second was in its transmission when reception was poor. Thirdly a mistake could be made in its decoding. There was even a chance of error by the teleprinter operator sending a stream of messages from the home radio station to Baker Street, SOE's London HQ.

George knew only too well the risks he ran of being captured particularly if his transmission became over long. Yet in 1942 it was not unusual for an agent to listen after sending his messages for the incoming items which had to be acknowledged. All the time German radios monitored all broadcasts in the frequency bands used by agents, throughout every 24 hours. This enabled three German stations, at Brest, Nuremberg and Augsburg to monitor and record all such signals traffic in northern France. If they found that someone—our George, perhaps—was transmitting every second night they used direction-finding (D/F geometric) radios to give them the bearings of George's location from the three stations. Draw these lines on the map and there was George's location within 20km, somewhere in a triangle shown by the lines. If he was say 30km south-east of Paris, then the crews of two German D/F cars, usually black Citroëns, would scan the triangle. The next time George was on the air they would have two bearings using the D/F radio at Claremont to give the third leg of a new triangle which showed to within 200m where George broadcast from. At this stage he had no way in the 1940s of knowing that he was being D/F-ed. The cars with a controlling van could therefore work their way closer to him each time he came on the air, but he was still reasonably safe if he was working in an apartment in a built-up area. Even when the German with a small D/F set began scanning a particular block, there would be time for George to slip into the street. With the D/F aerial hidden under his coat, strapped to his body, George might evade capture with luck, good papers and a sensible cover story, once he had reached the street. One operator working in a block of apart-ments in Prague probably expected at least 15 minutes to pass, if not half an hour, before he needed to leave the building even though the German search teams were in the block. Yet they caught him by switching off each floor's electric power. His transmission stopped when they turned off the power on his floor, which was searched in minutes.

Our George was not caught and by 1943 would be using lighter weight transceivers (see Appendix 3.7). These lighter sets were more easily moved and owed their small size to the new makes of compact radio valves supplied from America. Transistors would not be generally in use for another 20 years or more. The French and other exiled agencies used similar sets but the French codes had been broken by the Germans unbeknown to BCRA. And perhaps fortunately only the Poles were allowed to transmit to Europe in the weeks immediately prior to the Normandy landings.

Some ultra-small sets were in general use by 1944-45 throughout SOE's various Country Sections' circuits. The specific uses of some are referred to later but their development has interesting features. The original heavy British Type XV Set had a separate transmitter and receiver which had been carefully built for

reliability, using radio parts available to amateur enthusiasts in 1937. One such set was still operating in Paris at the time of the city's liberation, although its operator no doubt was still having trouble as the 'XV' tended to wander off the frequency to which it was tuned. Those smaller valves with metal cases which became available from America were much more robust than the 'XV's' glass valves, and were used in the BP3 transceiver designed by a team of very clever exiled Poles (see Appendix 3.7). One of the most remarkable small sets was the MC C 1 mini-receiver, 10,000 of which were made, half of them going to the French *maquis* and other guerrilla forces. It was about the size of a long, narrow book, being packed in a tinplate Huntley and Palmers biscuit box which gave it the name 'biscuit tin' receiver. Weighing only a kilogram with three batteries packed in the box, a headphone,

◀ The American special service transmitter-receiver SSTR-1 was designed along the lines of SOE's A Mark II set of 1942. The SSTR-1 became the standard OSS transceiver in the field, its construction enabling various modules to be concealed when necessary. More usually these were kept in the suitcase provided and might be powered by batteries or mains supplies ranging from 90 to 230 volts of alternating current. The range of signal transmitted could exceed 1,000 miles with the appropriate aerials. The centrally mounted tuning dial of this SSTR-1E set was operated by its concentric knob. To its left is the container for the crystal plugged into the set. A switch beside the headset socket (the BFO switch) could be set for continuous wave operation. The frequency selection switch and 'DIM Points' switch are at the top left of the set. Other controls regulated the volume, aerial trimming and power supply.

▼ The sections of an MCR 1 receiver are shown here with the power pack on the left, the receiver on the right with three of its interchangeable coil units. These were used for different ranges of frequency and plugged into the base of the receiver. Its control knobs were all on the same side, the large tuning knob moved

a graduated scale seen through a small opening on the top side of the set. It was supplied in a biscuit tin and therefore known as the 'Biscuit Receiver'. The graduations marked on the coil unit, showed the corresponding tuner dial settings required for particular frequencies.

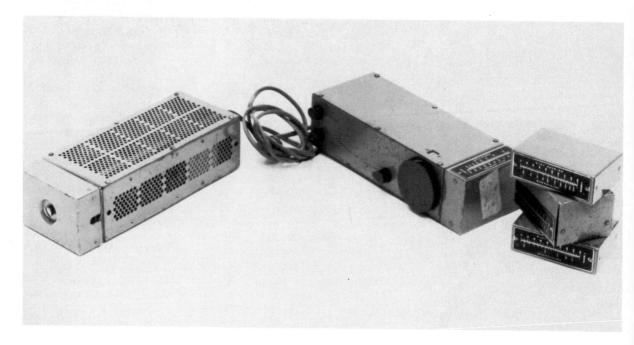

aerial and earth wire which plugged into one end, it had interchangeable blocks plugged into the other for different frequency ranges. It was one of several clandestine sets to the development of which Major John Brown made a major contribution. Another ultra-small set was the Type 51/1 transmitter weighing 565gm (about 1lb) which could transmit clear signals over 1,000km, being easily read in England from as far afield as the French Alps if used high in the mountains. But the 51/1 could only be used on 200 to 260 volt mains which precluded its use on the 110-volt Paris and similar supplies. This handicap was met with a design, the AP4, with a built-in transformer that worked on either voltage.

The development of 'burst' radios came too late for any extensive use in World War II but a Dane working for SOE built one. This recorded signals that could then be transmitted at ultra-high speed in a second or two. The message was recorded on receipt at the home station and then played at slow speed for the morse to be read.

OSS' Communications Branch was formed on 22 September 1942 for rapid and secret communications, taking over from the inadequately small staff of COI. They, on the formation of the service, could not meet its requirements for technical innovations as well as increased signal traffic. This was being handled by three clerks in December 1941 but by the end of the War there were 130 personnel in the Message Centre with its Code Room, Paraphrasing and Distribution Centre (where reports were abbreviated), and other facilities in Washington. There were also 400 staff spread over 25 major centres in foreign countries. A great deal of work was carried out by the R & D Division to complete new types of radio, since the original COI set for clandestine work proved inadequate. R&D modified it as the Strategic Service Transmitter Receiver the SSTR-I which became OSS' standard set (see Appendix 3.7). It was fitted into suit cases appropriate to the operator's region: the hand luggage carried in Europe; or the green fibre-board cases common in the Far East. Such luggage was purchased by OSS through combing secondhand shops and from Camp X's contacts with refugees.

A radio-telephone ('walkie-talkie'), the SSTR-3, was developed for the OGs, answering a need as we have seen in Norway, to communicate with scouts and others over short distances of up to eight kilometres. For long range signals the SSTR-5 with its 50ft antenna was built into a small case that could be carried in its canvas bag through the jungles of Asia. Other developments for assisting aircraft to find a DZ are described later but among such ancillary communications systems was a unique device for telephone tapping. This SSAA-401 was a very small gadget which had an amplifier and could be used without the need to physically cut into a line in order to eavesdrop on callers' conversations. Whenever possible, however, telephone lines were cut, forcing the enemy to use radio signals which could be intercepted. Another of what would become known as 'bugging' devices first built in 1944-45 was a tiny microphone from which conversations might be overheard 'in distant rooms'.

In all the early developments of OSS's clandestine radios SOE proved '. . . extremely co-operative, with the result that a complete interchange of information, models and operational reports was achieved . . .' OSS in turn helped to find special valves and other advanced equipment SOE needed from American sources.

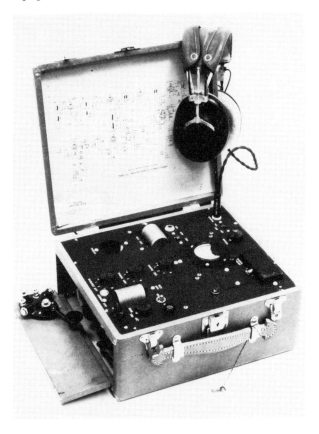

▲ US Military Intelligence radio operators used the AN/PRC-5 suitcase transceiver for continuous wave (Morse) communications. Seen here on its back with the key to the left, it was usually operated with the set stood upright and the case lid to the right. The key was then placed in front of the set. The manual issued with these sets states that they were for transmissions 'over medium distances from variable points'. They could also be used for voice communication in appropriate circumstances. Each set was supplied with a set of six crystals and four plug-in transmitter coils. The tuning knob for reception is seen to the right and below the D-C milliameter. This knob rotated a calibrated dial which could be read through a small opening at the top (seen on left 'top') of the milliameter. The three knobs running to the left of this opening were used in controlling the various current loadings in the aerial, the tuning capacitor and the power-amplifier circuits. The selected crystal was inserted into the circular apperture appearing top left in the illustration. Seen to its right is one of the plug-in coils, a second is on the lower left, and appropriate coils were needed for particular frequency ranges.

Many of OSS' clandestine radio stations operated in the Far East. There the signalling routines were little different from those in Europe, but the local conditions of high humidity and often damp storage facilities, created particular problems in maintaining the valve radios of the 1940s. Yet OSS operators kept Washington informed of political events as well as more routine military intelligence for Allied armies. From China there were reports of the many moves by Nationalists against the Communists, at times regardless of the fact that the Japanese were making inroads into China's defences. From Thailand, where the first four-man team from OSS lost two men killed by Japanese after infiltrating across the Chinese border, came reports no doubt on SOE's British-sponsored agents! Here as elsewhere in former spheres of British influence, there developed a number of time-consuming arguments on policy between the Foreign Office and the American State Department. In these and more important political matters OSS' intelligence reports proved of incalculable value in the furtherance of American foreign policy. Although OSS in general was more concerned with defeating the Axis forces than with political intrigue.

Returning to George in Europe; his life in many respects although still very dangerous was a good deal easier. His lightweight sets of 1943 could be carried by his 'niece' or other courier, in the panier of a bicycle. Its emergency crystals were taken by a second courier just in case the set was captured, as it was frequently moved from one safe house to another with perhaps three different locations used in one night by a busy operator. He might send messages to SOE for supplies needed by the local maquis, intelligence reports on German

activity and his own organiser's signals for London. The houses might be up to 15km apart, which foxed the monitoring stations, especially as George might use more than one call sign and frequency at any house. His frames of 35mm records by now could not be memorized but his job of coding was much simpler. He used a one-time pad, which is still used in the 1980s by many services including the British Army. It was first introduced in F Section in September 1943, but as with any new code some time was necessary before all operators in the field could be taught to use it. George encoded a batch of messages using a sheet of this pad. The decoder in London had a matching sheet: two sheets that were unique and therefore bore no relationship to codes of earlier messages taken from different sheets. All George had to do was select his key letters according to the length of his message, therefore in the message 'Harry in Paris from July' there are 20 letters, for which George needed four five-letter 'words' picked at random from the top line of the pad: say 'GRPQY SMBTO ANNFJ QRCHK'. This enabled George to take each letter of the message in clear, using the sequence beginning the vertical column 'G' to encode the first letter, 'H'. He then used column R to code the second letter 'A' and so on. When this message was received in London, the decoder took his matching one-time sheet and entered the grid on his message pad. He knew that it would be approximately half the 'words' of George's message. Then by looking up the letters in the second half of the message in appropriate columns as shown by the key, he or she found the letters of the message in 'clear'.

This system was not only unbreakable when a page of pad was used only for a single transmission but the pads

◄ This SCR-504-A radio direction finding set was used by US Military Intelligence. When carried as a normal suitcase, a small panel of controls was positioned below the carrying handle. These controlled the volume of signals received. Also on this small panel was a 'sense' button. When depressed this connected the rod aerial (or antenna) to the loop aerial. The user could then point the case towards the transmitting radio with greater accuracy than the general direction revealed by the increased volume when the set's aerial was pointing towards the radio source. The panel—immediately below the handle—also included a BFO on-off switch for use when D/F-ing Morse transmissions, a power on-off switch and the socket for the earphones. These were of the type that fits discreetly into the ears and were a common component of deaf-aids in the 1940s. The operator might therefore hide the wires leading to these ear pieces, under his clothing. Instruction for destroying this and similar radio equipment was specific: 'Smash—use . . . hammers, heavy tools etc. . . . Cut—use axes . . . matchete [sic] . . . Burn—use gasoline, flame-throwers, incendiary grenades . . .' The rod aerial is erected in this illustration but was concealed inside the case when this was carried. The loop aerial can be seen above the receiver's graduated tuning dial, below which is a large knob with a white pointer for the selection of one of eight wave bands. The small block on the left of the lid depressed a switch when the case was closed, transferring the volume control from the knob on the face of the set to the panel below the handle. The piece of fabric on the outer edge of the lid was folded upward when the case was closed. This flap was then outside the case, partially concealing the operator's hand. The set might also be used by rotating the open case standing on a 'suitable tree-stump and D/F from there'.

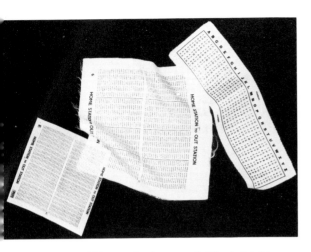

◀ These examples of one-time pad codes were usually printed on easily destroyed paper. The top item was used for numbers. The centre item is on silk and the bottom one is on a combustible synthetic material and could be hidden in some types of cigarette packets. Although the German Foreign Office had used these codes since the 1920s, SOE did not adopt them for use by agents in the field until the autumn of 1943. They had been used before then betwen SOE London and overseas headquarters since 1941. The figure 1 in the top example appears in the vertical column D as D. The figure 2 in column G is H and so on. The sender may then use two five letter blocks to encode the figure 12489. The first block gives the respective vertical columns he has used, say DGJWP and the second block are the letters in each of these columns corresponding to 1, 2, 4 and so on. The recipient then decodes these blocks—DGJWP DHOWE—by reading off the respective letters in each column to read in clear 12489.

themselves could be easily destroyed. The initial issues had proved difficult to burn. One agent even had to take to the hills with his pads in his haversack when German search parties located his once 'safe' house. Later versions of these pads had sheets of edible rice paper impregnated with compounds which made them both highly inflammable and soluble. No doubt the original pads had been of ordinary paper, as these had been used since 1941 for signals between SOE's home station and overseas headquarters in Cairo, New York, Bari and Brisbane among others. Such communications were also made in signals encoded by cipher machines when too long for easy use of one-time pads.

Traffic from France in 1943 was somewhat reduced by the reports that were carried by aircraft flying to clandestine air strips. But, as we will see later, this method of sending long reports had its drawbacks. Therefore in 1944 the heavy volume of messages to and from SOE's Section which handled communications to France, was mainly in radio signals. These along with signals from other occupied countries in Europe came into SOE's signal stations in great volume. Indeed there were so many that they swamped the Germans' attempts to D/F transmissions. Therefore in some cases the French radio networks could operate more as military than clandestine communications. George moved from safe house to safe house, as often as not being accompanied by armed *maquis* as his bodyguard.

The volume of work at the SOE signal centres was so great that an additional station was opened from April to November 1944 at Bicester in Oxfordshire, not far from Grendon Underwood and Poundon (station 53C) on the Oxfordshire-Buckinghamshire borders, which along with the station at Dunbar in East Lothian, were SOE's home stations. Over the years there had been all manner of technical improvements in transmissions from these home stations with, for example, powerful transmitters which could be heard over almost any amount of jamming. The solitary radio set on a special desk still stood clear of the banks of sets worked by signallers on routine work. This was for emergency calls, as it was manned all day and night so that an agent using his emergency frequency might expect a quick response to the content of his urgent message. He was guaranteed one in 70 minutes at the most. This may seem a rapid reponse but as he or she sat at the out station set, pistol near to hand, time passed slowly. Every creak in the floorboards, the rustle of unseen trees or other unusual sounds which the agent sensed might be the Gestapo, must have made each minute seem like an hour.

The signallers' receivers at the communications centre, like their transmitters, were now capable of accurate tuning, so enabling George's signals to be received without a heavy background of atmospheric 'mush'. His messages were automatically recorded by machines whch switched on recording wires or discs as soon as a signal was picked up by a receiver. This was sensitive enough to catch a transmission sent with only the power of a single watt, a tenth of the usual transmission power from a good aerial and fully charged batteries. Outgoing messages were also greatly increased in both length and number. They were therefore mechanically punched on tape which each night was used to send out the messages for various agents. George, no longer working in the park as he had to transmit during the day, could sit at home listening to the even flow of this mechanized morse. Easier to listen to than hand-keyed dots and dashes, he would take down the messages before decoding them by the appropriate 'pages' of the one time pad. His 'pages' were now on 10 pieces of film that could be read by a powerful magnifying glass. Half of these pieces were for codes he used in sending messages, his 'out station to home' set, and half for decoding 'home to out station' messages. These sheets were 11×10cm overall and would fit in some standard packets of cigarettes between the foil wrapping and the cardboard. Although each sheet had sufficient material to encode 1,000 five-letter code words, they had to replaced fairly frequently with new sheets parachuted to George.

Should he become parted from these sheets for any reason, he had a silk scarf which was personal to him. It

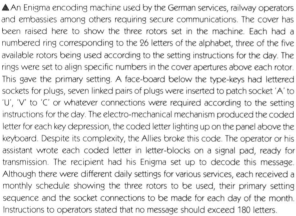

▲An Enigma encoding machine used by the German services, railway operators and embassies among others requiring secure communications. The cover has been raised here to show the three rotors set in the machine. Each had a numbered ring corresponding to the 26 letters of the alphabet, three of the five available rotors being used according to the setting instructions for the day. The rings were set to align specific numbers in the cover apertures above each rotor. This gave the primary setting. A face-board below the type-keys had lettered sockets for plugs, seven linked pairs of plugs were inserted to patch socket 'A' to 'U', 'V' to 'C' or whatever connections were required according to the setting instructions for the day. The electro-mechanical mechanism produced the coded letter for each key depression, the coded letter lighting up on the panel above the keyboard. Despite its complexity, the Allies broke this code. The operator or his assistant wrote each coded letter in letter-blocks on a signal pad, ready for transmission. The recipient had his Enigma set up to decode this message. Although there were different daily settings for various services, each received a monthly schedule showing the three rotors to be used, their primary setting sequence and the socket connections to be made for each day of the month. Instructions to operators stated that no message should exceed 180 letters.

▲The American M-209 cipher machine is shown with the mechanism cover raised against the box lid. The various rotors and other mechanical components of the machine can be seen, and these provided a relatively simple method of coding. It was used for messages that did not require a high degree of secrecy, but the messages could be encoded in 15 to 30 minutes depending on their length. Such speed was often more important than secrecy with such low grade messages, the content of which became unimportant once action had been taken on the message received. The M-209 was developed by Boris Hagelin with rotors that were easily re-set to the day's instructions. To encode a letter the operator aligned the marked dial wheel on the left with a mark on the mechanism lid. When this was closed the encoded letter appeared in a small aperture and was printed on a paper strip. This can be seen fed on the left from its spool in the box lid to the paper's feed rollers on the left of the mechanism. The intricate polyalphabetic cipher of this machine has a period of 101,405,850 before a specific letter's coding is repeated. While the number of different rotor and other settings in the machine are—in cryptographic terms—vigintillions.

carried the essential details of his codes, frequencies and transmitting times. He also learnt a poem by heart, which SOE's decoders knew, to be used if he needed more groups than were on his one-time pad material, or for some other reason. He also had a 50cm square of silk with abbreviations for standard phrases such as:

BNBN *meaning* 'assistance urgently needed in area of . . .'

AUAU *meaning* 'ambushed and killed enemy groups at . . .'

3H2 in a letter group referring to three containers containing explosives with detonators and fuses, 1H4 being a single container packed with incendiary devices. George—since 1943 his new colleagues referred to him as to all radio operators, as the 'Pianist'—would have left France in early November 1944 when the major part of SOE's communications networks closed in his area.

Throughout George's time in Europe, indeed since the summer of 1941, the BBC's World Service had broadcast a number of coded phrases. These were sent out among many personal messages to families in occupied countries. They were sent in the language appropriate to the region at which a programme was directed, but might be roughly translated as: 'Maurice S sends greetings to all in Papion', 'Juliet has arrived at her Aunt's'; and 'Harry will be home tonight'. The first was a genuine greeting, the second referred perhaps to a courier's arrival at a 'safe' house, and the third to the return from the UK of a specific agent to his circuit. These were nonsense messages unless you knew what to listen for, which tantalized the Germans, who wasted much energy in trying to make sense of them. A few— including some important warnings of the Normandy invasion—they persuaded agents to reveal to them, but failed to react to the Normandy alerts. At other times an agent could prove that he worked for SOE or OSS by having an agreed phrase broadcast. In this way any Europeans might hear it, even though they risked imprisonment for listening to the BBC.

All radios in Europe, not only clandestine transmitters, became increasingly dependent in late 1944 and 1945 on batteries, as power cuts became more frequent and of longer duration. An operator's set then needed recharged batteries at frequent intervals when he had a full schedule of transmissions. SOE had devised a number of different generators which unlike those commercially available, did not need petrol. The thermo-couple 'Genny' for example had 350 cadmium-chrome elements embedded in a fire-proof ceramic cover. Heated in a fire of twigs or charcoal this generated sufficient current to charge a six-volt battery to one amp, giving you an hour or more of transmission. A steam-powered generator was produced for SOE's clandestine stations in the Far East but it weighed over 30kg, needing a mule or six men to carry it over rough going. OSS also produced a 'battery charger', burning wood, charcoal or other solid fuels, which produced up to nine watts for charging six-volt batteries. But for many agents, ingenuity in the field—be it for charging batteries or fooling the security police—proved more valuable than complicated equipment. Therefore many a battery was charged in Asia by the agents' sweat as he peddled on a bicycle frame hitched to a 'Genny'.

N EITHER SOE nor later OSS apparently made any extensive use of secret inks for invisible writing, while the micro-dot technology was essentially a device of the Secret Services. These included no doubt MI 6 and the OSS department which dealt with similar espionage (see Chapter 6). SOE's agents going to France in the early 1940s were nevertheless taught how to make various invisible inks from items easily purchased in a chemist's shop. One used *Eau Blanche* diluted by five times its volume of water. This writing was later made visible in muddy coloured letters by dabbing the paper with cotton wool soaked in a liquid containing sulphur, such as that used to remove hair from the body. Another such ink was mixed using half a phenolphthalein (laxative) tablet, two coffee spoons of ammonia and two dessert spoons of water. It was later made visible by using a weak solution of soda crystals. There was also that school child's standby: a weak (one per cent) solution of alum in water. This was read by ironing the page with a warm iron. Urine, cow's milk, weak nitric acid, weak sulphuric acid, saltpeter (potassium nitrate) and copper-sulphate could all be used because on a dry page they are invisible until it is heated. Starch was only detected by blowing iodine vapour over the dry page.

In theory at least, you wrote your words which then became invisible as the particular solution dried, between lines of ordinary writing in a letter. But such a letter might hold a coded message without need of invisible inks, by cleverly constructing an everyday note. This might then incorporate the three words of a secret message as the fourth, tenth and sixteenth words in an apparently humdrum letter. At the other extreme of sophistication were codes created by the Enigma machine. Bill Stephenson was shown one of these in 1924 by its German manufacturers who were selling it for commercial business coding to 'frustrate inquisitive competitors'. However, apart from suggesting ways in which this manual machine could be redesigned to use an electric motor, Stephenson did not pursue the idea. German intelligence services saw a greater potential as they believed the messages coded on this machine would be unbreakable. With one version of the machine, deployed by the 1940s, the sender and receiver needed to know which wheels were being used and in which plugs the various key coding wires had to be set. These details were provided by a chart showing what they were to be on each day of a particular month.

The Poles, who had one of the most efficient secret services in Europe in the late 1920s, had discovered by 1928 that the Germans were using *Enigma* (the Greek for 'puzzle') machines. These were electro-magnetic and an improvement on those shown to Stephenson. They offered 150 million, multiplied by a million and another million: 150,000,000,000,000,000,000 solutions to any series of settings of keys and wheels. Yet Polish code breakers, their crypto-analysts, had deciphered some signals by 1937 using primitive computer-like machines called 'bombs'. In Britain Alastair Denniston was given the job in 1938 of building a replica of an Enigma machine. A short-statured Scottish Professor of German, who had worked in the Royal Navy's deciphering centre of World War I known simply as 'Room 40', he made remarkable headway with this difficult task. The French also made some discoveries: their agent, Hans-Thilo Schmidt, with access to German ciphers, was paid for several documents dealing with Enigma. Their content when later linked to machines provided by the Poles who had built several, would help towards breaking the code. Only the keyboards of these models had letters A, B, C in sequence, the German machines having a typewriter keyboard with Q, W, E . . . etc. By 1939 the Poles were no longer able to decipher Enigma messages, as they may not have been able to find the rotor settings, which changed each day. Other information, including charts of wheel and key settings, were later captured. One came from U-33, one from a weather ship and another, in late December 1941 from a German trawler boarded during a commando raid in Norway. These enabled the British Secret Intelligence Service to read some messages in Enigma

▲ A British telsonic receiver was made in 1945 for listening to enemy telephone conversations. The device with its wire aerial extended over a telephone line, picked up any conversation. This the operator could then hear on his earphones. The device worked on the principle of induction when placed 'in close proximity to telephone lines'. These in the 1940s were usually single not multi-flex connecting field or local telephones.

codes. These were deciphered at the ultra-secret establishment, Bletchley Park, in Bedfordshire, headquarters of the inter-service Government Code and Cipher School (GC & CS). This school had been reading German codes for a number of years but its ability to decipher Enigma messages was limited—a change of the German codes on 1 May 1940 took three weeks to break—until later in the war. Then, by 1943, all Enigma codes were read, albeit on occasions with a few days' delay before a change was mastered. The value of such a source of intelligence was almost beyond belief. Therefore the deciphered signals were distributed to very few people who disguised the source of these 'ultra' signals in case the Germans guessed that their radio signals were being read. It is difficult to judge how far this information helped SOE's operations, because after the occupation of France a great deal of important signals traffic went on teleprinters and telephone lines, making it at least secure from radio interception by the British. Yet it was not totally secure, as for example French telephone engineers of the Resistance broke into the German military telephone system in northern France.

The Germans also succeeded in listening to other peoples' calls by using a large antenna on the Dutch coast near Eindhoven. They had known of the 'Scrambler telephone to foil spies abroad' since it was headlined in American papers. The device had been developed by Bell Telephone Company to split a frequency band, jumbling normal tones to make speech '. . . sound like a Mah-jong game played too fast . . .' when first used in September 1939. This A-3 scrambler was later improved by adding an inversion element which gave a thin, squawking background to the sound '. . . ringing with bell-like chimes . . .' Matched channel-mixers shifted the transmitting and receiving frequen-

cies every few minutes when the telephones were connected by US Army operators in trans-Atlantic calls.

The German equipment automatically searched and found the new frequency in 20sec, using a device built by post office engineers whose ministry passed transcripts of conversations to Himmler. Little was missed in the 20-second gaps of what proved most revealing conversations, which from 1 March 1942 included not only those of the national leaders but of many other senior politicians and civil servants. By this interception Hitler learnt of Italy's collapse in September 1942, of the build-up in England for the invasion of Normandy and the planned conferences of Churchill and FDR.

The British had established a co-ordinated service to intercept all enemy radio signals, known as the 'Y' Service during World War II, which had recorded German signals since 1928. Even when these signals could not be decoded, they provided some intelligence by their numbers and frequency. This, linked to D/F bearings for the transmitter's source, could pin-point possible military headquarters or even heavy freight traffic on railways, since these used radios with important signals in a version of the Enigma code. The American equivalent of the 'Y' Service, known as Radio Intelligence (RI) Branch by the 1930s, had established a few stations in Honolulu (Hawaii) and elsewhere. These stations fed intercepted signals to the American Army's Intelligence Branch with its crypto-analysts, who in 1922 had cracked the Japanese diplomatic code. This had enabled them to read signals sent to Tokyo from the London Naval Conference, where the major powers agreed upon the composition of navies for the next decade. Knowing the details of Tokyo's replies, American negotiators were then able to force the Japanese delegates into accepting their government's maximum concessions. Stimpson stopped this eavesdropping but it was authorized again from 1938. By 1939 American Army intelligence was reading the highest grade of Japanese ciphers. The intelligence service distributed the decrypts as 'Magic' messages to a very few people, but a clerk with no proper security clearance photocopied some deciphered messages. These he sold to a German agent, but when the Abwehr passed on this information, the Japanese apparently refused to believe that their code was broken.

Collecting such intelligence by radio interception, communications with agents, instructing them and those local forces they advised, required complex organizations. But when the Americans and British were intercepting messages and decrypting codes in the 1920s and 1930s the secret services were small organizations. How they developed, so far as SOE and OSS are concerned, is sometimes due to a tangled web of chance as much as to forethought.

5
ORGANIZATIONS, SELECTION AND TRAINING

THE brilliant sunshine threw dark shadows under the palm-leaf roof of the hut in which Pete Ellis lay dying on Koror island. This south sea paradise surrounded by Pacific blue ocean, was in the Caroline Islands administered by the Japanese in 1923. Since November 1922 Ellis had been travelling in what was then known as the Orient, supposedly representing the Hughes Trading Company of New York but, as he proclaimed on several occasions, he was an American spy. A heavy drinker, he had been on a 'bender' probably for a day or two when on 23 May 1923 he stumbled towards a coast defence battery which the Japanese had built on this island. Whatever details he had discovered of these guns were not recorded, for he went back to the hut where a local family had befriended him, and died that evening. A few days later a European—the family never learned his name—ordered that Ellis' body should be disinterred and cremated. At this time also his few personal possessions disappeared from the island's police station, but not before a newspaper reporter had discovered that Ellis was a serving lieutenant-colonel in the US Marine Corps.

Yet in the tragedy of Ellis' last journey through these islands, there are many aspects closer to the realities of espionage in the 1920s and 1930s than the fictional adventures of a John Buchan hero.

The Japanese had watched Ellis throughout his travels while on leave ostensibly from the Marines. But his undated resignation was held by the Corps, should the American government wish to deny that he was a serving officer. This was a step they might have had to take although all nations' military personnel quite legitimately collected any intelligence that they might chance upon. Lieutenant (later Rear-Admiral) Kemp Tolley, US Navy, for example, was a passenger on a merchant ship in April 1937 when he saw Japanese aircraft drop torpedoes by parachute from 300m. This was at least six times the height at which airborne torpedoes were being launched by the US Navy.

All departments of the US intelligence services in the 1920s and 1930s were small. This was the main reason for OSS in 1942 taking the roles in intelligence work which in the British clandestine services were carried out by SIS. US Naval Intelligence had only 20 officers in 1920, who worked on old fashioned filing systems by the commercial standards of office practice in those days. The Military Intelligence Division (MID) of the general staff had about 20 serving officers and 48 civilians on its staff in 1938, even though the Japanese

threat had sharpened with their occupation of northern China and invasion of the south. Counter intelligence was handled by the Federal Bureau of Investigation (FBI). Although its agents had no legal authority to work outside the USA, later they would be authorized to work in Central and South America in order to penetrate Axis circuits.

Much of what might be called the pure espionage of both Britain and America in these years fell to private individuals, two of whom became key figures in World War II espionage. They had met by chance in 1916. The American, a large man known as 'Big' Bill Donovan was an Irish-American lawyer working for the American War Relief Commission in France at the time. There he met the young Canadian fighter pilot, Bill Stephenson, who as we have seen travelled Europe later in his commercial work which enabled him to collect intelligence. 'Big' Bill by 1918 commanded the 69th (Fighting Irish) Regiment in France before returning to his law practice on being demobilized. He also undertook delicate missions for the American Government. He visited Russia in 1919 and Germany in 1920 for the Rockefeller Foundation when he discovered how much the German people still idolized their army. This was one of many pieces of intelligence which he passed to Franklin Roosevelt, who became a close friend of Donovan. The future President put great store on the lawyer's reports and after FDR was elected President in 1933, he asked Donovan to undertake several delicate enquiries for the State Department. 'Big Bill' therefore had direct access to the highest levels of government. Just as 'Little Bill' would have similar contacts when his close friend Winston Churchill became Prime Minister in May 1940.

There appears to have been no formal exchange of intelligence between the two future Allies, although the two Bills provided informal exchanges of information from time to time. These included discoveries of the Germans' secret rearming of their military forces, although this was against international treaties. Then in 1935 Hitler admitted that the *Luftwaffe* had been re-formed and for a time hoped to equip it with British aircraft for his war against Communist Russia. Indeed Squadron-Leader F. (Freddie) Winterbottom and a British aero engineer were invited to visit German factories, the squadron-leader's subsequent report providing good intelligence. The Germans, however, learnt little on the reciprocal visit. Others were collecting intelligence for SIS, including a Lancashire cotton goods salesman who travelled in the Middle East. At this time in the late 1930s, the mercurial Johnny Owens also gathered technical data on his business trips, which he passed to Naval Intelligence.

A second strand of our story has its origins in the British Army's involvement in Ireland before the creation of Eire, There in the 1920s the nationalist leader Michael Collins had a circuit of agents. These included a middle-aged lady holding a responsible position in a British government office in Dublin. Through her and other sources, Collins was able to steal from the office of the Dublin Special Branch Police, files which incriminated him and others in the Irish Republican Army (IRA). This army had only sufficient weapons for 3,000 men but kept 80,000 police and soldiers fully occupied in trying to contain it. These deployments provided a lesson in guerrilla warfare that made a lasting impression on Lieutenant Jo Holland, DFC, Royal Engineers, and Captain Colin McV. Gubbins, MC, Royal Artillery, who were serving in Ireland during the early 1920s. Both officers were to make a major contribution to British tactics and strategy in guerrilla warfare during World War II.

The main stream of British intelligence in the early 1930s, though a small one by 1980s standards, was influenced by the work of Admiral Sir Reginald Hall who had been chief of Naval Intelligence until he officially retired in 1920. 'Blinker' Hall—one eye twitching as if to disguise the sharpness of his intellect—knew that the analysis of deciphered enemy radio signals was the key to twentieth century espionage. Therefore after his retirement he set up an unpaid group of academics to work on methods of breaking enemy codes. Also in Hall's group was the 26-year-old Stephenson, who in 1922 was beginning to make his fortune from home radios and who never—even when head of SIS operations in America during the 1940s—took any payment for his work for the British.

The British had also set up in 1919 the Government Code & Cipher School which later became involved in breaking the Enigma code. Much of their activities, however, fall outside the subject of this book, as do most SIS operations, because such secret work requires the minimum of obvious activity while the role of SOE's agents was to create disorder and eventual revolt. Only three aspects of SIS' work had an indirect bearing on SOE activities. In December 1939 nearly all SIS' operations in Europe were closed down when the Germans captured two officers running SIS circuits from Holland. These had connections with anti-Nazi elements in Germany. The officers were tricked into visiting the Dutch-German border where they were snatched by enemy agents who had crossed 200m into Holland in a car. Many of their agents were already known to the Germans who had systematically photographed visitors to the British Passport Office in the Hague. This office had been one cover for SIS operations. A second SIS operation which certainly helped SOE was known as 'Double X'. The 'Double X' Committee, with a success not entirely explained by subsequent publications on its history, 'turned' all the German agents who survived in the UK to send information back to their controllers. Once turned into double-agents—hence double cross or 20 Committee—they fed the German Abwehr with misinformation the British wanted them to have. Finally there was the general rule that SIS operations took priority over those of SOE. Therefore if SIS wanted an area undisturbed for their operatives, SOE agents might have to lie low for a time. This was specially applicable to times and places where SIS operatives were being landed secretly.

German intelligence had two main divisions (see Fig. IV) but for OSS and SOE agents in Europe and the Middle East, there was little if any difference in being caught by one or other of these security forces. In 1934 and for some years after this, Hitler forbade any espionage agents being sent to Britain, another aspect of his hope that the British might become his allies. Nevertheless some agents were sent without his knowledge but were caught, except for an Iraqi military attaché who provided the Abwehr with reports on his visits to various military demonstrations before he returned home in 1940. In America both the Abwehr and the SD had a number of circuits through the 1930s mainly among Americans of German parentage and anti-British Irish-Americans. The Japanese also had agents particularly on the west coast as explained later, but their activities were penetrated by American signals intelligence and the FBI.

Both in Britain and America few people had considered the possible consequences of the Axis powers overrunning Europe and south-east Asia. But in 1938 Jo Holland took over what became the British War Office's section of Military Intelligence Research (MI R). He and his secretary—the pair of them being the only staff at the time—began work on a host of ideas which would eventually lead to not only the formation of SOE, but many aspects of Commando and Combined Operations (the British amphibious forces headquarters). Holland was not only a man of ideas but as his staff increased in numbers, he was also able to delegate work to others who developed his original ideas. He was joined by Colin Gubbins who became one of MI R's few field operatives to visit Poland in the summer of 1939, when he secretly flew across the marshes on the German border looking for possible guerrilla bases. He later flew down the Danube to see the Iron Gate gorge. After this flight he met a ship owner who headed Section D's

Fig. IV The German counter-intelligence services worked independently, until Admiral Canaris was dismissed. He had headed the Abwehr but after February 1944 the Abwehr agents were absorbed into the SD. The Gestapo was recruited originally from Nazi party members, as were other Schutz Staffel (SS) units including infantry and armoured regiments. By 1944 these units had several million personnel not all of whom were ardent Nazis. The Gestapo with 40,000 men and women, however, remained ruthlessly dedicated to the Nazi cause. The SD never exceeded 3,000 in its staffs and agents but all were even more ardent than the Gestapo in their support for Hitler.

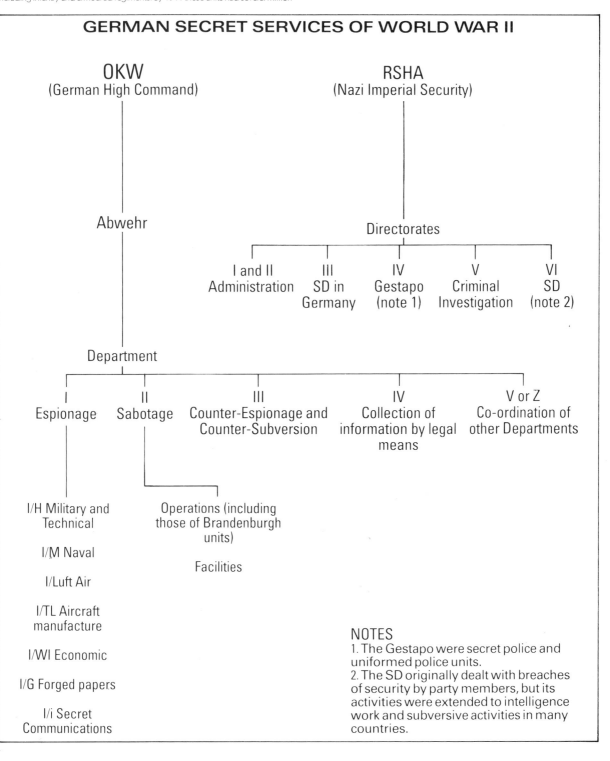

GERMAN SECRET SERVICES OF WORLD WAR II

OKW
(German High Command)

RSHA
(Nazi Imperial Security)

Abwehr

Directorates

| I and II Administration | III SD in Germany | IV Gestapo (note 1) | V Criminal Investigation | VI SD (note 2) |

Department

| I Espionage | II Sabotage | III Counter-Espionage and Counter-Subversion | IV Collection of information by legal means | V or Z Co-ordination of other Departments |

I/H Military and Technical

Operations (including those of Brandenburgh units)

I/M Naval

I/Luft Air

Facilities

I/TL Aircraft manufacture

I/WI Economic

I/G Forged papers

I/i Secret Communications

NOTES
1. The Gestapo were secret police and uniformed police units.
2. The SD originally dealt with breaches of security by party members, but its activities were extended to intelligence work and subversive activities in many countries.

Balkan operations in what was a typical interchange of ideas between the Army's MI R and SIS Section D.

Gubbins was much more than a field operative but in 1939 he, like many others, turned his hand to whatever was required. He wrote two pamphlets in one of which, *The Partisan Leader's Handbook*, are suggested methods of sabotage including: '**Burning of Soldiers' Cinemas**—cinema films are highly inflammable [being made of celluloid]. The cinema should **be fired during a performance** by firing films in the operator's box. This should be easily arranged.' The bold type face of the original stressed what was considered in those years to be a most unchivalrous act. But after the fall of Poland, France and Norway, the British faced up to the barbarity of total war.

In the more conventional fields of military intelligence the British found sufficient numbers of the right calibre of officer for field intelligence with operational commands. However the Army's Intelligence Corps which had been disbanded in 1919 was not reformed until 1940. The Middle East Intelligence Centre was also set up, co-ordinating reports for the British Headquarters in Cairo. Their sources included a radio interception station of the 'Y' service manned by a company of Royal Signals on the Libyan border. In Europe as the Germans began their advance of May 1940, an officer of Section D brought out most of the industrial diamonds from Amsterdam, vital components of high-grade machine-tools used in making armaments. Three others, after the Dunkirk evacuation, landed on the French coast but brought back little intelligence. They had missed their rendezvous, however, with a navy ship and had had to row for 13 hours. They at least proved that landings were possible but information would be hard to find, as two small parties of Commandos discovered when they landed in occupied territory later that summer. The collapse of France had indeed cut off the British Army from all the usual sources of field intelligence: prisoners, recce patrols across no-man's land and so on. Far wider changes had also to be made as the Allied strategy for defeating Germany had to be totally replanned.

The peoples of the occupied countries would have to provide much of the manpower that might eventually be needed to overthrow the occupying forces. But the British and Americans might provide them with the arms and other means to do this. A small beginning in this direction had been Section D's arms caches left north of Paris. More, far more, would be needed as Churchill knew when he became Prime Minister on 11 May 1940. Within a few weeks he asked Sir Maurice Hankey, Secretary to the Cabinet, to report to him on the organization of the secret services. In the course of these inquiries Hankey had a meeting on 13 June with Grand of Section D and Holland of MI R. He also looked into the operations of the Foreign Office's small propaganda department. The staff of this EH Department, named after its location in Electra House, thought more in terms of influencing opinions overseas than what had become the unpleasant business of misleading people by propaganda. (In time the Allies became adept at putting out 'black' information to mislead the enemy, but that was not part of the SOE story.)

Subsequent to Hankey's report a committee of government ministers set in train the events which would give Churchill the organization he demanded '. . . to set Europe ablaze . . .' Known as the Special Operations Executive from its conception, the staffs of Section D, MI R (but not MI Rc Section of inventors of explosive devices) and EH Department were to form the nucleus of the Executive. It had two principal roles: sabotage, which required bold adventurers; and the raising of guerrilla armies requiring tactful organizers with calculated daring. Although intelligence was a secondary feature in both roles, SOE especially in the Far East became deeply involved in supplying information. This included targets for Allied airforces and details of the enemy's order of battle among other items of field intelligence for Allied armies. But first SOE would pass through a frustrating year of largely paper battles in the centre of British government administration, Whitehall, until the organization was remodelled (see Fig. II). There must also have been changes in SIS after Hankey's report, for this service appears to have recruited more capable field operatives after the summer of 1940.

In the early days at least, some SOE agents were recruited through members of SIS. Pat Howorth was interviewed by a vice-consul in Poland in August 1939 who had returned to London by September. Pat later reported to 68 Baker Street, to find the same gentleman was working there. Those already in MI R included a number of men who were used to the pressures of big business: Tommy Davies, a director of a large textile firm, Courtaulds, became the first SOE head of facilities with the rank of colonel. Another senior staff officer was Douglas Dodds-Parker, formerly a British civil servant in the Sudan who provided the back-up service for MI R's operations in Abyssinia. There its agents, including Orde Wingate, were arming local tribes in the west fighting the Italians in 1940. Section D also had men in Abyssinia who Professor Foot has explained were '. . . striving to wreck it [the operation] by independently appealing to the Galla tribe . . .' to secede from those in the west. D's staff at this time included the Australian businessman George Taylor, a ruthlessly efficient organizer who became SOE's first chief of staff. Under him were inherited the various Country Sections, the bricks of the organization each running agents into particular countries or regions. While clearly Taylor ran the operations side of the Executive and Davies the supply of equipment and advisory help, there was no sharply defined organization until November 1943. Then a senior civil servant was appointed to set up proper systems of administration.

The political head was first the Socialist Member of Parliament Dr Hugh Dalton, Minister of Economic Warfare, with Sir Frank Nelson, a 56-year-old former Conservative MP as the executive director. Grand and Holland went back to their military careers in which they both rose to senior rank. Nelson took the title 'CD' possibly as 'C's' deputy although 'C'—traditionally the letter by which the head of the SIS was known—never had any direct control over SOE. Nelson was to burn himself out in dedicated determination to make SOE successful, although the confusion of its ever changing organization in the early years slowed down its development. He was replaced by Sir Charles Hambro who had worked for the Executive in Scandinavia. He had much wider claims to his new post, a tall, experienced banker with good organizing ability and an MC. He had held a directorship of the Bank of England at the age of 30, and later held other senior appointments in commerce. He promoted Colin Gubbins, who after leaving MI R for Norway stayed with the army until recalled to SOE in November 1940. Gubbins became director of operations. Later he was CD's deputy and a Major-General by the end of 1942, and has been aptly described as the 'mainspring of SOE'.

The expansion of SOE during these years would lead to much wider recruiting than the friends of friends. Yet Davies' business lawyers are said to have volunteered all their partners under 50 years of age. Certainly several of this legal firm of Slaughter & May served in SOE, including Harry Sporborg who was CD's political assistant. The net for recruits was spread wide and at Gubbins' suggestion included insurance assessors, since they were likely to know which machines were valuable targets in a factory. Many recruits came from the armed services and retained their rank as SOE staff were all military personnel, although rank seems to have been of little importance to more senior members. A few recruits joined after chance meetings, the way Dodds-Parker found Peter Kemp who had fought in Franco's forces during the Spanish Civil War and would spend 10 months for SOE in Albania. He was imprisoned by the Russians after working in Poland, and later this man of fearless bravery served SOE in south-east Asia. Some agents in the field were women like Yvonne Cormeau who for 12 months was a radio operator in France, but fewer than five per cent of agents working directly for SOE were women and the proportion in OSS was probably smaller.

The Country Sections also recruited some foreign nationals, but this had its difficulties apart from the obvious one of screening such volunteers for enemy double-agents. The Free French who worked for Section F were regarded by de Gaulle as traitors, since they might have worked for his Secret Service Bureau. This difficulty was only overcome in 1945 by back-dating their commissions in the French Army to match the date of the British commissions as junior officers. Some Sections did not directly employ any nationals of the regions in which they were working: like the EU/P (Europe/Polish) Section formed to give assistance to the large Polish communities living in France. Yet this Country Section at one stage was the only link between disputing departments of the Polish Government in exile, not a role included in the official tasks of SOE.

The Executive required a 12-line switchboard for the telephones of the staff who moved from MI R, Section D and EH Department to new headquarters in Baker Street. This was in the former offices of the Prison Commission; but by late 1943 SOE had been expanded to occupy five adjoining buildings and use a 200-line switchboard. It was now an organization with efficient training facilities as we will see, its own seaborne ferry services or at least responsibility for their organization, and close liaison with the RAF. By this time its special operations flight and other squadrons were flying regularly in support of SOE missions.

IN the summer of 1940 Bill Donovan visited England. He was shown not only the Baker Street headquarters but also GC & CS at Bletchingley and other secret locations from where the British were carrying the fight back to occupied Europe. These and other visits enabled Donovan to refute American Ambassador Kennedy's belief that 'the British are through'. The President's envoy also made a number of other arrangements including those for two American intelligence officers to be trained by SOE the following February. At a higher level British and American staffs were already working on strategic plans should America enter the war. In November, a year before the Japanese attacked Pearl Harbor, other American officers visiting Melbourne studied Australian plans for a coast-watching service that would secretly put teams on many Pacific islands to report by radio the movements of Japanese ships and aircraft.

Donovan returned to Europe in February 1941 and went on to visit the Middle East. While in the Balkans he carried forged documents prepared by SIS to suggest that there was an Anglo-American plan to help local leaders. The Abwehr lifted the details which were believed in Berlin to be from a genuine document, according to one report. This ploy was no doubt part of several British deceptions to suggest that they had

▲ Brigadier-General William ('Big Bill') J. Donovan won a Medal of Honor for gallantry in World War I. In the 1930s this Wall Street lawyer was known as President Roosevelt's 'mystery man' after making several trips to Europe on which he made secret reports. On 11 July 1941, at the age of 58, he was appointed Co-ordinator of Information and became the Director of OSS when COI was reorganized on 13 June 1942 as the Office of Strategic Services. After World War II he was an adviser on the formation of the Central Intelligence Agency (CIA) in 1947 and American Ambassador to Thailand in 1953-54.

greater influence than they in fact had in occupied territories. For many Europeans were sceptical of the British ability to win the war, until America entered the fray in December 1941. Knowing that such an event would undoubtedly go against his interests, Hitler encouraged German political activity in the autumn of 1940 aimed at preventing the President's election for a third term. The Germans also fostered subversive activity which in 1940 and 1941 consisted of sabotage in America by anti-Communist Ukrainians and Irish-American sympathizers—if not actual members—of the IRA. Reportedly the latter were paid $200,000 for their work. However, the FBI's investigations into 20,000 incidents of supposed sabotage during the 1940s proved that they were mostly accidents or damage caused by disgruntled workers with no political motive.

Donovan's experience and the President's trust in him, made this investigative lawyer almost an inevitable choice to head, as Co-ordinator of Inform-ation, a new agency the President created for clandes-

tine activities abroad. COI set about recruiting a wealth of talent: corporate attorneys, advertising executives and distinguished academics. Ian Fleming, the author of the James Bond books, is said to have suggested these recruits should be discreet, sober fellows, devoted to duty and aged about 40. Such individuals were more suited to SIS work than duties in the field with resist-ance forces, but Donovan needed a wide range of people with differing talents as his organization initially covered both SIS- and SOE-type roles and political propaganda. He told the President that he was recruiting '. . . young officers who are calculatingly reckless with disciplined daring, trained for aggressive action . . .' in the field. His administrative officers, on the other hand, were older men in their forties. Their devotion to duty at times clashed with the field agents' calculated recklessness. The State Department also took what was a similar line to the Foreign Office in wishing to curb the agency's activities in neutral countries.

The American Under-Secretary of State rightly anticipated that Donovan would '. . . get into everybody's business . . .', although or because—COI had offices in an annexe of the State Department. The political sections of COI's organization were transferred to that Department in June 1942, however, when the agency became the Office of Strategic Services. Throughout his service as head of OSS, Donovan's overbearing manner did not endear him to many who worked with him and not only those in the State Department.

The FBI had reservations about a new agency, trying to prevent it working with Stephenson's American branch of SIS. His staff 'traded' as British Security Co-Ordination (BSC) with contacts in the FBI. There were other clashes as when COI's agents broke into the Spanish Embassy in April 1942, only to be surprised by two FBI cars arriving with their sirens wailing. Such an obvious disturbance was a more effective means of preventing OSS agents making any further break-ins, than any formal protest against COI encroaching on the Bureau's sphere of activities. These illegal entries into embassies which for the Americans in 1941 were technically at least not hostile, were in some ways paralleled by US Naval Intelligence's burglary of the office of Stephen K. Ziggly. This short, fat, self-important European banker took an office suite in Chicago in the summer of 1941. At this time he was suspected of espionage by the intelligence agencies who had kept tabs on him in Europe during 1940. Willis George of USNI explained this to the superintendent of the office building without naming Ziggly. For three months, George was then able to acquire the waste paper from Ziggly's office and from several others to avoid revealing who was suspected of being a spy. The waste revealed nothing, but did show that the spy's doodlings were more concerned with warships and planes than banking. This provided sufficient justification, along with his regular dealings with Germany, for intelligence to make a surreptitious entry—a euphemism in the profession for illegal searches—of the suspected spy's office. George and other agents entered the office no doubt using the superintendent's keys. They then searched it but removed their finger prints from the desk, re-set the safe combination to its original reading, re-waxed the floor, and the last man to leave swept the rug to remove any footprints. Nothing was taken. Nevertheless, names on a list in the safe, instructions on use of microfilm and secret inks all pointed to Ziggly operating a dozen agents. This circuit was one of several that the Germans were running in America with four major circuits which had been established since 1940, nearly all of which were penetrated by American intelligence. Simon Koedel, however, a German who went to America in 1906, worked for the Abwehr until caught in October 1944. He had sent over 600 reports in the 1930s and 1940s to Germany, and had spied for them in World War I. At 62 years old, he was 'a sinewy grey-haired man with little eyes . . . as hard and as cold as he looked . . .' when sentenced to 15 years in prison.

Very different in manner was the green-eyed American girl who worked in Washington for the SIS, Betty Pack. During 1940, she succeeded in *seducing* information from a number of Axis officers working quite legally for their embassies in Washington. These contacts led to the FBI suspecting that she might be working as a German spy, not suspecting apparently that the British would be carrying out espionage in a friendly but neutral country. Betty nevertheless succeeded in gaining access to both the Vichy French and the Italian embassies' code books, which SIS copied and returned without the thefts being discovered. There is a report that the FBI followed her to the French Embassy but were deceived into thinking her intentions went no further than love on a sofa. Had they known her true intentions their Director, J. Edgar Hoover, would no doubt have taken action as he threatened to do from time to time in the stormy relationships he had with Bill Stephenson.

Relations between SOE and the burgeoning OSS were on the competitive level of professional football teams. At times the British felt that their American counterparts were apt to be brash, on occasions operating without the knowledge of army commanders in a theatre, or creating other misunderstandings rather than deliberate affronts. Gubbins viewed OSS as an efficient service and he was in a better position than others to make such a judgement. He also saw the work of many Allied secret services, although their commanders knew him only as a liaison officer, not realizing that he was head of SOE's operations.

Spheres of influence were agreed by the Allies that June in so far as OSS took the lead in North Africa, China, Korea and Finland. SOE were to predominate in India, West Africa, the Balkans and the Middle East; with both agencies working jointly in western Europe. There on 1 May 1944 they formed a joint command, the Special Forces HQ which controlled missions in France, Norway and other occupied countries. The other Allies' secret services in exile, especially the French, do not appear to have accepted any British or American lead in clandestine work in their countries. This was a political aspect of operations which both SOE and OSS agents were under orders to avoid, as successful ones like Ben Cowburn with his 'Tinker' circuit always obeyed.

SOE had been a highly secretive organization since its inception and by all accounts its detailed secrets were well kept. The Germans learned of it and by 1942 knew something of its methods, but its full range of activities were never penetrated except perhaps by Philby. In 1941 there was an understandable fear that German agents might be preparing the way for an invasion of England—only a dozen people knew of the Double-X operations. Even digests of military intelligence sent to the Chiefs of Staff continued to stress that England or possibly Ireland might be invaded, until the Germans were clearly committed to their invasion of Russia. In such an atmosphere and as a matter of good security, since what other people do never seems quite as important as your own secret work, staff at Baker Street did not enquire what others were doing. This led to one agent feeling that he would have grasped his job more quickly had someone explained 'what SOE did and what it had to do it with'. In later years others would be more adequately informed once thorough training courses had been established. In earlier training the field agents of Section D and MI R had been given some grounding in clandestine warfare, with a short course at the Cavalry School at Weedon, Northamptonshire. Some agents were also trained in the Arisaig area of Inverness-shire, where Gubbins acquired a house in the winter of 1939-40 for trainees in this remote part of the western coast of Scotland.

Late in 1940 Colonel Wilson, who later commanded the Scandinavian Section, was appointed as SOE's first training officer to set up co-ordinated training. This had three levels of difficulty: introductory; basic; and specialist. Our George the radio operator might well have volunteered for some unspecified duty requiring languages. He then would report to a pleasant country house requisitioned by the army. This was one of thousands used for various military purposes and furnished with a mixture of army-issue beds and tables, the owner's less-treasured furniture and such items for

▲ SOE trainees in a lecture room possibly at F Section's Wamborough Manor near Guildford, Surrey. Posters on the walls show German uniforms and badges of rank (possibly cinema film reconstruction).

▲ A sand table model used in training agents on the choice of routes to a target and no doubt similar models were used in briefing agents. On the wall (at left) are tabulated details of 'Reception Committee [No.] 81'; while the enlarged photographs pinned to a display behind the trainees, appear to show specific details of boats on a river and Maquis(?) in training.

their own comfort as the training staff could scrounge. SOE had 12 such houses for their introductory course, although George like most of the other volunteers did not know what he was being introduced to. He was to spend a fortnight doing mainly cross-country runs and PT, being shown the elements of Morse code and simple radio procedures. There was plenty of booze in the mess for which as an officer he could sign a chit (voucher) whenever he wanted a drink. What he did not know was that the instructors would note the size of the bill for these chits: too large a bill and he might be considered a drunk, or there could be other signs that he was not a stable character. Then he would have been sent back to his army unit or civilian job, without SOE being compromised, for he did not even know of its existence, although for the fortnight he had been using a personal codename. Volunteers from different countries were usually sent to particular houses for their selection courses. Special groups might also be segregated at other stages in their training, as we have seen with the Norwegian team going to Vermork.

George went on to four weeks of para-military training living in one of three large houses—Drumintual, Glenmore and Forest Lodges—near Arisaig. He saw no civilians as the navy had closed the area on some pretext, in fact at the request of SOE. Here there was little doubt about what he understood to be a commando course, for he learnt to use explosives in practical demolitions training on old railway waggons. He was taught how to fire German, Italian and other foreign weapons, how to clean them and how to use British weapons he had not previously seen. For like many volunteers he had only received basic infantry training and some, including the girls on the course, had no previous experience with fire arms. He may well have guessed that this was more than a commando

course because there were as far as he knew, no girls in the commandos, yet here were members of the First Aid Nursing Yeomanry (FANY). Some of his fellow trainees had dropped out on the selection course, others now found the going too tough for they had on some exercises to live off the land, survival training as it is known in the 1980s. No precise figures of the failure rate are known but one course of six men was reduced to two before they went to Ringwood near Manchester.

There the RAF had a school for parachutists. George, like most trainees, feared he would break his nose on the far edge of the hatchway hole through which he jumped, or break an ankle on landing. Some did, but most came through two jumps from a captive balloon and five from aircraft without more than a few bruises, because the instructors were expert at teaching how to land without mishap. Having received his 'wings' on passing the course, George went with the rest of his course, perhaps three or four other trainees, to Beaulieu in Hampshire.

Here in the New Forest there was no pretence at commando training. George and others were told that they would be dropped into occupied territory. He learnt how to play the part of whoever he was supposed to be—park keeper, railway porter or whatever—not only in obvious ways but also in mannerisms appropriate to the role he acted as his cover. One night he was suddenly woken up by men in German uniform. They hauled him off for interrogation and he had to withstand the hard-nosed bully's questions and those of a kindlier 'Abwehr' questioner who offered him easy ways to make his confession. This kindly questioner casually talked about this and that until George was tricked into telling some incriminating fact. Of course he never got the full treatment: he was not plunged naked into an ice-cold bath, half drowned as a few

▲ An SOE instructor demonstrates the positioning of an explosive charge on an electricity sub-station transformer (cinema film reconstruction). In many 1940s transformers this oil was inflammable and therefore likely to set on fire easily when gushing from a fracture near the base of the transformer.

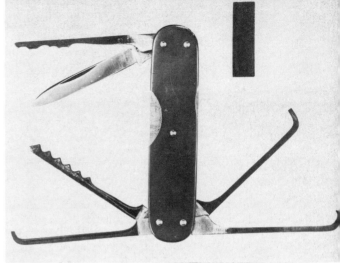

▲ This SOE lock pick knife was provided in a leather case. The knife blade was one and a half inches long, with five lockpicking tools that folded into this penknife. The user only required some form of small torsion bar to use with this otherwise complete kit, for making surreptitious entries through locked doors or into cabinets.

▼ This kit for making keys was provided by OSS. An impression of the key was made in the soft material (centre right) which had been placed in the mould (top centre). A low melting point metal (seen in box to left of mould material) could then be poured into the mould after its two halves were clamped together. The candle provided sufficient heat to melt this special metal which was sufficiently strong when cast to open a lock. The duplicate key was used with a torsion bar.

giggling girls watched this torture repeated, until in his confusion he might break and confess his involvement.

Having survived what was nevertheless a tough basic training, George would go on to train as a specialist. Those who failed the course might after the first stage be sent back without more than the comment that they had failed to be selected for the commandos. Although one writer has suggested that they were given 'scientific help' to forget what they had seen, there is no other evidence to support this and it hardly seems to have been necessary. After Arisaig those who were to be returned to their units needed presumably some persuasion that they had to forget all about the course. M. R. D. Foot has written that '. . . they might have to spend some time in the cooler [prison] at Inverair . . .' before being sent back to their normal life. This presumably gave the failed trainee reason for being sent back to his or her previous job. Throughout the basic selection and Arisaig courses George had a number of SOE's F Section watching his progress, getting to know him and later commenting on his suitability. For no agent, however acceptable to the instructors, was passed to join a Country Section unless he was acceptable to its staff. Having been accepted George went to Thame in Oxfordshire where SOE had its radio (wireless in those days) school. Here he learnt to send Morse at 25 words a minute, was taught how to use the various codes and given complete training in how to maintain his radio set.

Those agents who specialized in sabotage went to Brickendonbury Manor near Hertford where George Rheam had taught the Norwegians how to destroy the heavy-water cells at Vermork. A large man with great imagination, he considered the Norwegians the bravest of the agents he instructed, but had great sympathy for all those in exile. The methods he used at this Station XVII taught an agent amongst other things how to spot the essential component on a machine or locomotive he or she would sabotage, ensuring that it was not easily repaired. His methods were later used at other SOE sabotage schools opened in North Africa and Italy to train men from partisan groups who had been selected as agents.

Other specialist courses in lock-picking, photography and clandestine printing were run at various centres, in one of which the Russian agent, Kim Philby, worked while waiting to be transferred to SIS. His cover part was played to a bizarre perfection for the next 25 years. George no doubt played his park keeper's role almost as well but before he was finally sent on his first mission he slept in a safe flat in London or near it, where microphones—if not the curvacious 'Fifi'—checked whether he talked in his sleep in the language of his cover.

IN Canada Bill Stephenson bought small parcels of land near Oshawa between Lake Ontario and the Toronto-Kingston highway. These became the site of Camp X, the British Government later refunding the purchase price to 'Little Bill'. It was guarded by uniformed troops who like sentries in the field hid in the surrounding woods with darkened camouflage on their faces, while more obvious Canadian Mounted Police patrols barred any unauthorized entry from the road. Approved visitors were usually brought 40 miles across the lake from the American shore just east of Niagara Falls. Here in 1942 the first OSS agents were trained for action overseas. Their training included all those techniques taught to SOE agents, including the finer points of weapon handling. Fairbairn came to North America and stayed for most of the latter part of the war, teaching not only close-quarter combat but those other tricks he had shown SOE, including the pistol stance with knees bent and a two-handed grip on the aimed gun. OSS trainees learnt how to make concise reports, short enough to be transmitted in 100 words of five letters. Yet the detail in these messages was precise in identifying not only German tanks but '30 PzKwfw IVs, 8 IIIAs and two Tiger 1s'. They were advised on who might be a reliable sub-agent and who an agent with greater potential for responsibilities among the clandestine recruits. They learnt how to spot and avoid someone tailing them which might require more than jumping on a tram: were there any taxis about for the enemy security man? Having avoided this tail, they were practised at casually dropping an identifying password into bar conversation. Some were taught what in those days was loosely called propaganda but since the 1960s has been known as 'how to win hearts and minds'. Most important of all they learnt how to be unobtrusive, as the best British and American agents were often uncommunicative companions in peace-time, not given to proffering more than unhelpful replies to any who wanted to make light conversation. Yet these obstinate characters had also to be calculatingly aggressive. They had to be prepared to respond by reflex to any enemy's surprise appearance, although not so touchy that they precipitated trouble when the French policeman or Chinese merchant was no more than normally inquisitive. Then the agent's papers or cover story got him by, since in living this cover his reaction was calm, not jittery.

OSS had other training centres with Recruit Training No 11, 20 miles from Washington, for Special Intelligence training, and in 1942 also for some basic training. Later an area 30 miles north of Baltimore became OSS' main initial training centre for recruits. The Maryland Centre, often called the 'Farm', consisted of several country houses as did the centre near Baltimore which was known as Area E. Areas A, B and C were in wooded country, near Quantico Virginia, the Catoctin area of Maryland and a second area in Virginia, respectively. These three areas were used for para-military training and the training of Special Operations' Operational Groups. Also near Quantico from March 1943 was the maritime unit on the Potomac.

The Service originally had only an assessment centre for volunteers on the West Coast, established by the summer of 1944. But after that summer new agents

▲The British Security Co-Ordination (BSC) organization in America produced these metal cap badges but there is no evidence that they were ever issued or worn.

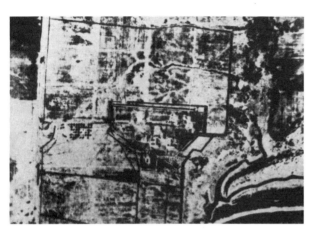

▲ This aerial view of Camp X suggests that it was well camouflaged. The shore of Lake Ontario can be seen at the bottom right of the picture. Both British and American agents were trained at this Canadian camp for SOE and OSS personnel.

▲ This large barn at Camp X was used for training sessions in unarmed combat. The smaller lean-to building was a store. An unidentified building is in the background and smoke (centre left) suggests this photograph was taken during a demonstration or exercise. Two men are crawling towards the smoke or taking cover behind it.

▼ RDX charges placed on a railway track during a training exercise at Camp X. A double line of instantaneous fuse links the charges with—the photographer noted—the 'charge on left bears a primer'.

were being trained for operations in Asia and most training was moved to western areas, while camps on the East Coast were used mainly to debrief and reassess agents and OGs withdrawn from Europe.

At these various schools there was a general atmosphere which provoked '... an undercurrent of tension and nervous pressure beneath a relaxed surface ...' to quote the OSS War Report. At Camp X for example, several second generation Americo-Hungarians first met in a room fitted out as it might be in their parents' homeland with Hungarian folk-art pieces as part of its decoration. Here the recruits were served as much wine as they wanted while eating Hungarian food. This was meant to be a test for strong heads, not as generous as it might seem, for much of the recruits' course was a continuous round of physical tests of endurance, of demolitions and operational exercises outside the camp. One team of Hungarians 'stole' a locomotive from a Toronto railway yard, they 'raided' local factories and ships in harbour. At other times they used the underground firing ranges, learning to sense where a target might be in the dark. Only nine of the 22 Americo-Hungarian volunteers passed this introductory course, and those who came through successfully were trained in Lysander pick-ups on an airfield in the camp.

Some training was carried out overseas, OSS instructors being sent to army schools in various theatres. But in Algiers OSS had its own school for teaching guerrilla leaders (see Appendix 3.4). The parachute school here trained 2,500 agents and guerrilla leaders from early in 1943 until it was moved to China in the winter of 1944-45.

The training of OSS personnel covered a wider field than that of SOE, for SI agents learnt the Special Intelligence techniques similar no doubt to those taught to SIS agents. SO personnel had courses which differed little from those of SOE's agents, while OGs' training was closer to that of the SAS than SOE.

T HE first operation in which both OSS and SOE were involved in numbers was the 'Torch' landings on 8 November 1942 in North Africa. This brought out some of the Allies' political difficulties not spelt out during an agent's training, but of which his SOE Country Section or OSS equivalent would have warned him. Preparations had been made in 1941 for American diplomatic contacts to be established with the Vichy-French authorities, who ran their North African administration to the orders of the government allowed by the Germans to rule southern France. The

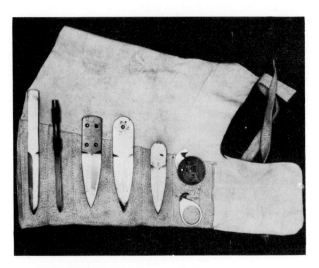

▲ A set of blades for use by an instructor at SOE training schools. This set was unopened until 1986 and shows from the left: a form of thumb knife; an SOE 'dart' blade; two variations of thumb knives; a lapel knife; a tyre-slasher pivotted on an English penny (agents in the field would use a coin of the country in which they operated); and a tyre-slasher used by slipping the ring over the forefinger. The set was carried in a chamois leather roll. The thumb blade with four holes might be tied to a pole or otherwise secured to make a stabbing weapon. The single hole was used for a finger thong. This might be slipped over the forefinger and the blade concealed in the palm. It could then be 'flipped over' to stand vertically between thumb and forefinger which gripped it for slashing an enemy's hands, side of the neck, ears or face. Or it might be allowed to fall on its thong when the arm was lowered, to be gripped between the fore and second finger. Then when the user clenched his fist for a thrust at his victim's eyes, the blade protruded from his fist. Care was needed to ensure the thrust was a 'direct extension of the forearm, otherwise the blade might tip back cutting the knuckle web'. The roll was found in New Zealand and had been packed on 3 February 1945, its official description of contents names the SOE 'dart' as a 'Commando Nail' and probably the four-holed thumb knife as 'knife, thumb (NZ)'.

contacts included the work of 12 American officers who as Vice-Consuls ostensibly supervised the distribution of food given by America for the people of Morocco, Algiers and Tunis. These 'twelve Apostles' as they became known were described in one Abwehr report as being '. . . mainly interested in social, sexual or culinary activities . . .' This underestimation of the officers' abilities was also shared by de Gaulle's secret service. He was regarded by the American State Department as a British protégé and the Americans favoured General Giraud. A number of French circuits like *Alliance* owed their allegiance to Giraud as in 1941 de Gaulle had by no means the support of all Frenchmen. Yet Giraud would not leave France and told Robert Murphy of the State Department that he expected an Allied landing in France to support a national revolt, which he would lead.

Other plots and counter plots among Allies and enemy alike need not detain us; but when OSS smuggled out of North Africa two men with detailed knowledge of Moroccan harbours—a senior ship's pilot and a tug boat captain—General Patton gave his consent. Eisenhower did not know of the mission and the British SIS are said to have disapproved of the methods used. Be that as it may, OSS were forbidden to assassinate several Gestapo officers in North Africa but were allowed to drug them to sleep during the vital hours of landing. SOE helped to consolidate OSS' links with anti-Vichy commanders and young Frenchmen who were to seize the docks at Algiers. Many were arrested on the night of 7/8 November because the Allied troops were two hours late in landing there. In French Morocco, however, the pro-Allied military commander arrested the Vichy-ite governor.

Giraud, brought out of France by the SIS, refused to take part in the landings, spending 7/9 November in Gibraltar trying to persuade the Allies to land also in France. (De Gaulle had only been told of the invasion three days before it happened and would not arrive in Algiers until the following May.) Giraud went to Algiers a day or so after the landings but the French colonial forces continued to take their orders from the Vichy Admiral Darlan, who had known sympathy for the Germans. Later Darlan was assassinated by a young Frenchman who was serving in SOE; a cause of mistrust between the French and British, not entirely removed by the youth's execution. The Vichy old guard still held some positions of authority even though the Allies controlled these French colonies after the invasion. These officers were not replaced even when Giraud took command of French forces in north Africa after Darlan's death that Christmas. They continued to believe that de Gaulle's secret service was behind the Admiral's assassination and took steps to arrest any agents that they could find. Several hid in one of SOE's offices, others were rescued from prison by OSS teams, before eventually de Gaulle arrived. He dismissed all officers in the colonial forces who had Vichy sympathies, forcing Giraud into retirement. He died in relative obscurity in 1949.

OSS teams continued to operate from Algiers with one party of 20 agents trained for work in neutral Spanish Morocco. They were led by Donald Downes, who at 37 had some experience of this work as he had been in Stephenson's branch of SIS before joining OSS. The agents were mainly young Americans who had served with the Lincoln Battalion fighting Franco five years earlier, or Spanish communists. Before they were sent to Morocco however, OSS' veteran Colonel Bill Eddy, an American Marine, wanted to show the US Army that OSS could provide teams for field intelligence, and against Downes' wish his men were sent to the Tunisian front. There one 'gung-ho' major and a young ex-Lincoln soldier were captured, when making a reconnaissance.

Downes wanted to use Spanish communists in exile in Algeria, but the former Vichy colonial officers refused to release these men from prisons. Downes therefore helped several of them to break out of a concentration camp deep in the desert but unfortunately they included at least one double-agent. He later informed the Spanish Moroccan police of a safe house used by Downes' men and several were arrested with American weapons in their possession. During the summer of 1943 Downes got permission from the US Fifth Army HQ in Algiers to send agents into Spain. This caused some concern to State Department officials as it did to their counterparts in the British Foreign Office, because if the agents were discovered by the Spanish this might lead Spain into closer ties with the Axis powers. SOE were unable therefore to help Downes and he had to create his own ferry service from a stretch of the French Moroccan coast into Spanish coves. This Moroccan base was guarded by OSS and the ships crewed by former communist officers of the Spanish Navy.

OSS and SOE agents would continue to operate into southern Europe sabotaging Axis installations, gaining intelligence and recruiting local support before their roles changed as the Allies went on the offensive. Then both agencies became more directly concerned with equipping partisan armies. These were roles which Gubbins had seen in 1938 as suited to guerrilla forces working in concert with an army's main battle force, and which inevitably brought the clandestine forces in closer liaison with military staffs planning campaigns. SOE Cairo's headquarters was put under control of the General Headquarters of the Mediterranean theatre in September 1943, mainly for this reason. Baker Street then no longer had direct control of its agents' operations in this theatre, a change in the Command Structure over which Charles Hambro resigned as CD. He was succeeded by Colin Gubbins.

B EFORE looking at some examples of OSS and SOE intelligence circuits—the spy-rings beloved of novelists—a brief summary of the agencies' operations throws a little light on national resistance forces.

Abyssinia—agents of MI R and Section D helped to organize irregular forces which were briefly trained by a few British soldiers. In January 1941 1,800 of these irregulars marched into the mountains from the Sudan in the west. At the same time British and Indian troops attacked the Italians from the north and the south-east, driving the enemy from their defences as the irregulars did coming from the west to enter the capital Addis Ababa on 5 May when the Italians capitulated. This campaign showed that patriotic forces could fight effectively, if given some training and the support of a few experienced officers and NCOs.

Albania—Italy had annexed this small state in April 1939, although the tribal independence of the mountain people of the north occasionally led to raids against the occupying forces. But neither Section D's agent nor later SOE's agents were able to raise any sustained guerrilla operations. By 1943 rival tribal and communist guerrillas (from the south) were fighting each other. Then SOE's supplies of arms to both factions were used apparently less often in fighting the Germans than the British had hoped. The Communists received the bulk of these weapons perhaps because there were one or more staff officers of SOE in Cairo who were confirmed communists. Five OSS teams went to the Communist south where from November 1943 they established networks independent of SOE's contacts, and continued to provide intelligence until 1945 when the 'cold war' separated the communists from the British and Americans.

Algeria—after the 'Torch' landings SOE's base 'Massingham' was established at Guyotville just west of Algiers. It had schools for training saboteurs and partisan leaders, supply stores where containers could be packed albeit often inadequately; and other facilities. OSS had a similar but separate and larger base (see Appendix 3.4). The work of the two agencies was more closely co-ordinated after May 1944 when a joint Special Projects Operation Centre was formed. This also included some French officers after 20 June.

Asia and the Far East—see Chapter 9.

Austria—SOE did not know apparently of a small anti-Nazi resistance movement that had grown up since Germany annexed Austria in 1938. In 1944 SOE missions were mounted from Italy and Yugoslavia on foot and by parachute but achieved little; seven of 12 OSS missions that winter succeeded in sending useful intelligence from southern Austria. Late in 1944 one OSS agent was killed and at least nine others were captured or forced back to Allied territory. Their difficulties were mainly due to the Germans' widespread use of fake agents who had trapped many Austrians disposed to be friendly to the Allies.

Belgium—by December 1941 Walthère Dewé had set up a similar circuit to the one he had operated when Germany occupied Belgium in World War I. Later over 100 agents were inserted with SOE's support, although the resistance forces which they raised had little time for action as in 1944 the Allies advanced through Belgium in a few days. Nevertheless these patriots prevented the retreating Germans demolishing the cranes and other installations of Antwerp Docks

Bermuda—some of Bill Stephenson's SIS operatives intercepted mail held over night from the Americas, when flying boats refuelled here on their way to Europe. The mail was read without the knowledge of the recipient (see Chapter 6).

Bulgaria—apart from Donovan's visit in 1941 and the work of the US naval attaché before America entered the war, there were apparently no Allied clandestine operations here except perhaps by SIS. The Russians had the centre of their Balkan espionage based in the capital Sofia, which may have accounted for the lack of other Allied activity.

Czechoslovakia—after the assassination of Heydrich (see Chapter 2) a few SOE supported teams parachuted into these provinces for intelligence work. In 1944 one SOE officer joined forces with an OSS group in the Tatra mountains of Slovakia, after the OSS team had contacted officers of the Slovak army which had been in revolt. All but two agents were caught in the mountains on Boxing Day 1944, the survivors escaping through the Russian battle front. In May 1945 another OSS officer organized a small resistance group in Prague during the last days of the war.

Denmark—although a neutral country a group of young staff officers and senior policemen in 1941 formed 'The Prince' circuit. They sent intelligence to a journalist in Sweden who passed it to SOE. The first sabotage teams were established here in the winter of 1943-44 and supported by joint SOE/OSS operations. The following June the railways went on strike for three weeks at the time of the Allied landings in France; this strike prevented the movement by rail of six German Divisions. In early 1945 Danish teams carried out a series of sabotage raids, after RAF planes had bombed the SD's offices the previous October, destroying their files of information on Allied circuits.

Eire—SIS had control of the Abwehr agents here and the IRA had only weak links with the Germans. One OSS operative worked mainly with the Irish security forces to provide reports on enemy agents, shipping and Irish politics. In 1942 the Irish Government allowed their Embassy in Rome to pass OSS information on targets worth bombing in Tokyo, details of which had been collected by the Vatican representative in Japan.

Finland—America never declared war on Finland and therefore maintained diplomatic contact with the Finnish Government. Two OSS operatives visited the country gaining some intelligence through senior army officers but were unable to influence the Finnish Government's decision to avoid any action which might antagonize the Germans.

France—during SOE's formative years, 1940-41, its French (F) Section and de Gaulle's *Bureau Central de Renseignements* (BCRA) supported by SOE's R/F Section established circuits: F had started nine; BCRA about six. There were also a number of spontaneous circuits like 'Alliance' created by French men and women not owing allegiance to Section F nor to BCRA. In some of these circuits were French railway employees who carried out many minor acts of sabotage which had an accumulative effect on German transport. The first major Free French operation was carried out by paratroops who severely damaged a power station near Bordeaux. The explosives for this raid were included in one of the first parachute drops of supply containers, made in June 1941. In December 1941 F Section began to use agents in teams of three: an organizer, a radio operator normally with no other duties, and a sabotage instructor who also acted as quartermaster. These and earlier teams during 1942 led some two dozen active circuits although some earlier ones had been closed by German penetration. BCRA had probably more and began taking former free-lance circuits under its wing. OSS worked with BCRA to the discomfort of SIS whose senior staff limited their co-operation with OSS in London for a time. BCRA made no distinction between military and political operations, as at that time de Gaulle needed to establish himself as the only leader of France. After the political difference in North Africa had been resolved, however, OSS, SOE, and BCRA co-operated in raising armies of resistance fighters (see Chapter 7).

Germany—SIS contacts with anti-Nazi organizations in 1939 were cut by German counter-intelligence (see Holland), but a few lone SIS and OSS operatives worked in the Nazi fatherland and the Double-X operation from London mounted its radio 'game' of deceptions. No SOE or OSS agents worked here before the winter of 1944/45 to establish contacts with anti-Nazi movements, which in 1943 looked to Russia as most had communist sympathies. A major Russian circuit, known to the Germans as 'The Red Orchestra', included many well placed agents with a senior government official and a *Luftwaffe* intelligence operator working until caught. The quality of intelligence beamed to Russia was probably good but the circuit's radios are said to have been designed only to transmit eastwards.

Black propaganda from the British Political Warfare Executive (PWE not part of SOE) was distributed in various ways to deceive the Germans and German military forces in the occupied countries. There were broadcasts, newspaper articles, rumours and counterfeit documents purporting to be of German origin. The lies and half-truths included 'evidence' of individuals who had disobeyed Nazi regulations, and escaped punishment. There were exaggerated reports of Russian victories in 1942. By 1944 OSS' Morale Operations had a 600,000-watt transmitter broadcasting a 12-hour programme each night to Germany. This, like two other MO regular broadcasts, was laced with black propaganda once the programme's popularity had been established. This was achieved because German listeners enjoyed the music and other aspects of the broadcasts.

OSS successfully parachuted 32 teams 'blind' into Germany during the last nine months of the war when there were few SIS operatives there. The British were surprised at the number of infiltrations, but only four succeeded in contacting their controllers who received intelligence transmitted on Joan-Eleanor equipment to USAAF aircraft. The first agent to land was a German who from September 1944 had a circuit in the Ruhr, eventually with seven sub-agents. His reports came by courier to Switzerland.

Greece—All operations here were bedevilled by civil war between the Royalists and Communist groups. The British left behind some contacts when they evacuated Greece in April 1941, but only once did Communists and Royalists work together. On this occasion, in the autumn of 1942, they captured the guards, or at least drove them off while an SOE team destroyed an important railway bridge near Thermopylae. The

▲ Sergeant Charles W. Magill of SOS Operations Group, in the mountain village of Kastania, Greece. The 28-year-old sergeant is wearing a uniform jacket with its American flag shoulder flash, but no other badges. Horses were a common form of transport here in late 1944, for both OGs and other personnel of OSS and of SOE.

following June, without local support or any Greeks in the SOE team, a viaduct was destroyed, closing the line for months. SOE teams were active also on the Greek island of Crete from 1941 until its recapture. Patrick Leigh-Fermor and Stanley Moss captured the German commander of the island in April 1944, driving him through his own road blocks to rendezvous with a submarine.

Between May and October 1944 80 Special Intelligence agents operated in 30 OSS teams including 'Horsebreeders' (see Chapter 10). Eleven of these provided not only military but also political intelligence. During this period Operational Groups with over 200 personnel destroyed trains, and caused over 1,700 Axis casualties. After the civil war began, on the Germans' retreat, 33 SI and SO officers remained, providing political intelligence. They and SOE officers caught 120 German agents left behind to disrupt Allied attempts to reconcile the various Greek factions.

Holland—after the Abwehr had snatched the SIS officers working from the Hague in 1939, the surviving British agents of several nationalities were further compromised, as the Germans invading Holland in May that year found a complete set of accountant's records in the Hague Passport Office of the British Consulate. In the next year several agents working for the Dutch Government-in-exile were parachuted into Holland, and one working for SIS was captured with a pile of encoded messages in his pockets. Others were caught that summer of 1941 and later, the Germans controlling all SOE's agents from March 1942 until 1 April 1944, sending misleading information in a radio 'game' known to the Germans as 'North Pole'. In the early summer of 1944, however, SOE and the Dutch-in-exile successfully armed the resistance forces here.

Hungary—SIS' principal agent was head of the Hungarian military security forces before he disappeared in 1940. The following April the Germans took command of Hungarian military services with encouragement from some Hungarian generals. In late 1943, however, the Hungarian Government wanted to make peace with the Allies and an emissary contacted SOE in Turkey. He was sent back to Hungary with two wireless sets that were operated by police radio operators until March 1944 or soon afterwards when the Germans occupied the country. Attempts the previous winter by an SOE agent to encourage resistance in the south had met with no success. On the other hand attempts by the Germans to infiltrate OSS through Hungarian contacts were blocked. An OSS team which parachuted into the country on 15 March, four days before the occupation, were caught. A later drop by an SOE team met the same fate with only one survivor of German prison camps.

Italy—SOE made little if any headway in establishing circuits before the fall of Mussolini in the late summer of 1943; but one of their radio operators who had been captured was able to transmit for the new government, several messages of surrender which the Germans could not decipher. Later SOE and OSS provided weapons for the Italian resistance, after the first OSS team had contacted political leaders in German occupied Rome during October 1944. Intelligence circuits were also established by OSS far north of the battle area and others close to it. By April 1945 there were 75 other OSS teams training and supplying Italian partisans in the north, as well as a number of SOE teams.

Libya and the Western Desert—this was SIS' province; but British military intelligence was helped by the work of the SAS and the Long Range Desert Group (LRDG) far behind the Axis battle front. Probably typical of SIS agents here was Colonel J. E. Haselden, the Egyptian born son of an Englishman, and his Greek wife. The Colonel often passed for an Arab in moving through Axis held territory. He was killed in September 1942 during a major raid on Tobruk, the raiders having been betrayed by a double-agent.

Norway—the importance of the sabotage at Vermork has been explained in Chapter 3 with its consequent setbacks to the Germans' production of atomic bombs. The local resistance—the military organization, Milorg for short—was built up with SOE and OSS help to 60,000 by 1945. Milorg then helped to ensure 350,000 Germans were held in Norway to fight the Russians on the north-east border and a possible Allied invasion from the west. SF HQ sent several teams to southern Norway in 1945 for sabotage that would disrupt the German movement of troops.

Poland—despite the long flights—14 hours in 1941—which had to be made by RAF and later USAAF crews, 348 agents-cum-soldiers (all but five of whom were Poles) parachuted home. They and 600 tons of weapons were dropped from some 500 flights. Many of these were made by Polish airmen at the cost of heavy losses, trying in August 1944 to supply their Home Army during its rising in Warsaw. The Germans put down this bold attempt at freedom, and an SOE mission was flown in from Italy to assess the morale and surviving strength of Polish resistance. The team was overrun by a sudden Russian advance and its five men held for a month in Russian prisons before being repatriated.

Portugal—the capital Lisbon was a centre of SIS, Abwehr and other secret service activities, the British identifying many, if not all the men or women passing through Lisbon for espionage in Britain or America. The

▼ Patrick Leigh-Fermor and Stanley Moss of SOE dressed in German uniforms for the operation in Crete. There in April 1944 they captured the German commander of the island, later taking their prisoner off the island by submarine. Perhaps ironically each carries a commando fighting knife. The one worn by Moss (on the right) appears to be in an American 'pancake flapper' scabbard. Similar knives had been captured by the Germans during operations on Crete in 1941.

Germans even discovered that through currency deals in the city, they could trace the likely note numbers of money given to Allied agents before being dropped in occupied Europe. MI 9 agents were based here in 1940 but active aggression against Axis interests in this neutral country was forbidden by Allied governments. This did not prevent OSS having close associations with several Axis diplomats who provided political intelligence.

Roumania—Abwehr agents frustrated Section D's attempts to destroy the very productive oil wells, which the local people had no wish to destroy as they were the main source of the country's wealth. A young Roumanian operated a Section D radio from the time of the Germans' arrival in October 1940 until he went off the air on 23 June 1941; an SOE colonel re-established contacts here in late 1943. The King eventually overthrew the pro-Axis dictator, Antonescu, in August 1944 but the Russians were soon to take the country under their control. In the few days before they arrived

▲ A British trained Italian paratroop officer, Ezio Mario, prepares his kit for a jump behind the German lines. At this date, 20 April 1945, he was working for OSS in Italy. In addition to his sub machine-gun he is packing various grenades and explosives. The parachute wings on his left shoulder are below what appears to be a cloth insignia of three vertical bars (possibly the Italian national colours). The badge below the 'wings' has not been identified, but like the several Italian badges—on his British utility battledress collar and left pocket—this lower cloth flash on the left shoulder may also be of Italian origin. His sub machine-gun appears to be a Beretta, its barrel rests on a drum of instantaneous fuse (Cordtex?). In front of this is a box of No. 82 Gammon Mark 1 grenades, with a fighting knife resting on the box. To its right is a Very pistol. This pistol lies on a drum-tin of slow fuse, '48 feet of safety fuse Mark 11' according to the label. In front of this is a box of detonators (possibly of American origin by the appearance of the box). Two phosphorous grenades lie beside a No. 36 fragmentation grenade in the centre foreground. Ezio has in his right hand what might be three cartridges of PE, and the black square 'tin' in front of his haversack may be one of the incendiary devices to which the official caption refers. These could also include the black cylindrical item under the haversack flap and a similar item behind the box of detonators, although one of these may contain Very light cartridges.

▼ Men of the Italian partisan Modena (V) Division in the Vidiciatico area, being addressed by their commander, General Ricco M. Armando. On his left (in a waterproof jacket) is Lieutenant Elton L. Kennedy of OSS. He was one of several OSS officers attached to the American IV Corps who worked with partisans. The Modena Division was closer in size to an Allied brigade. The 1,500 partisans in this formation 'secured information behind the enemy's lines'. Their weapons included Italian, German and American sub-machine guns, rifles and carbines.

an OSS team of 21 personnel organized the evacuation of POWs, inspected the oil fields and collected intelligence from the German HQ, with some co-operation from the Russian NKVD unit until 9 November.

Spain—the British Government prohibited SOE operations in Spain in order to maintain Franco's neutrality. This in the early years of the war had a bias toward the Axis powers, as General Franco had been helped by German and Italian forces during the Civil War, and escaping Allied soldiers were usually handed back to the Gestapo by Spanish police; nevertheless SIS had an 'escape' line through Spain in 1940. Later in the war SOE teams were deployed but not activated in Spain against the possible occupation of this country by Axis forces or in the the event of Spain even joining the Axis powers. After about 1943 the chances of such a commitment by Franco receded. Gibraltar, as a naval base provided a haven for SOE's fishing craft inserting agents into occupied France (see Chapter 10). OSS had an SI operative in Spain from April 1942 as a member of the US diplomatic staff; from this small beginning the OSS expanded by 1943 to 40 circuits each of 20 agents or sub-agents. Their reports included evidence of the Germans being given access to Spanish diplomatic reports from overseas, which contained some military intelligence.

Sweden—after initial setbacks for SIS when a senior policeman worked for the Germans to have operatives deported, SOE established a secret training camp for Milorg leaders. They came from Norway, the British instructors working with those of OSS from 1942 although for security each agency had its own offices. Other activities were directed at espionage and SOE's smuggling of important steel ball bearings through German shore and off-shore patrols (see Chapter 10). There was such a pattern of Axis disloyalties here that a Pole working for the Japanese was spying on the Germans.

Switzerland—SIS, SOE, and OSS all had senior men in this neutral country, organizing operations in adjoining occupied countries. Allen Dulles established a major if small OSS centre for intelligence which also provided points of contact for Axis peace feelers without the risk of American diplomatic commitment.

Turkey—Axis and Allied secret agencies had innumerable missions here. The Germans in turn paid £300,000 in forged bank notes to the Turkish valet of the British ambassador for photographs of documents, including minutes of top level Allied conferences which reportedly gave the proposed date of the Normandy landings. SOE recruited some agents for operations elsewhere through their Turkish offices, and with OSS identified 1,500 Germans agents controlled from Turkey including 30 trained to penetrate Allied clandestine agencies.

Yugoslavia—SOE had a passive but propaganda role in encouraging the rising which replaced the Regent with young King Peter. But before the army could be fully mobilized the Germans invaded the country. The next SOE contact was with the Royalist Colonel Draže Mihailović who had set up a resistance force in the mountains. He soon became an international hero but analysis of sabotage operations and ambushes—by a quirk of fate in Enigma signals provided by Bletchley to a senior SOE officer in Cairo—showed that Tito's communist partisans were far more effective. By another chance an SOE agent had met Tito and when the Royalists began seeking German help in fighting communists, SOE switched their full support to Tito. OSS continued for some time to help if not arm the Royalists. This support was given as the Americans had landing strips of their Balkan Air Terminal Service (BATS) in the territories of both factions. At that time these rescue services were flying hundreds of Allied airmen to safety after their aircraft had crash landed.

Between January and November 1944 OSS also supplied shipping for the evacuation of 20,000 civilians, the shipment of 2,000 partisans for training in Italy and their return to Yugoslavia. And in addition to their work in supplying partisans, OSS set up four meteorological stations, organized escape routes for airmen, and distributed the MO Branch's black propaganda leaflets.

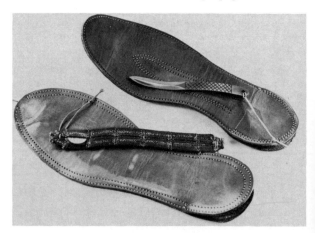

▲ These leather insoles were fitted into SOE agents' shoes to conceal a knife or money. They were particularly useful when the agent was wearing only light clothing with no other convenient place to conceal items. The sole on the left was designed to carry five gold coins, which in the Balkans and Middle East were often gold sovereigns. This one-time £1 coin was an accepted medium of exchange in many parts of the World in the 1940s and later. On the right is the knife-sole, its blade is shaped to fit comfortably under the arch of the foot. It was used in a similar manner to a thumb-knife.

6
COLLECTING MILITARY AND INDUSTRIAL INTELLIGENCE

A S Eric Erickson stepped from the Swedish air liner onto the tarmac at Berlin airport, he was confident of his cover. Invited by the German Government to visit their oil refineries in September 1941, he was known for his pro-Nazi sympathies and a recognised authority on oil supplies. Yet, when he saw the two SD officers checking the passengers' papers as they filed into the reception building, a cold chill of fear gripped him, tightening his stomach to steel his resolve not to panic. One of the officers took his papers; his visa was genuine, and his authority to visit Berlin supported by the correct documents. Yet Eric was not absolutely certain that this German did not suspect the reason for his visit. His passport showed that he had been born in America, still a neutral country but hostile in many ways to the Nazis; but his naturalization as a Swede was genuine and pre-dated the war. Could there be any obvious reason to doubt his personal support of the Nazis? Apparently not, because the officer smiled, nodded a welcome to Berlin and handed him his papers.

A relaxed Eric could play his pro-Nazi role as the ministry car drove him to his first meeting of this trip. It would take him to the centre of German economic planning for the continued supply of oil. In Sweden his views had met with support from some business colleagues but cut him off from his American relations. They were not to know that these pronouncements in praise of Hitler were prompted by none other than an American ambassador who during a visit to Sweden had met Eric by chance. In the course of this and later meetings, Erickson was recruited for the secret services, working first for the SIS before America entered the war and later for OSS. During his first and later visits he obtained details of German refining and oil storage facilities in great detail. At the same time he arranged to sell major quantities of oil to the Germans, no doubt having bought this ostensibly for refining in Sweden.

In 1942, after transferring his services to OSS, Eric got the permission of his American controllers to recruit two sub-agents: Baron von Oldenburg, an advisor on fuel consumption to the German Government; and Otto Holtz, an old friend of Eric's. The Baron insisted on having a letter confirming his work for OSS, which might be used in his defence should he be tried for war crimes after the war. Erickson also gave his friend Holtz a similar document. With these insurances against possible prosecution, the Baron and Otto supplied details of bomb damage and other information on German oil refineries. On a visit in the summer of 1942,

OSS asked Eric to collect also reports from Marianne von Mollendorf. She had worked for the Office for some months, was well connected through her family who were wealthy, enabling her to travel and learn several languages. Eric could not decipher the codes of her secret reports but visited her regularly. At first they posed as lovers, unitl in 1943 he actually became the lover of this statuesque, dark-haired lady. That year OSS set up a bogus synthetic oil refining project for which Eric was given detailed plans and a brochure, supposedly produced by his company. This had obvious appeal to the Germans for a plant in Sweden could not be bombed, and they encouraged Eric to build it, showing him around their own synthetic oil plants of which he took photographs.

Spies' motives are always difficult to determine but the Nazi responsible for these plants decided to work for Eric, as again this would stand him in good stead if he was tried after the war. Erickson's own motives seem clearly to have been a dislike,—to put it mildly,—of all that the Nazi movement was doing in Europe. For he persisted in his trips to Germany, despite many setbacks as his biographer explains in *The Invisible World of Espionage*. Holtz died suddenly and there was a frantic search through the dead man's papers for the incriminating letter. On another occasion Eric was arrested for listening to BBC broadcasts, but satisfactorily misled his interrogators. On one trip he arrived at Berlin airport in 1944, passed through the SD officers' security check and got into the waiting car. Its driver did not take the usual route for the government offices, but instead took Eric to Moabit prison. He expected the worst but experienced an even more agonising shock: the once stocky Marianne now dishevelled, gaunt and manacled, no doubt, was in a line of 50 prisoners to be executed. Eric and others had been brought to watch what happened to those who were traitors to the Fatherland.

The SD must have known that he was Marianne's lover but he was allowed to continue his visits to refineries until the autumn of 1944. On a visit to Leipzig, he was recognized by a business acquaintance who knew Erickson's firm had at least one Jewish partner. Before this man could contact the Gestapo, Erickson knifed him and fled to Berlin. There he learnt from the Baron that other sub-agents of OSS had been arrested, as apparently was the Baron after Eric was safely on a flight to Sweden.

Erickson's cover must have enabled him to use an

ordinary camera as Stephenson's men used in 1940 when code books were brought to them for copying. For at that time SIS apparently preferred to 'borrow' the code books for an hour or more while they were photographed in some 'safe' building. Getting the books away from the Italian embassy in Washington was a job assigned to SIS' blonde and beautiful Betty Thorpe Pack, described earlier.

Photographing papers in enemy headquarters or some office that might be visited by a night guard on his patrols, needed ultra-small easily concealed cameras. Alternatively some convenient deception—as in Erickson's case—might give the agent reason to be carrying a camera. But since there were areas of Europe like the zone along the west coast of France which were forbidden areas for civilians, the chances of openly carrying a camera even for taking holiday snaps, were very few in any region that could possibly be of military interest or associated with the Axis war effort.

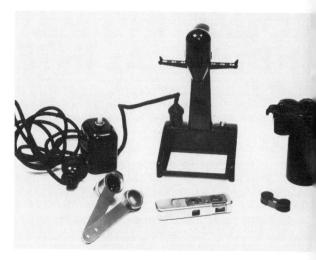

▲ This Riga Minox camera (bottom centre) is shown with associated equipment for developing prints without a dark room. Walter Zapp designed it in 1934 and by 1939, 17,000 of these cameras had been sold worldwide. British intelligence services bought all that were available in the UK in the autumn of 1939, OSS had a standing offer of $400 for any available in the USA in 1942. Insufficient supplies later let to the production of the Kodak 'matchbox' camera. The Riga Minox has an F/3.5 anastigmatic lens with a focal length of 15mm. Exposure speeds ranged from half a second to one-thousandth of a second and there was a setting for time exposures. The 8mm film cartridge (bottom right) provided 50 negatives of 8 x 11mm. These could be developed in the special tank (top right) which could be loaded in daylight and used only 1 oz of developer. The miniature enlarger (top centre) was only eight inches high but produced good quality 3½ x 2½ inch prints. Its controls and transformer are on the left. Also provided was a special magnifier-viewer (bottom left) for examining negatives. The Minox's 'natural sight' was in focus from six feet to infinity, but could be focused down to eight inches. This made the 3⅛ x 1 x ¾ inch camera ideal for photographing documents.

I N 1940 trans-Atlantic flying boats on their flight to Lisbon, stopped overnight at Bermuda. Engineers could then service and refuel the aircraft while its crew were entertained at perhaps the yacht club or some restaurant, to which they were taken by British residents of this colony. One suspects that the crew knew what went on while they left the British Airways Clipper, but since there were many American tourists on this island even in 1940, there had to be no apparent interference with the cargoes of mail bags. Certainly no one was supposed to examine the contents of diplomatic bags on their way from South America to neutral countries. On one such flight were perhaps 200,000 letters, several hundred of which Stephenson's staff on the island wanted to inspect. Nadya Gardner knew what to look for in an address or style of handwriting, for she was one of the 'trappers' who checked through this mail at the Princess Hotel. As pretty as Betty Pack, her job was less glamorous, although SIS girls on the island are reputed to have made up a ditty which included the line: 'My legs it was that got me in, still I wait for my bit of sin'.

Nadya could recognize perhaps 30 particular styles of writing and knew by heart the addresses of many firms which were business fronts for the Abwehr or the SD. She worked in one of the many offices hidden away in the vaults of hotels or in large family houses, along with perhaps 20 girls and their supervisor. One night in February 1940 she drew his attention to a letter skillfully extracted from its envelope, bearing the address of an SD front company in Berlin. The typescript might be genuine enough as a business enquiry, although the English phraseology of its American author seemed quaint, indeed Germanic in

tone if not in actual words. The supervisor had the pages passed to one of the laboratories also hidden away in the building and there the pages were tested for secret inks. None were found on this occasion. However when another letter from the same firm was tested for colourless ink made from the pain killer Pyramidon, the wording stood out in all its detail of ship movements, aircraft numbers freighted from USA to Europe and other intelligence. These tests must have taken time for the pages had to be left unscarred by such treatment if the Germans were not to know the secret messages had been read. (There was always the dilemma of what intelligence to let pass to preserve the secrecy of its interception and what must be lost in the post, so to speak.) The passengers on the Clipper were no doubt comforted with adequate reasons for any delay caused while the letter was tested, or a particularly heavy post caused the 'trappers' to take longer than the engineers in servicing the flying boat.

The American who wrote this and several other letters intercepted in Bermuda, signed himself 'Joe K' who wrote also to addresses in Spain and Portugal. Some, but not all, the contents of this secret writing was

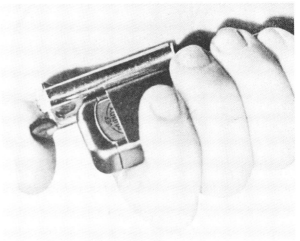

▲ The screwmount Leica camera of c1937 (top centre) was of the type used by a German agent to photograph documents in the British ambassador's office in Ankara, Turkey. For comparison a Minox camera is shown on the left. On the right is a French equivalent of the Kodak 'matchbox' camera, this had speeds from 1/20th to 1/250th seconds with 45 exposures. The 'matchbox' camera (bottom) is a rare example of the OSS' Kodak camera disguised as a box of Chinese matches. The Kodak 'matchbox' was $2^{3}/_{8}$ x 1½ x ⅞ inches and could be supplied with Swedish, Japanese or other manufacturer's labels. In some cases the agent provided a suitable matchbox label. The camera took 34 exposures, each negative being 14mm² on any 16mm film. 100 feet of Plus X and 100 feet of Super XX unperforated film was provided with each camera. Its wide-angle lens had two openings of f.5 and f.11 set by adjusting the focal length with a pin. There were two shutter settings: one for a seventy fifth of a second; and one for time exposures when using an air filled bulb to activate the shutter. The fixed focus gave a clear picture at 4½ feet to infinity. A tripod for use in photographing documents was available. In June 1944 a compact developing kit was 'in preparation and will be ready in the near future' to quote an official source.

▲ An adaptation of the Minox camera that appeared to be a cigarette lighter. This was built by MI 9 the British escape and evasion section of SIS, with a team that produced many clandestine devices.

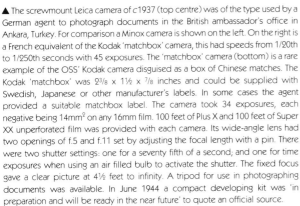

passed from SIS to the FBI who began a search for 'Joe K'. They discovered his associate had been killed by a hit and run taxi in circumstances which needed some explaining. SIS then told more of what they knew of 'Joe K'; and without perhaps admitting any guilt, had an explanation for the taxi accident. The FBI discreetly left the case on their files and later arrested 'Joe K', Frederick Ludwig, a German-educated American. He had returned 'home' in March 1940 when he was 48, to recruit sub-agents through the German-American Bund intended to foster good relationships between the two countries.

Bermuda lies 580 miles due east of the Carolina coast, ideally placed to intercept radio traffic on America's eastern seaboard. It appears that this was monitored by a station of the 'Y' service. After the late spring of 1940 Churchill set up Stephenson as controller of not only SIS operations in America, but also prepared to take over all its agents should the Germans invade Britain. Not surprisingly therefore some 1,200 staff of SIS worked with the 'trappers', chemists and code experts in those secret offices on the island. In one, perhaps under the pink-walled verandas of Hamilton's Princess

Hotel, was a powerful radio transmitter able to contact Europe and further afield.

Other interceptions were made in Jamaica and Trinidad where several international telephone and telegraph lines crossed the islands, phone tapping which added to the information passed to the FBI. The British were dependent on neutral America to prosecute German agents, since there were obvious limitations to the number of fatal taxi accidents that might be arranged. Bill Donovan knew of Stephenson's work as he visited 'little Bill' when he was living quietly in Bermuda in 1940. There the future chief of OSS was updated on information the 'trappers' had found in mail from the Export Sales Vice-President of Texaco. He, without the knowledge of his other vice-presidents, had shipped oil ostensibly to neutral countries, but in fact for delivery to Germany; he also supplied the Germans with various detailed figures on American oil output, amongst other intelligence. Both transactions broke American laws of neutrality and therefore he had to resign, Texaco then ceasing to supply any Axis power, even neutral Japan.

A more difficult case, indirectly aiding the Germans, was Standard Oil's agreement with the Swiss-financed subsidiary of I. G. Farben. This arrangement probably could not have been challenged in the courts, but—to the fury of Standard Oil's executives—a book was published explaining just how this deal worked. *Sequel to the Apocalypse: How Your Dimes Pay For Hitler's War* may not have been a best seller even if it was circulated to American embassies and government departments. These departments and others who received complimentary copies of the book, might be

▲ Willis George, one-time aeroplane salesman, US undercover agent for the Treasury in Cuba, worked there also unofficially for the FBI and naval intelligence in 1936. In 1940 he advised the British on the suitability of American volunteers for the RAF. During 1943 he was working for Naval Intelligence in Bermuda before joining OSS in January 1944 as an expert on surreptitious entry. In this illustration he is using a special tool to extract a letter from its envelope without breaking the seal.

interested not only in Standard Oil's deals but in those of other American corporations, knowingly or unknowingly trading with companies secretly owned by the Germans. The author and publishers of this revealing work were not traced at the time, because SIS had it written, printed and published at Camp X on the Canadian-US border.

Mail interception continued to be a source of much useful intelligence, whether the seals of diplomatic bags were '. . . not immune to the fingers of skilled investigators . . .' or only less sensitive mail had to be read. In all cases care was needed to avoid any sign that a letter had been tampered with. Willis George, one of OSS's most inventive technicians, designed a device by which a letter might be removed from its envelope without breaking its seals or gum. The technique was to insert two slim rods like knitting needles some three millimetres in diameter, that were slightly curved and could be pushed beneath the unsealed gap of the envelope flap. The rods were now inside the envelope and when held downwards it was possible to jiggle one each side of the letter. By inverting the envelope you could get a grip on the pages with sufficient strength to wind them onto

the rods and then slide the letter out of the second unsealed gap (wartime envelopes seldom were sealed completely at the corners). This was all far more difficult than steaming open the flap, but any tampering with mail that softened the gum left a telltale thin line where the gum had flowed when softened. Once the letter had been read or copied it was again rolled onto the 'needles' and re-inserted into its envelope, this being pressed flat to remove any sign of the letter having been curled around the rods.

The Germans must have realized that any mail might be checked for secret writing, and as the war continued the Axis agents overseas had to find a better means of sending their reports than writing them in invisible ink. The answer was the microdot, a pin-head sized picture which the recipient could enlarge to get perhaps 300 words of a report or details of an engineering drawing. Before 1940 these pin-head pictures could only be made in a well equipped photograph laboratory, when a 35mm stamp-sized piece of film was in effect re-photographed through a microscope used to reduce rather then enlarge a picture. This required equipment that was not suitable for use by agents. Professor Zapp of the Dresden Institute of Technology, however, simplified the process. His microdot making cabinet produced pin-head negatives that had been 'fixed' in the photographic sense and were printed by the recipient before he enlarged them. They were clear minute dots of plastic unlike the printed earlier dots. These had to be placed using the modified tiny tube 'point' of a hypodermic needle, to represent punctuation in printed or other texts. Zapp's clear dots could be fixed beneath the stamps of an envelope or on the inside of almost any innocent container, like a lady's powder-box. Allied agencies no doubt used them but no details have been traced because such techniques are still in use. There is no evidence that the Germans intercepted any microdots, although in Bermuda several German agents' reports were deftly 'smudged' probably by treating the microdot negatives with photographic chemicals.

IF espionage can be as ungentlemanly as reading other people's mail the collection of military intelligence—'int' in military slang—was even more ungallant. No holds were barred to obtain vital information, not only on German and other Axis troop movements. For instance a French girl surprised an agent of F Section taking notes of train schedules in a railway office and she had to be killed. Less dramatic but often nearly as important was information on the amount of a sugar ration or the local rice distribution centre, as it was to have the correct detail on a printed identity card. An agent in Europe might also require: a work permit showing his trade qualification; a ration card; a tobacco card whether or not he smoked; a permit to visit a frontier or coastal area closed to civilians; demobilization papers for a man of military age; and—after the summer of 1942—a medical certificate explaining why the bearer could not be sent to work in Germany. (One SOE agent, the gallant Wing-Commander F. F. E. Yeo-Thomas who worked for RF Section, carried his papers in a wallet with a clear plastic holder showing the distracting picture of a naked girl, opposite his identity card. On more than one occasion this diverted a policeman's attention from the fabricated details of Tommy's identity.) Without the right papers an agent knew that he or she might be caught, but it took experience to understand the importance of that sugar ration. Casually ask for more than your entitlement and not only might the grocer be suspicious, but other shoppers might gossip about the stranger's ignorance. Such tittle-tattle in France could reach the ears of a member of the

◀ This 'Zapp' cabinet was designed to produce pinhead-sized microdots. These reduced a 35mm negative to a negative 250-times smaller than the original. German agents used this equipment after its development in 1940. However some microdots were intercepted by British 'trappers' working for SIS in Bermuda. Although the device was invented by Professor Zapp, this cabinet was built by Ernst Leitz of Wetzlar (in modern West Germany). It had been used until 1945 in one of the German embassies in South America before it came into the possession of the FBI. The 35mm negative was apparently placed in its holder under the hinged cover at the top left. The microdot was produced at the end of a glass phial-like holder mounted with part of the chemical processing mechanism below the large hinged cover.

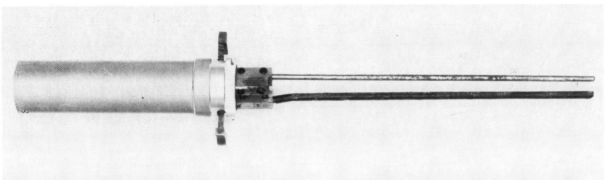

▲ An American device for extracting a letter from its envelope without breaking the seal. After examining the letter and photographing it if necessary, it was replaced in the envelope by the same tool. The envelope might then be 'ironed' to remove any obvious creases.

▼ A British device for extracting and replacing letters in unopened envelopes.

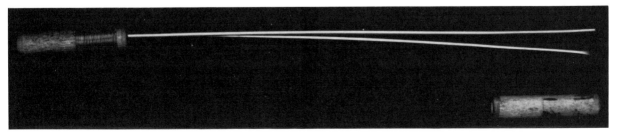

pro-Nazi *Malice*, a paramilitary force of Frenchmen under German control, who lived in their hometowns. They were therefore particularly dangerous for an agent might be noticed as a stranger or they might realize that a prominent citizen was missing from his usual cafés and work place and report his absence. Later still the *Malice* infiltrated some *maquis* units, but in 1940 they were eavesdroppers reporting the gossip of the town.

The British and French had no means of even hearing the gossip in June 1940 after their armies had withdrawn from Dunkirk, but that August de Gaulle's BCRA began attempts to send agents back to France. In December the 38-year-old senior officer in the Bureau, Lieutenant-Commander Honoré d'Orves decided to go to France himself to set up resistance movements. Earlier reports had shown that the German forces were accepted in many towns because they were generally courteous and correct in their behaviour giving the French no reason to fear them. Nevertheless, since August 1940 if not before, there had been isolated acts of sabotage by brave men and women who wanted to fight back against the occupying forces. The Commander was landed by boat at Plogoff on the Brittany coast on Christmas Eve 1940, a time when the German sentries along the coast were likely to be off their guard. But he was only in France a month before he was denounced by an informer and imprisoned. In May he was tried and sentenced to death but remained in prison until August. That month a German midshipman was the first of the occupying forces to be assassinated, or at least the first whose death the Gestapo could attribute to the Resistance. He was killed on 21 August in the Barbès Rochechouart Metro Station, and eight days later d'Orves was executed in a series of German retributions.

In later years the Resistance would have traced the informer who denounced d'Orves and followed the advice of Gubbins' pamphlet: they must be killed, and, if possible, a note pinned on the body stating that they were informers. This could not be done in the summer of 1940 but four years later no informant was likely to survive the *maquis'* rough justice: even a mother and her pregnant daughter were shot for telling the Germans of secret camp sites.

This pamphlet, giving advice to partisan leaders also set out in its Appendix VII details for a guerrilla information service. Advice which in 1940 could equally be applied to the search for information by SOE's agents. Gubbins' list of likely sources of information included innkeepers, barmaids, railway staff, barbers, newsagents, camp followers (his inoffensive word for 'prostitutes') and civilians employed by the enemy. The appendix goes on to explain how women domestic servants—and there were many of these in 1940—could gain the confidence of soldiers who react favourably to

kindness when stationed in a hostile country. Not everyone in authority, however, in 1940 had Colin Gubbins' appreciation of total war.

Even in February 1941 the RAF did not want to be associated with '. . . the dropping of men in civilian clothes for the purpose of killing members of the opposing forces . . .' as they regarded SOE's agents as '. . . what one can only call assassins . . .' The air force was, however, persuaded the following month to drop six Frenchmen to attack a key aerodrome. From such small beginnings grew a close liaison between SOE and the pilots of 161 Squadron's Lysanders, together with 138 Squadron, whose bombers were used mainly to air drop supplies to resistance forces. In 1944 this became a regular job for many British and American squadrons, with whom SOE and OSS had the closest co-operation. Long before then Lysander pilots lifting their 'Joes', as they called their passenger agents, out of occupied countries, were regarded by their squadron-leader as carrying out routine transport flights. They were not pilots doing tricks as if in some air circus. Yet men like Whippy Nesbitt-Durfort ('Whippy' since he had crash landed in Whipsnade Zoo) needed all the skills which he had learnt when flying for the RAF's acrobatic team. He flew his Lysander Mark II across the coast of France watching for night fighters and avoiding concentrations of anti-aircraft batteries. Navigating by the map strapped to his knee, its detail barely readable in the light of his hooded torch, and flying solo, he flitted the gull-winged aircraft over the moonlit countryside.

For the last few kilometres of his approach to the landing field, he flew at perhaps no more than 100m for the emphasis was on *field*; he would put the aircraft down on just that, without any ground control and no more than a torch and a few flares to mark the cleared strip. As he crossed this the first time he saw only the flashed recognition letters of the ground organiser's torch. Three letters, 'A' in morse to which Whippy might respond with 'GMC' on his signal light, as he banked to line up the aircraft to come in over the organizer in the direction of two lights, which made the bottom strut of an 'L'. This showed Whippy in which direction the ground wind was blowing. As his wheels touched the field by the organizer standing to the left of the flight path, the Lysander began to bump and bounce over rough ground for perhaps 350m. Whippy could pull his plane up in less, before turning right to taxi back to the organizer of this reception committee. As the aircraft rolled towards what would be the pick-up point, Whippy made those checks on fuel levels and ground wind speed that were needed before take off, which he made almost as soon as he swung the plane back into the wind. Sometimes pilots were horrified to see spectators in the taxi 'lane' watching the show as if it was some kind of entertainment. Nevertheless once the

▲ A prototype of the special duties Lysander in June 1941. It had a wingspan of 50 feet, a maximum speed of 350 knots and cruised 275 knots. The large auxiliary fuel tank and absence of armour, weapons and heavy radios enabled this aircraft to fly from southern England to airstrips in the French Massif Centrale, and return without refuelling. The matt black camouflage for night operations was later changed to black only on the undersides of the aircraft. Conventional European aircraft camouflage was then used on the upper part of the fuselage, of the wings and tail assembly, with the tail fin in these lighter colours. Illustrations of the 'Lizzy' indicate that it was not always used with the reserve tank. The Mark II aircraft for special duties was an adaptation of the Mark I used for artillery observation. The II had only an HF TR-9 radio for communication with an airfield's control tower, signals to a reception organizer were made by lamp. But in 1943 VHF TR-1143 were fitted for voice communication with ground controllers and an S-phone for communication with the organizer of a landing zone.

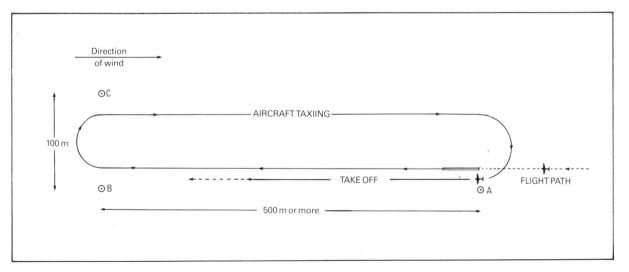

▲ The diagram shows the simple drill by which Lysanders and other aircraft including Ansons and Dakotas were guided to an airstrip. The pattern of lights showed to the pilot the wind's direction. He landed heading into this before taxiing back to the point where the organizer stood with any agents due to be flown out. The whole operation took three minutes or less. 'A' is the position of the ground reception party organizer with his S-phone and signal lamp. At B and C are men with signal lights. These mark the windward end of the cleared landing strip.

Lizzy had turned ready for take off, two of three Joes with just a suitcase each, no parachutes, would be crammed into the rear seat area of the cockpit. The pilot then 'opening his boost control to override' was back in the air withing three minutes. Once three Lysanders used the same field and were headed for home with their passengers within nine minutes, not the permitted 30 for three aircraft. At times the field was so humped and runnelled that the overloaded aircraft seemed about to jar itself to pieces, especially if packed with four Joes: two in the rear seat, one on the shelf behind it and one on the cockpit floor. They made up a weight far greater than the guns, armour plate and long-distance radios which had been stripped from the 161 Squadron's Mark II Lysanders. Without this equipment the aircraft could maintain its performance with the usual two Joes in the seat intended for a navigator-observer, when this type of aircraft was used in directing artillery fire. There were many difficulties and mishaps which could easily occur in such pick-ups. Sometimes the Lysander did not come to a stop but was still moving at 25kmph when one particular Joe had to leap from the ladder '. . . with a hell of a wallop as you hit a grass field . . .' On at least one

occasion the reception committee set up their lights on the wrong field causing Whippy to land on a strip he thought had been prepared '. . . for the French Grand National . . .' He took off in a series of violent jerks as the wheels skipped from hillocks to ruts. Becoming airborne, the Lysander then collected several metres of electric cable wires which caught the undercarriage, but he reached his home airfield on Newmarket race course near Cambridge. His radio aerial had been damaged in the take off and he had to land without contact with the control tower as he came in through a morning mist. He was less fortunate in his last mission in January 1942, his plane icing-up on the return flight he was forced to crash land in a field and join one of the escape lines.

One of the first Lysander missions on 4 September 1941 brought one or two agents—sources differ—from Vichy France. There in the unoccupied zone there was less risk of being intercepted, and an area the size of England and Wales in which to choose a landing field.

▼ A light aircraft of an American Army Co-operation Flight takes off from a typical landing strip near Epiausy in France. During the late summer of 1944 such airstrips could be used in daylight. A group of Maquis are on the right of the picture and women with their children are watching the take-off.

▲ Colonel F. W. Nicholls CBE, MBE a veteran of the operations in Arabia in World War I, served as SOE's director of communications. He was awarded the Légion d'honneur and the Croix de Guerre. He was held in high regard by French agents.

▼ Colonel Maurice J. Buckmaster OBE was head of SOE's French (F) Section from the autumn of 1941 until its major activities closed down. A tall man with a gentle manner he was in his late 30s when in charge of F Section, having been a journalist in France before the war and worked there for the Ford Motor Company. He had many qualities of leadership but was not universally popular, he is seen here in about 1944. He was awarded the Légion d'honneur and the Croix de Guerre, and an American decoration.

This was chosen by the local organizer although as air landings became more widespread in occupied countries both USAAF and RAF officers worked as agents choosing these sites for the secret services. In 1941, however, clandestine routes by sea were used (see Chapter 10) and the two men brought out on 4 September had been reconnoitring secret landing points on the Mediterranean coast. As soon as they or any other Lysander took off, the reception committee removed all evidence of the landing. In occupied countries this might involve re-digging the trenches, filled in to give a level landing strip. There might be poles to replace, which like the trenches were intended to prevent aircraft or gliders landing in a field. On other sites there was old farm machinery or other obstacles to be put back. In each case the field when seen from the air or in a casual glance from a passing German vehicle, looked as it had done the previous evening. Nevertheless there were some signs, like freshly dug earth which were hard to hide from German soldiers patrolling on foot, or the curiosity of a *Malice* snooper. In this way a number of landing operations were discovered by German security forces, news of a few reaching their ears before the landings. This was an unnecessary risk when an agent from the 'Cod' intelligence circuit in the spring of 1942 had no justifiable reason for a lift, which in his case was flown despite appalling weather.

After the 'Cod' incident strict rules were laid down for pick-ups. For instance, only RAF trained organizers could supervise operations on the ground. Pilots would not land if there was a crowd; and if they had turned ready to take off, anyone approaching from the right would be shot by the pilot, who carried a service revolver. By 1943 the scope of air pick-ups expanded to landing Hudson aircraft in France, able to lift out 12 Joes or others. Even larger aircraft were used in later landings with Dakota DC3s making regular trips to airfields in France. In the Balkans the USAAF were landing four-engined Liberator bombers on airfields protected by partisans.

Back in 1941 as SOE were learning their clandestine trade they established a number of intelligence circuits in occupied countries. Although sabotage was SOE's stock in trade at that time, the Executive had on occasion to send reconnaissance or intelligence missions in order to establish what opportunities there were for raising guerrilla forces in the future. One such mission in Vichy France was undertaken by Count Dzieřugowski for the Europe/Polish (EU/P) Section, which arranged his parachute drop. His radio contacts, however, were with Polish signallers in London at the time when all radio communications for SOE were handled by SIS. After he had recruited 87 Poles working in France as miners and farmers, their Prime Minister in exile heard of the mission. He was angry at what he saw as British interference in Polish affairs, and therefore SOE had to abandon the Count to a Polish controller, who no doubt received the benefit of the reconnaissance. SOE had dropped some sabotage supplies to the Count but ceased any further supply and this 'Adjudicate' circuit does not appear to have carried out any major sabotage after its role was expanded from intelligence gathering.

Such political problems were not confined to Polish services, and some circuit organizers managed to cut across political differences, as did the 32-year-old barrister, Francis Suttill during 1942 and 1943. His father was English, his mother French but he was not familiar with the wartime habits of daily life in Paris when he first arrived from England in October 1942. Nevertheless he was a conscientious and careful organizer—though not careful enough—who by the late spring of 1943 claimed 10,000 supporters for his 'Prosper' circuit. They were drawn from as wide a range of the political spectrum as communists to country gentlemen. His second in command was the poet Armel Guerne who had not been trained in Britain as had the other senior agents: Gilbert Norman the efficient if over-trusting radio operator; and the courageous Andrée Borrel who had helped to set up an escape line before she came to England in 1941. All four were based in Paris during these years but travelled widely, so that the information their circuit collected was drawn from a vast area of northern France, stretching from the Ardennes to the Atlantic seaboard. The details they acquired were of particular value to the Allies but gathered in some cases without the usual safeguards of sub-agents meeting only couriers. Yet there were 20 agents in the circuit trained and paid by SOE, whose sub-agent couriers would normally be expected to deliver and collect letters from secret mail drops. One was the 'post-man' knowing only the sender and a second was the collector, knowing only the recipient. This method of 'cut-outs' in the delivery of messages was probably used by the communist cells in the organization, as they were never entirely penetrated by double agents. For added security Yeo-Thomas instructed his circuits only to use verbal messages between couriers.

Suttill and his top team became overconfident. The team met nearly every day for lunch at the same restaurant and played cards each evening in a café near the Sacré Coeur. These habits could have been dangerous enough, but in addition they occasionally stopped using French. They believed no doubt that their regular waiter was a friend—yet the Gestapo employed such staff in the way Gubbins had suggested—for their own purposes. The language lapse might have been due to forgetfulness or maybe they did not want their friendly

neighbours to understand what they were saying, but whatever the reason attention was drawn to the group. The waiter, perhaps, or some other informer reported the team's conversations. (At that time 32,000 sub-agents and informers were controlled by the Gestapo headquarters in Paris.) Suttill and others were arrested in the third week of June. Suttill was tortured, his arm broken and he was kept awake without food for three days. The others were interrogated with varying degrees of severity, but Norman fell for the 'don't suppose you can help us' insinuation that he had a minor part in the organization. Later evidence suggests that he told his interrogators a good deal but not the security checks for his transmissions to London. Therefore when his set was used by the Germans in an attempted wireless game, Baker Street soon realized the radio was being run by the enemy. Later he and others were executed by the Germans. But one of F Section's agents avoided becoming caught up in the fall of 'Prosper', as he used more cut-out contact techniques and thus heard of Suttill's arrest without exposing his interest in the circuit. There seems no doubt that Suttill and some of his senior agents had been in France too long, for the months' of stress sapped the concentration of even the best agents who, like a bomber pilot who has flown too many missions, begin to make careless mistakes through apparent overconfidence. Such casual disregard of what would seem to be the simplest of security precautions had been not infrequent in France as, for example, the imprudent behaviour of Mathilde Carré and the Pole, Roman Czerniawski, who had been a senior intelligence officer with 1 Polish Division. They had maps on the walls of their flat marking the position of German sentries on key Paris buildings early in 1941. Yet there was no look-out posted outside the door and it is unlikely that the German officers among her many admirers were unaware of her espionage activities. Nevertheless this self-appointed organizer and courier of the 'Inter-Allied' circuit built up a network of more than 200 agents with four radio teams in Paris before Roman was flown to London on 1 October 1941; Mathilde became the mistress of a German officer and a double-agent.

How many of 'Prosper's' sub-agents died as a result of this penetration of the circuit is not known, but the communist cells, or at least some of them, survived. Another circuit, 'Alliance', a rather amateur organization at the outset, lost 500 of its 3,000 members, who were executed or died in concentration camps. Originally founded in Vichy with Paris connections, its leaders intended to assist General Giraud raise a revolt in southern France. In its early days there were many setbacks, not least of which was the capture by the Gestapo of a typed list of members' addresses. Nevertheless it survived. Some of its leaders, among them

Marie Fourcade, the mother of two children, escaped to England by way of the Pyrenees and Spain.

Some of the intelligence gathered by this circuit was no doubt flown out of Vichy by the RAF's Lysanders. This means of communication should have been extremely secure provided any addresses or names were given in code in the reports. Yet many such reports from circuits in France were to be seriously compromised, because F Section's organizer of flights—the man who chose the landing areas if not the precise fields, scheduled dates and co-ordinated local reception committee organizers, was himself working to some extent with the Germans. He was a former free-lance French air pilot, Henri Déricourt, whose keen intelligence and steady nerve contrasted with his flashy clothes. Allowed by the British to return to France from the Middle East in 1941, he married a lady he adored. Later when he had been trained in England and sent back to Paris in 1942, his love for his wife may have provided the hold that the SD had over him. Certainly the Abwehr's Sergeant Bleicher in his smooth way let it be known that Déricourt was working for the Germans. Maybe he intended to deprive the SD of a useful double-agent because their Josef Goetz is said to have remarked on Déricourt's recall to England, 'Ah well, that's four million [francs] down the drain.' Whether the pilot and the sergeant had known each other before 1942 has never become clear, but in 1943 they were neighbours. SIS knew Déricourt had German contacts and warned SOE not to employ him, but he satisfied F Section that he was loyal. Later he claimed that he only gave the Germans information of little consequence, in order to be able to continue operating in France. He was acquitted of collaboration in a trial after the war, but clearly the Germans had seen many reports before they left for England. They had also been able to organize French criminals to follow agents from landing fields, and might have caught Victor Gerson, one of F Section's cleverest agents, had he not been careful enough to evade those following him on one occasion, but many were arrested after being followed from the landing zone.

By contrast in Poland no agent was caught near the place to which he parachuted, a security record that tells much of the Polish underground's well guarded secrets. These secrets they were unwilling to share: even the eccentric engineer Stanislow Witowski who ran the 'Musketeers' for SIS, was distrusted by the Poles in London. Their secret service organizers in Cairo imprisoned the Polish girl, 'Christine Granville', (an English name chosen for her passport) after her fourth visit to Poland for SOE. She helped to establish escape lines from Poland and may well have known of underground operations that the Poles in exile wished to keep from the British. Otherwise these might have come to the knowledge of the Russians, a sensible precaution in retrospect now we know of Kim Philby's activities. The gentle Christine—she never carried a gun, relying on charm and bribery—was released from jail, and sent to France in 1944 for F Section. This mission she survived, but she was murdered by her lover in 1952.

Christine's use of bribes was a practice that Allied agents often used in central Europe. A great deal less messy than killing a border guard or knifing a local policeman, it nevertheless had its risks, for the gold an agent carried led to several being murdered. Bribery was not confined to sweeteners for border guards for the Allies could offer large sums to achieve their purpose. For example, when Yeo-Thomas was in the Fresnes prison in Paris and about to be sent to Germany, SOE offered four-million French francs to a Gestapo officer to lose Tommy's record file in the prison office. However, the officer was killed that July (1944) when making another arrest and Yeo-Thomas was sent to a concentration camp from which he later escaped.

ON 11 April 1944 three operatives of OSS' SI Division, Lieutenant M. Basset with R. Beugnon and A. Martin (who are described as NCOs in OSS' War Report) parachuted to a reception committee northwest of Paris. They were to establish 'Beggar' circuit for SOE's F Section in one of the examples of SOE/OSS close co-operation in preparation for the landings in Normandy the following June. Basset with the cover name of 'Ludovic' went to considerable but well worth while trouble in establishing his cover, while spending several days walking the streets of Paris to familiarize himself with the local life. He bought newspapers read by Nazi sympathizers and frequented black market cafés, gathering on these journeys such trivia as a lottery ticket, bus tickets and other odds and ends, all of which a Parisian might have in his pockets. He had a friend write to him at his 'safe' house, then carried the letter in his wallet as another piece of identification which proved he was a Parisian. He also looked up people with his cover name in the telephone directory, later calling on them to give himself some distant relatives. He found an employer, who was prepared to substantiate his work permit was genuine. This deception later paid dividends when Basset was picked up in a random police check with a hundred other civilians. When the police telephoned his employer, the man confirmed that 'Ludvic' worked for him and he was released as he was on another occasion after a spot check by the police.

He established rendezvous with the local resistance in the Creil, Senlis, and Beauvois districts, in order to be able to give instructions on the use of explosives, how to keep their circuit secure and other clandestine work. Yet none of his contacts knew where he lived. His care and the group's good sense in not involving people who had not been carefully screened for loyalty, led to a circuit of 91 sub-agents being established by the time of the invasion. Since these sub-agents were brought together in only eight weeks, it seems possible that they were communists or other associates who already had close connections before 'Ludovic' arrived. He divided them into eight teams one of which was a reception committee to receive air-dropped supplies. The other seven were saboteurs who damaged the telephone system as well as attacking railway services. On 12 June 'Ludovic' learnt of 500 German tanks hidden in the *Forêt de Bez* which were a target for Allied bombers, as were the V-I rocket depots which he reported 12 days later in two quarries and underground hangars near Creil. 'Beggar' continued to attack German communications and provide valuable intelligence until the Allies reached Paris, after the citizens had seized key points during the third week in August 1944. 'Beggar' had 505 men in its organization that month and like other SOE/OSS circuits had made their contribution in providing arms for the citizens.

The intermingling of sabotage with intelligence work was inevitable although the two roles do not ideally run together. In May 1943 SIS proposed to OSS that 50 two-man intelligence teams should be dropped throughout northern France, to collect military intelligence from areas as far apart as Brittany and the Belgian border in anticipation of the Normandy invasion. These became known as 'Sussex' parties for which an OSS staff was sent from America in September. This staff overcame some opposition from the British SIS as its *éminence grise* the cold-eyed Colonel Claud Dansey was reluctant to have independent OSS circuits in Europe. Eventually some 87 of the Sussex agents came from de Gaulle's forces as there were insufficient bilingual American nationals available, but even these reinforcements took time to reach England from North Africa. Therefore the first Sussex team was parachuted into France on 9 April 1944, only eight weeks before D-day.

In Italy OSS had 63 agents providing similar military intelligence through circuits they established among Italian partisans in the summer of 1944. These agents, designated as part of OSS' Company D from 20 July 1944, expanded their activities in northern Italy to train partisans and carry out some sabotage raids by OG teams. In one of these three OG officers in uniform spent four months in the region of the Brenner Pass after landing on 3 August; but after September sabotage operations were suspended, for as long as the USAAF received details of potential targets, these were more easily destroyed by bombing than by ground attacks. However, the airforces had been unable to block the Brenner Pass, and in December, having sent his two companions back to the Allied lines, the leader of the team in this area, presumably with partisan help, suc-

ceeded in blowing up a section of steep hillside to block one approach to the tunnel. He was caught, however, tortured and executed.

Other OG teams had their difficulties especially as the communists and other factions vied for supplies of arms; disputes which may have led to Major William Nolohan being killed although he was more probably murdered for the $16,000 of money, gold and gems which he carried. He had been working 80km north of Milan, far from the main battle areas. Other teams from Company D worked with the US Fifth Army on the west coast, the 80 men of the Company being reinforced by 30 from OG 2671st Provisional Reconnaissance Battalion. These teams worked close to the battle front either infiltrating through the German lines or being parachuted not far behind them. They were able to report German movements, answer specific queries from the Army's staff and even direct long range artillery fire on to targets.

C OLLECTING military intelligence was a prerequisite of partisans' guerrilla operations leading to the national revolts in occupied countries. Such a reconnaissance was made by the legendary 'Xavier', Richard Heslop of SOE's F Section. With a companion, Jean Rosenthal, the 30-year old jewelry salesman from RF Section, Heslop contacted a number of *maquis* leaders in the autumn of 1943 while travelling through the Jura and other mountains in eastern France. There he met Henri Romans-Petit who had been gathering bands of young men in the valley of the Ain river 20km from the Swiss border. Heslop and Petit apparently got on well together from their first meeting and would develop a strong friendship, the Englishman deciding that if the somewhat dispirited young men of the *maquis de l'Ain* could be armed and trained they would become a formidable force under Romans-Petit. He therefore flew back to London, explained his plans to Gubbins and others, returning to France within 48 hours. He brought with him two Americans, Denis Johnson, who would be the radio operator, and, Elizabeth Devereaux-Rochester as the courier. Elizabeth had been educated expensively in England; and is said to have been surprised at the 'common' manners and speech of pilots she later helped to reach escape lines. The Hudson aircraft which brought Heslop and his companions to a field near Lons-le-Saunier in the foothills of the Jura mountains, touched down on 21 September 1943. This date forms a convenient starting point to the history of revolt in these mountains, for although in nine months Petit had gathered perhaps 3,000 men in this remote area, they were unlikely to achieve much without arms, food and the other necessities which SOE could supply.

7
RAISING REVOLT

'Sabotage alone will not suffice . . . it must be accompanied by efforts to promote revolution.' From a report to William Donovan from his Chief of Staff, Robert Solborg, October 1941.

'Xavier', an apostle to the *maquis* not only in the Ain valley, after a brief welcome by the reception's organiser, was driven to the local headquarters. The mud-bespattered Citroën was shabby, as suited a country doctor's car but its driver, whatever his identity papers claimed, seemed a trifle too skilled in handling the car for a country doctor. Up the mountain lane, sliding on loose stones before being brought to the next corner, he did not even use its hooded lights. Otherwise some German patrol might have been attracted to enquire why the 'doctor', two jewellry salesmen and others had been in the mountains. One was the bespectacled Rosenthal who had dealt in jewellry as well as furs in the family business; the second was Heslop whose cover of jewellry salesman suited his mission, although his peacetime occupation had been in the teak trade of Thailand. (Few details have survived of Heslop's exploits and this reconstruction is based on typical receptions.) Driving perhaps 20km east up into the hills the driver then reached the farmhouse headquarters, a safe distance from the landing field. Here Henri Romans-Petit and several of the captains of his companies met on occasion to arrange possible ventures against German patrols, but mainly to discuss how they were to get food for the men. Petit, a decorated veteran of World War I although only in his forties, must have spent as much time trying to organize supplies as in training his men. Being a good commander he appreciated the need to provide regular rations for the companies which might otherwise degenerate into roving bands of brigands. A capable organizer, he used the skills of persuasion he had shown as public relations advisor to French fashion houses of the 1930s to win support from local townsmen. Be that as it may the *maquis* were short of food that autumn.

The *maquis* in the woods beyond the farmhouse brewed their acorn 'coffee' by makeshift shelters under the trees, with old canvas cart covers, sacking and carpets probably providing the materials for most of their lean-tos, while a few more fortunate men lived in tents. 'Jacques', a typical hybrid resistance fighter of 1943, had trained as a conscript in 1940, far from any battlefield. Demobilized without ceremony, he re-

turned to Grenoble where he repaired sewing machines in a glove factory. There he heard rumours of bands of fighters in the hills or, as some of his father's generation described them, men who preferred a life as brigands to factory work. Then in August 1942 the Germans decreed through the Vichy Government that able-bodied men should be conscripted for work in armaments factories. To avoid this likelihood of being sent to Germany or some other country far from France, Jacques left home with some friends from the glove factory. They were ordinary young men, dull in many ways, as Harry Rée of SOE pointed out, with '. . . ordinary selfishness and cheerful humanity . . .'

Most of them seem to have enjoyed their freedom in the woods and heaths, and gained some respect as the *Maquis* (after the Corsican word for brushwood), although Jacques and others occasionally bullied village storekeepers into giving them food. They were no doubt still regarded as little more than brigands in some quarters. The Germans certainly did not regard them as any threat but sent patrols into the mountains to round up any men that they could send to armaments factories. Petit meanwhile organized some training with the few weapons available, including sporting guns. The instructors were mainly former officers and NCOs of the French army who did their best to instil some discipline into these bands of civilians. By the autumn Jacques' only coat was in tatters, one shoe had a hole in the sole, and in the steady rain of the mountain valley, he was becoming not only bored but weak from lack of regular food.

He was not even enthusiastic when the man from England, Xavier addressed his 'platoon' with promises of guns, uniforms and food from the RAF. But the stocky Xavier's quiet manner, his explanations of how they would be taught to fight by others trained in England, impressed Jacques who took this jewellry salesman to be as French as himself, not an English lieutenant-colonel of F Section. The cover gave Richard Heslop reason to travel as he co-ordinated Petit's *maquis* with others in the Allies' overall strategy. In 1943 this was by no means as clear as it should have been, but Heslop rose above the tangle of politics in the Allied headquarters. These were problems which Jacques knew nothing about nor did he know that this 30-year old British officer spoke perfect French, having spent much of his early life in France before going to work in Thailand. He had joined SOE in 1942, been caught by the Vichy police but allowed by them to escape with others when the

Germans entered what had been the Unoccupied Zone before November 1942. Heslop's square build matched his character for he was no more ruthless than he had to be: cradling a dying *Malice* woman in his arms rather than firing a second shot to kill her. She had caught him stealing a list of troop train movements, during one of his earlier missions to France.

After a month in the Ain valley, Heslop and Rosenthal flew to England for a brief visit. Rosenthal as Petit's liaison officer with de Gaulle's headquarters, would be mainly responsible for supervising the strategy of this resistance force, the details of supplies and of instructors it required. Richard Heslop would have wider responsibilities and as the strength of the fighting resistance forces grew, his inspired leadership gave Petit's men an assurance and confidence, in part because Heslop never sent them into action without having properly assessed the risks. He had also proved able to find them the weapons, food and a thousand other items needed to keep them in action—during his brief visit to England in October he arranged for one of the most successful series of parachute supply drops to any of the *maquis* forces. Not all of these drops were accurate since the Allied airforces had difficulties at times finding the DZs despite the use of homing beacons and radio-telephones: 220 containers intended for Heslop's *maquis* fell in an area they did not control that February, and were snatched up by the Germans. The number of drops was so numerous, however, in 1944 that such losses did not seriously damage the *maquis* faith in SOE and OSS. In the three months of 1944 6,750 containers were dropped in France, 619 by the USAAF who in the following six months dropped 20,000! (see Appendix 3.10).

Warning of a pending drop was often given in the 'personal' messages put out on the BBC's World Service. Then the dropping zone could be prepared on an open piece of heath 600m across and 800m long, the ideal size, with only a spinney or two, for the woods lay at the upwind end of the zone. (This, of course, is an ideal operation; in reality the wind might not come from the expected direction, there might not be such a convenient area without lakes or rivers, but the organizer would have to make the best choice he could, always allowing for German road patrols not only at the DZ but on the roads by which the supplies would be distributed.)

Three men with hand torches stood in a line marking the DZ. The torches would be lit on the shouted order of the organizer who wore a transmitter radio, that gave a signal beam and provided an ultra-high frequency radio telephone, both beacon beam and conversation being received in the aircraft. The beam activated a dial pointer showing if the pilot was flying to its left or right. The beacon could be picked up on its matching dial at 64km by a plane at 3,000m and at 10km when flying at 150m, but the radio of this S-phone could only be heard when the aircraft was close to the beacon. Then it was heard by all the crew on the plane's intercom, and the organizer could hear them. Should the phone not work for some reason, signal lamps were used to exchange messages. The S-phone tended to be used when men as well as containers were to be dropped, because an SOE or OSS officer controlling an operation might fly with the incoming agents. He could even recognize the voice of the organizer of the reception on many occasions, because they knew each other, helping to ensure that this was not a compromised landing.

Once the organizer and pilot were satisfied that all was ready, the pilot, perhaps in a Halifax, approached the DZ and passed over it at 100m as the men marking the 'L' lit their electric torches. 'Bloody awful lights', as one rear-gunner remarked, to be answered from the ground with: 'So would yours be if the Gestapo were only a mile away'. On the second pass the bomb aimer would release 15 of the black-painted containers suspended in the Halifax's bomb bay. Good judgement and little wind ensured that these all fell in the DZ, but when as frequently happened some drifted away from the zone, they had to be found. *Maquis* stationed among the sentries around the DZ had the specific job of noting where the wayward containers had fallen, and were supposed to take a compass bearing, or preferably two, from different spots to pinpoint where the 'chutes fell. More often than not, in practice, there was a frantic search for the missing containers. These had to be found before daylight when a parachute would be revealed hanging in a tree, inviting the attention of the security police.

On its third pass our Halifax would drop wicker panniers and other packages on 'chutes, pushed through the one-metre diameter hatch specially cut in these aircraft, (providing a floor exit on other occasions for agents parachuting into occupied country). These packages contained delicate items. These included 1943 radios, tubes of printers' inks for clandestine presses, medical supplies and occasionally such special items as the artificial brass foot of one of F's agents. All these items needed special packing, sometimes in kapok or other padding.

Later in the war containers were dropped with parachutes that did not open until they were 100m from the ground and would not drift too far on the breeze. They could be released from 3,000m far above the light anti-aircraft fire which caught many aircraft dropping supplies over Warsaw in 1944. The number of containers carried by aircraft on such supply runs was also increased: the 22 Stirlings 138 Squadron RAF received in May 1944 each carried 18, as did the USAAF's B-24 Liberators. Six of these, commanded by the Norwegian-

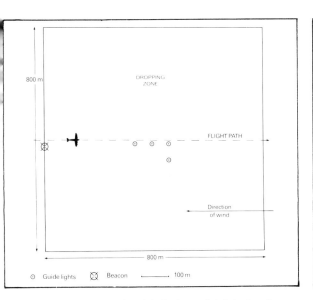

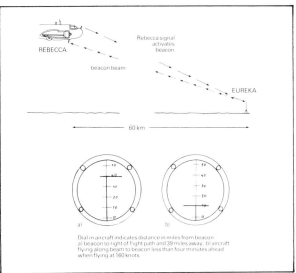

▲ Hand-held torches might be the only indication to pilots that a dropping zone (DZ) lay below them. Although from 1944 they might be guided to it by a Eureka beacon or the beacon signal of an S-phone. By the end of that year, as the Germans retreated from occupied territories, signal fires replaced lamps on occasion. Men or women holding three red torches (shown as guide lights) stood 100m apart to mark the centre of the DZ. A man with a white guide lamp stood 50m to the left of the others, his lamp marking the up wind side of the zone and flashing a recognition signal. The aircraft's 'bomb' aimer released the containers when above the centre of the three red lights. Halifax bombers approached the DZ at about 100 knots, flying into the wind with the aircraft's flaps down.

▼ The S-phone provided a beacon signal to guide aircraft to an LZ or other rendezvous (a DZ or a point at which agents might be landed from small boats). It was worn on the organizer's chest and could also be used for radio-telephone conversations with the aircrew once their aircraft was within a few minutes' distance of the DZ.

▲ The Eureka beacon had a five-foot retractable mast on its seven-foot tripod. This was connected to a totally enclosed box which only required to be switched on, no other adjustment was necessary. The Rebecca radar equipment in an aircraft could then activate the Eureka's beacon signal. Although many of these were distributed to SOE agents there appears to have been a reluctance to use them. The airborne forces including the SAS used them with great success, as did a few agents but other Eurekas were hidden away. By the spring of 1943 its secrets were known to the Germans, although often not fully explained to agents. The ground equipment weighed about 110 lb and its carrying box was 30 x 15 x 10 inches. Batteries could be easily changed. The coded radar which activated a Eureka was transmimtted from a 25-foot aerial which could not normally be fitted into a Lysander, but according to Pierre Lorain was fitted in some 'Lizzies'. It could be fitted in any Allied bomber or in Hudson aircraft and Motor Torpedo Boats.

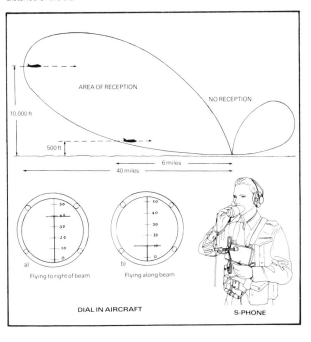

born Colonel Bernt Balchen, flew from Leuchers in Fife during the summer of 1944 to drop supplies to Milorg units. Prior to this the British had considered the risks too great to justify such missions in daylight over Norway. OSS improved the quantity of stores these aircraft and others could carry by replacing containers for clothing and other less fragile items, with strong double-skinned hessian bags attached to light weight 'flare' parachutes. But the procedure at the DZ was much the same as it had been since 1943.

On the ground Jacques and three companions could lift a C-type container by pushing two poles through its four lifting handles. However, it was more difficult to carry even over the short distances the organizer had planned to hiding places near the DZ, than the H-type which split into five separate drums when the tie bars were unbolted. After our ideal supply drop, SOE hoped that Jacques and his friends would gather in the containers and packages '. . . in rigorous conditions of silence and security . . .' This they probably did if Petit or Rosenthal were at the DZ. At other times the collection party was less cautious, calling to each other,

▲ As the Germans retreated from areas such as north-west Italy, partisans could mark DZs with parachutes laid out in line. Here near Cuneo three partisans mark a DZ. When the Allied aircraft approach the field, the straw bales will be lit to give an indication of the wind direction as the smoke drifts acrxoss the field. The French Alps are in the background.

▲ British Army officers working with Italian guerrillas watch two hessian wrapped packages drop to a DZ near Cuneo. These packages followed a drop of containers and were flown to the area from North Africa where both OSS and SOE supplies were packed for parachuting to guerrilla forces.

smoking cigarettes, with torches flashing as they searched spinneys for missing containers. Some—horror of horrors for the *maquis* quartermaster—opened packages looking for cigarettes or other 'prizes'. Yet packing a container on a flat hard floor in daylight required great skill, never fully mastered by the packers in Algiers. Repacking would be quite impossible at night on a muddy field. Then all too easily a clip of ammunition or other signs of the drop might be left for the Germans to see next day, after the *maquis* had attempted to remove an opened container from the DZ. Petit's well disciplined teams in the Ain valley apparently never caused such a foolish breech in their security but regularly collected food, uniforms, boots and weapons which equipped them as a formidable fighting force, as we will see. Had anyone been as un-disciplined as to open a container, one suspects that they would have been put in the make-shift cells most

▲ A number of C-type (on left) and H-type containers stacked for distribution by horse and cart. The H-type are painted a matt black but others are in their natural metal colour. The photograph was taken 'somewhere in France' in 1944.

▼ The H-type container was divided into sections which were easily carried once the tie bars were released. The earlier C-type was a single container that could be heavy to lift when full of weapons and ammunition. The containers might be packed with one of several standard loads (see Appendix 3.10) which in Europe might be sufficient to arm the equivalent of a platoon of guerrillas. Another standard load included explosive charges for saboteurs. The components of the sheet metal container were: a. the section which held the parachute; b. handles to lift the assembled container, usually carried on poles; c. strap-handles for separate sections; d. hollow metal sphere to absorb shock on landing; e. tie bars; and f. inter-locking lids of container sections.

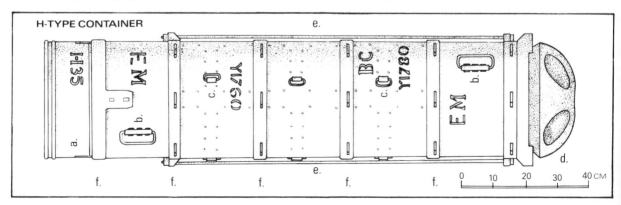

H-TYPE CONTAINER

maquis had for the *Malice* and other prisoners.

We will come back to Petit and Heslop, but in the spring of 1944 they had established not only a viable resistance force in the Ain valley, but Heslop had worked to co-ordinate this *maquis* with others in the Jura and Haute-Savoie, the Alpine area of south-east France. There this travelling 'jewellry salesman' became known to all the *maquis* leaders, establishing a legendary reputation as the provider of the people's needs through supply drops; and an enviable reputation for his wise counsel at their meetings. His couriers crossed over the Alps to Switzerland where they had contacts in the 'Gilbert' circuit, a large French intelligence network controlled from Switzerland.

Other aids to aircraft navigators in finding a DZ included the Eureka beacon, which although simple to operate, appears not to have been used as widely in France as SOE had intended. The reasons for this are not clear because it was an improvement on the S-phone as its signal could be activated only when the incoming aircraft transmitted from its Rebecca aerials. The beacon signal might therefore transmit for perhaps 10 minutes if activated at the maximum range of 60km. It was unlikely to be intercepted by a German aircraft in the way that they had at times picked up S-phone signals leading to the bombing of reception committees. The accuracy of the Eureka signal enabled navigators to pinpoint its position to within 200m, enabling agents on at least one occasion to be parachuted to a DZ hidden by the mist. However there was no voice communication with the Eureka, it was only a beacon signal. Perhaps surprisingly there appears to have been no regular attempt to use its homing signal and then to switch on an S-phone for a brief exchange of messages. The S-phone itself was superseded in OSS by the Joan-Eleanor (J-E). Three of these were fitted in the British Mosquito aircraft, the light high-speed aircraft used to mark targets for bombers, and for photo-reconnaissance. The tail sections of these planes were rebuilt to provide space for an OSS radio operator and his airborne part of the J-E, while the agent on the ground had a compact 1.8kg set with long-life batteries. The cone of its high-frequency transmission made a set difficult to D-F precisely yet could be heard by an aircraft flying at 10,000m in which the conversation was recorded. The agent's controller could also fly as the J-E radio operator and hold a two-way conversation with the agent, perhaps lasting 20 minutes in which a great deal more information might be passed than was possible in Morse transmissions.

OSS also developed the SSLD-321 a mirror reflector with three planes at right-angles to each other. These reflected directly back to an aircraft, the beam of light from a night-landing headset (SSLV-322). The beam could only be seen by a person placed between the mirror and the aircraft, which seems foolproof enough although how effective this was in locating a DZ is not disclosed in the OSS War Report.

DURING the time Heslop was organizing supplies and much else for the *maquis* forces of the French Alps, plans were being considered for SOE's and OSS' participation in operations to support the Allied landings in Normandy, code named 'Overlord'. The final details of SOE's operations were not settled until 3 June, three days before the landings, when the head of SOE's operations in north-west Europe and his OSS counterpart visited the headquarters of the Twenty-first Army Group. There it was agreed that the Resistance should make its maximum effort on the night of the invasion. There were also plans for British sponsored parties to parachute into France on the night of the invasion. These 'Jedburgh' parties were of mixed nationality, being provided mainly from the British Special Air Service (SAS), 100 American personnel from OSS, and a like number of Frenchmen. Each party had two officers and a sergeant signaller, all three of different nationality, who had attended courses at SOE schools. The Jedburgh parties would then be able to provide liaison with the main Allied armies, supply drops and other support, supplementing the work of the SOE and Free French agents already in France. Thirteen of these so-called 'Jeds' were landed in June, followed by 80 more in later months. All were in uniform, yet none was captured although 21 of their men were killed.

OSS also had Operational Groups (OGs) each with 34 members of all ranks (see Appendix 3.11), drawn from service personnel and fighting in uniform. In this way they differed from OSS' Secret Intelligence (SI) personnel who worked under cover as did Heslop and other SOE agents; SI included civilians doing similar work to that of SIS' operatives. The roles of the Operational Groups specifically barred them from missions in neutral countries, their instructions set out in their Field Manual being: (1) '. . . to organize, train, and equip resistance groups in order to convert them into guerrillas and to serve as the nuclei of such groups; [and] (2) '. . . be used to execute independent operations . . . as directed by the theater [sic] commander.' Such roles the British gave to their Special Air Service and other Allied SAS regiments, which were not a part of SOE. Once the invasion had begun men of these regiments set up bases far behind the main battle areas, working at times with the resistance forces not only in France but in northern Italy. Much has been written of their glamorous—if they will excuse this superlative—operations ambushing German transports, but SAS' major contribution to the Allied victory was in providing intelligence that could not be gathered by aerial reconnaissance. One team, for example, spotted the fords

▲ Specially formed teams of British, American and French officers and senior NCOs formed 'Jedburgh' parties. Each team of three men landed usually by parachute to provide military advice to *Maquis* forces. The team here are using an MCR 1 receiver to listen no doubt for information on the progress of the main Allied operations. These were aided through the teams' guidance of resistance forces, to provide co-ordinated actions against the German forces in France and later in Burma. This 'Jed' team was led by Major G. (Jerry) Davis on operation 'Eono' in Brittany during the summer of 1944. At that time several Jeds and SAS parties were operating in Brittany. The French Colonel Eon took control in August of resistance operations that cleared Brittany for the American advance to U-boat bases on the coast.

▲ The signaller with a 'Jed' team using a British B Mark II transceiver. His key is on a board resting on his right knee and this set is in a metal container used by paratroops. The power pack is lying across the righthand side of the set and an open box. The aerial wire has been suspended from a tree above the set, or by some other means which provided seven to 15 feet of aerial for transmissions over ten to 300 miles.

▲ The signaller of this Jed team is using a one-time pad to encode a signal. The American sergeant of this team is sitting on the bonnet or hood as he called this engine cover of their jeep. They had infiltrated no doubt through German lines in this vehicle.

which Germans had built with bridges beneath the surface of the Loire. Once such targets had been identified, Allied bombers could destroy them. They also armed resistance forces more readily than SOE had done. The Executive's caution arose because there was always the risk of putting arms in the wrong hands, when the political repercussions, if not those of double-agents, might adversely affect the Allied war effort.

One change of organization 24 days after the landings, helps to explain the background to SOE and OSS operations in France that summer. On 1 July all but EU/P of SOE sections working into France were moved from Baker Street to the offices of *État-Major des Forces Françaises de L'Intérieur*, near Marble Arch. The EMFFI, under the Free French General P-J. Koenig, was intended to establish a united French resistance movement with political affiliations to de Gaulle. Such political roles were one reason why the EU/P section, with its most secret contacts with Poles in France, did not move under EMFFI's wing. Koenig had a difficult task but understood the nature of the Resistance's secret war as did many of his staff. Some, however, had joined this headquarters after serving in Algeria and knew little of this type of operation.

Nowhere were these difficulties and confusions more apparent than in the Vercors, a high plateau 200km south of the Ain. Since 1941 civilian refugees had been living in remote camps in this natural redoubt, a massive arrowhead of limestone cliffs 50km from north to south with Grenoble lying to the east of its tip. The refugees looked to the dour communist, Eugène Chavant as their 'Patron'. A sergeant in World War I, this veteran politician from Grenoble did not always see eye to eye with the officers commanding a military force composed largely of cavalrymen from the 11th Cuirassiers and mountain troops of the 6th Battalion Chasseurs Alpine (BCA), which formed the nucleus of trained resistance fighters on the plateau. Nevertheless, by the summer of 1944 funds had been provided from Allied sources (through a bee keeper's bank account), as had such arms and explosives as SOE could provide. With these and a great deal of daring, several raids had been made into the Rhône valley to the west, and against vehicles on the main roads which skirted the cliffs of the plateau. The Germans countered such threats to their communications with punitive expeditions which from time to time destroyed specific camps of resistance forces, and with terror tactics to intimidate the population, as when a unit of *Malice* spent a week in April 1944 at La Chapelle. A number of men were taken back to the German headquarters in Grenoble and others were tortured for information on the where-abouts of *maquis* camps: one hotel-keeper was forced to sit on a red hot frying pan; a woman was dragged behind a car, with her feet tied to the fender.

▼ The Vercors plateau in south-eastern France where the *Maquis* fought several pitched battles with German forces in the summer of 1944. The defeat of these French guerrillas underlined the dangers for such lightly armed if very brave men, when they attempted to engage regular forces in set piece battles.

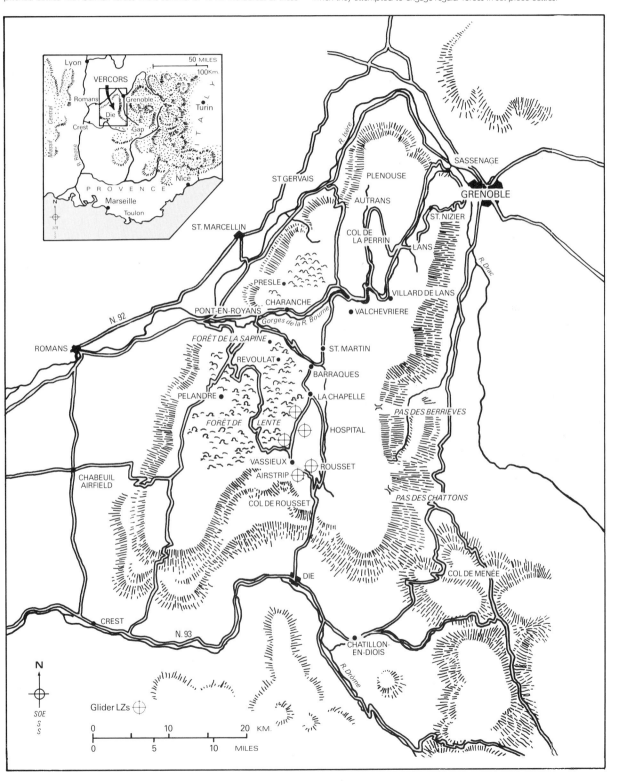

Colonel Marcel Descour had his headquarters on the plateau, from where he commanded de Gaulle's Rhône Valley Region, one of 20 set up to control the resistance forces. Also on the plateau was the safe house from which Francis Cammaerts co-ordinated all SOE's missions in south-eastern France. This smiling, bronzed giant of a man in his late twenties was one of SOE's most successful organizers. A former schoolmaster, his ability to organize agents owed much to the care with which they were recruited. Few could contact him although he kept in touch with each circuit. Like Descour, he and his couriers had little difficulty in moving around the region surrounding the Vercors although in May several of his senior agents were arrested in Lyons. To replace them and provide better communications between both London and Algiers, SOE planned to send in the 'Eucalyptus' military mission. At that time it appears that London did not expect any major operations to be mounted from the Vercors, although there were a number of French officers who saw this redoubt as a base for a major offensive by a battalion or more of paratroops. They might attack German lines of communication to the Mediterranean coast 240km to the south, where the Allies planned a landing by four French and three American divisions.

This landing was probably the one General G. R. Cochet had in mind when the Patron was brought from the Vercors to Algiers late in May 1944. For the General gave him a written order: *'Bouclez le Vercors le Jour J'* (Call out the Vercors on D-day). This confusion in orders, was to have disastrous results for the Vercors *maquis*, in proving what SOE staffs knew all too well: guerrilla forces should never attempt pitched battles against regular troops. The Patron had the tricolour raised on 7 June after the Swiss radio confirmed that the Allies had landed in Normandy. Colonel Descour ordered the mobilization of the local Resistance the following day, although François Huet who was commanding these forces did not believe his superior was making a sensible decision. Nevertheless as a regimental officer with a disciplined sense of command, the 39-year old Huet, obeyed the order. He had only been on the plateau for a couple of days, but began to organize his military force of about 300 men in training several thousand *maquis*, in mounting raids into the Rhône valley and guarding the approaches to the plateau. At first only German reconnaissance aircraft flying over the Vercors, gave any indication of the enemy's reaction, but these aircraft, made a detailed study of the plateau. Flying from Chabeuil, an airfield near Valence only a few minutes from the plateau, these aircraft would later support ground forces when, for example, 400 men of the 157th Regiment advanced up the road and railway tracks leading to St Nizier on the

north-east of the plateau. They were held briefly on the afternoon of 14 June, *maquis* dropping Gammon grenades on the advancing column at one point. At another, men with sten guns and rifles lying concealed on the reverse slope of a ridge, caught an advancing German company in withering fire. But such temporary setbacks for the Germans were overcome next day when they captured St Nizier, killing not only the wounded but digging up the corpses of those recently buried. Maybe these bodies needed identifying but more likely this was part of the grim intimidation of the villagers, for the Germans later withdrew leaving only Gestapo and *Malice* units to control the high ground which formed the tip of the Vercors arrowhead.

Huet and his forces withdrew across the 50m wide Gorges de la Bourne, a deep cleft in the blue-grey rock which cut the southern part of the redoubt from the north. Huet's forces then had some 65km of cliff tops and passes to defend, with mines laid in the gentler passes, while all tunnels through the cliffs and the gorge bridges were prepared for demolition. These defences and been set up on the understanding that this so-called Free Republic of the Vercors would soon receive reinforcements. Yet when 60 German aircraft including Ju 87 dive-bombers moved to Chabeuil airfield, the Allies had no aircraft available to attack them. Nor were the resistance forces encouraged to make raids, for the Free French in London realized the dangers of untrained *maquis* being trapped by German forces before Huet's men were adequately prepared. Yet once they had been trained, these men could be invaluable in attacking German transports and supplies. Meanwhile they were to build up their suplies, and a dropping zone for containers was cleared near Vassieux, on the southern rim of the plateau, which later became an airstrip.

Major Neil Martin's 'Monocle' Jedburgh team was parachuted to the Vercors and apparently brought in a Eureka beacon that would help aircraft navigators to find the DZ. The beacon was not needed in the bright sunshine on 25 June, when the crews of the 36 USAAF Liberators flying from the UK to the Vercors could clearly see the DZ into which they dropped over 600 containers.

Three days later SOE's Eucalyptus mission made a night drop on the plateau. It was led by Major Desmond Longe (pronounced Long) who had served in SOE since 1941, with his friend, Captain B. Houseman as second in command. Neither spoke more than a few words of French but the bilingual American Lieutenant' André Pecquet of OSS and J. de Croix, the French radio operator acted as translators. Their landing was made with some difficulty: Longe injured a vertebra; Pecquet gashed his right hand which as a signaller was more serious for him than for other agents; and one of their two radios was smashed due to faulty packing in

Algiers. A section from an OSS Operational Group dropped at the same time its 11 Americans and four French-Canadians commanded by young First Lieutenant Vernon Hoppers from South Carolina, whose second in command the Texan, Chester Myers was also in his early twenties.

Huet welcomed them, no doubt with some apology as Longe's car had overturned in the driver's enthusiasm to show him some feature of the defences. However, the French colonel's somewhat stiff manner belied his friendliness as he chain smoked his way through a gift of American cigarettes. Whatever he thought of the tall English major with his clipped military moustache, his bank clerk's background and lack of knowledge of conditions in the Vercors, does not seem to have inhibited their co-operation, for Huet welcomed the opportunity to get the supplies his men needed. Boots, blankets, weather-proof coats and other necessities for the growing number of men in training, would be supplied through the SOE mission, either by radio contact with London or Algiers as appropriate. The OG working in pairs helped to provide the much needed training, for some maquis '. . . did not know how to aim a rifle . . .' according to Hoppers' later report. Hoppers would also provide training in ambush tactics and within a couple of days of landing he gave a practical demonstration of this art.

On the Saturday the OSS men with eight maquis set out to recce the Chabeuil airfield. On their way there, they learnt of a German armoured car and two troop carrying half-tracks moving from the airfield to La Vacherie along a road passing through a deep cutting. Here they set an ambush in which they killed 18 Germans and destroyed the half-tracks. However no action was possible against the well guarded airfield, although its long perimeter, six and a half by eight kilometres had been studied carefully for weak points. By this date the Germans were well experienced in protecting airfields with interlocking zones of fire from heavy machine guns. The following Wednesday the OG had better hunting for they ambushed a truck convoy near Lus-la-Croix-Haute below the south-eastern ramparts of Vercors. The men, with 20 maquis took up positions on the steep bank of a horseshoe bend, when at about 0745hr Sgt Nathan Richman hit the leading truck 300m into the bend. Immediately the convoy's escort of infantry dismounted from the rear trucks and went into action, getting three machine guns behind the Americans. These were knocked out but German mortars in the dead ground by the road began to range on the OG's positions and they withdrew. Over 100 Germans had been killed or wounded for the loss of only two men of the maquis. One was killed outright and the second savagely tortured, his bones crushed one by one, his eyes gouged out and 20 painful though not fatal bayonet thrusts wounded him, before he died. (Such torture was not confined to German or Malice savagery: some unauthorized interrogations of Malice sympathizers led to a schoolteacher in the Vercors having hot coals dropped on the soles of her feet, although she was later proved innocent of any collaboration.)

The Germans believed that at least a battalion of Americans had mounted the Lus ambush, but only a few agents reached the Vercors in that and the following week. An airfield construction engineer parachuted in on 5 July, and with him, as a courier for Cammaerts, came the vivacious Christine Granville. Lieutenant Conus, a large, bearded big game hunter drove onto the plateau the following week. He had been parachuted to the Ain maquis before making his way south, as he and his radio operator were part of Longe's mission. Others came and went with some difficulty when the Germans set up unexpected road checks, yet the Patron continued to move around the region, using the cover of his supposed job as a road engineer. At this time in mid-July German patrols were active in the area by the Drôme river below the south-eastern cliffs. Huet found it hard to understand these enemy probes at the time, because at this point the cliffs were particularly steep. By Friday 14 July the airstrip near Vassieux was over a kilometre long and 140m wide. That morning 72 Flying Fortresses flew over this airstrip in tight formations of 12 to drop their containers with red, blue and white chutes that identified different containers' contents. As the trucks moved out to collect these, however, German aircraft shot up the DZ, and anything that moved on the roads in the next few hours was attacked from the air.

Next day the Germans made the opening moves in their assault on the plateau. This operation would take them over a week, but was mounted with a thoroughness and care that ensured success with minimum casualties. The first step was to seal the plateau from the surrounding countryside. That Saturday they blew up tunnels and bridges to block two access roads, placing a road block across a third. They would block another five during the week but people of the Vercors could still pass to and from the plateau by way of the road to Die in the south. The civil administration also continued to function with all the legal niceties of impartial justice which led to the trial of one collaborator being deferred until his attorney could attend— no brief delay because the lawyer had to travel from Paris! However the Germans had tightened their blockade of the access roads to such a degree after the weekend that Huet declared martial law at 1400 hours on 18 July. There had also been some looting after German air attacks, but the cohesion of the civilians and the military on the plateau became greater, while the strength of the maquis rose to 3,200 as more volunteers came from outside the Vercors. They were too few, however, even if they could have been trained for the continuous defence of the plateau to which they were committed. This plateau, nevertheless, offered strong defensive positions with its many steep ridges running across wheat lands, and the woods cut by ski-runs sweeping down from the high ground around the rim of the Vercors. The defenders would also need anti-aircraft guns and, as it turned out, anti-tank guns. Longe requested these and repeated Huet's requests for reinforcements. Yet none were sent. Much post-war analysis of these operations hinges on what policy was to be followed: hold the Vercors or operate as guerrillas? In all probability the answer lies in the general consensus of senior officers in London, if not in Algiers, that *maquis* resistance forces should not be used in set piece battles. This they might be tempted to do if they were provided with heavy weapons. This was the principal reason no doubt for not sending anti-tank guns but these in the 1940s also required specially trained crews for which instructors would be needed.

On the following Thursday afternoon, 20 July, summer rain clouds piled dark thunder storms over the Vercors and the high Alps stretching away to the east. Huet had known these hills and farms since he was a boy, memories which may briefly have come to mind as he thought of his wife and six children in their home, 15km north of the Vercors. But now a stream of reports on German movements were reaching the villa headquarters in St Martin. These showed that strong German forces were moving along both the east and west ring-roads to seize Die and close the southern exits from the Vercors. From Die they could also move up the pass into the mountains near Vassieux. Further east artillery batteries were being positioned where they might bombard the south-eastern cliff tops of the plateau. Difficult though an assault on these crags might be, a battalion of mountain troops was deployed to attempt it, no doubt using information from the recce patrols of the previous week. In the north, platoons and companies of German infantry garrisoned each ring-road hamlet and village, tightening even further the Germans' grip on the Vercors.

Captain Costa de Beauregard's 88 men must have seen these movements in the valley below them, as their *maquis* company with their 30-year-old BCA officer took up defensive positions on the Col de la Croix Perrin. These were the defenders' most northerly positions 10km from the tip of the 'arrow'. The company might counter-attack any German attempts to force their way from St Nizier onto the plateau. Further south was Sergeant Abel Chabal with his specially trained team of 82 sharpshooters, most of whom had served in the BCA. They could see from the tourists' observation platform at Valchevrière, the trees of the hillside falling away to their north and the Bourne

Gorge. The cavalrymen had their horses in the centre of the plain at La Rivière, where Captain Narcisse Geyer was in touch by telephone with his colonel at St Martin. The slightly built cavalry officer had led several successful raids and put greater score on such tactics than did his seniors, the cause of some friction between them, as Geyer doubted if any plan might succeed in holding all the access roads and hill tracks around the rim of the plateau.

The key to the French defence and ironically to the German assault, was the airstrip near Vassieux. Huet received a signal on the Thursday night to say it was still 60m too short for any available Allied aircraft to land. Therefore the colonel's 3,000 to 4,000 men—the numbers had grown daily as men came from the valleys—had to face some 10,000 Germans drawn mainly from the 157th Division, elements of the 9th Panzer Regiment, assault engineers and other specialists. Some 2,000 of these troops moved onto the plateau from St Nizier about 0600 hours next morning. Dividing into two columns, one swung north to face Beauregard's company and the second moved towards the Bourne gorge but by 0900 hours had made no attempt to attack the defences in either area. Huet must have wondered which other German units had to move up to some starting line—those advancing towards Die?—the mountaineers in the south-east?

The answer came in a telephoned report: aircraft were approaching from the south, flying low in close formation. They could not be Allied aircraft as no radio signal had warned of their coming, and soon their German markings were clear even in the watery light of that Friday morning. The towing aircraft slipped their gliders at 0930 hours and these disgorged the 200 or so airborne soldiers who would seize the airstrip. As they moved down the length of its new runway, they fired on the women, youths, and some children who had been working to extend it. Many were killed as were the two Frenchmen who managed to shoot down at least one towing aircraft. Others died when the fighters covering the landing strafed nearby woods. More gliders put down near four hamlets which dominated the approaches to the airfield and Vassieux from the north, the east and the west. A second wave of gliders came in later that morning and the large village of Vassieux was secured as there were 500 German airborne troops in the area.

To the east the mountain troops broke over the cliffs along a mule track and at other points, despite the *maquis*' attempts to block these routes. One such attempt involved 10 Frenchmen on the Pas de Chattons who were outflanked by a company of *Gebirgejäger*. These Germans were moving towards positions where they might provide cover for tanks climbing up the road from Die. There the German forces were closing in from east and west, sweeping aside *maquis* road blocks and the men defending the bridge east of the town.

Huet's only reserve was Geyer's cavalrymen at La Rivière whom he now ordered to retake the airstrip. At this time German artillery shells began to cut several of the telephone lines which were the *maquis* officers' only means of keeping in direct touch with the various defence posts. Geyer in this sense had been 'tied to the telephone', waiting for a report on the German positions around Vassieux, 12km from his headquarters. No report reached him until the afternoon, when he was able to make plans for a counter-attack. These included an attack from the scrub-covered hill south of the airstrip and simultaneous attacks on the four hamlets north-west and north-east of Vassieux. They would involve 400 of Huet's force, including the cavalrymen and Hoppers' OG Section, but they were not to be launched until after dark at 2100 hours.

During the morning German infantry in the north forced their way into the Bourne Gorge, taking a couple of hamlets at its western end. Meanwhile Jean Prévost had 400 *maquis* spread in a series of defence positions along the eastern ridges of the plateau. During the afternoon he and his men held these defences behind mined appproaches, as the Germans moved onto the plateau. But in the early afternoon, Prévost lost touch with Beauregard's company which had been overrun. German columns then turned south, closely supported by their air force. The aircraft provided warnings of *maquis* positions on the line of advance, strafed the French positions or gave the artillery details of their positions. But after dusk the aircraft could not make such recces and therefore the Germans consolidated their positions, having reached the outskirts of Valchevrière. To the south Hoppers had moved his men into positions where they overlooked open ground leading to the outskirts of Vassieux. On his right were Geyer's 11th Cuirassiers who already had been in action against the mountain troops advancing from the east, as the cavalrymen moved towards the airstrip. Nearer to the Americans were some 300 *maquis* whom Hoppers considered had barely any training, many being '. . . raw recruits who had joined the *maquis* just two days previously . . .' as he later reported.

These forces had a difficult task because the village lay in open ground, across which German machine-guns had cut down any who attempted to move forward in daylight. Even at night some of these guns fired periodically in defensive bursts along pre-set lines. Nevertheless Hoppers decided to make a further recce after dark, even though Huet was pressing Geyer to put in the attacks as planned at 2100 hours. The American officer by this time was accepted as the commander of this southern attack, although no orders placed him in charge. Probably the other officers were as conscious as the American of the friction between Huet and Geyer. This may have led to the order for the southern attack, although the other units were not ready to attack the hamlets.

Hoppers' three mortars and two light machine-guns gave his men some covering fire as he led the advance along a line picked out during the recce. The OG Section then reached the outskirts of the village as did Lieutenant Cathala's *maquis* company, but there was no way that they could break through the German airborne troops' defences. The Americans' bazookas, their Thompson sub machine-guns and grenades were not sufficient firepower to subdue one group of strong points, let alone the Germans' series of defences. Therefore Hoppers gave the order to withdraw, the French doing so with some reluctance. Elsewhere the French were unable to dislodge the Germans, as senior officers of the Resistance knew when they held a conference in the St Martin headquarters. General Henri Zeller commanding all the Resistance in the Free French regions of south-eastern France, Cammaerts of SOE, Chavant (the Patron) and Desmond Longe with several members of Huet's staff went over the alternative courses of action. These were: (1) the assembly of as many men as possible to break out in force through Villard or through Die; (2) to break out in small groups; (3) hold the plateau until all were killed or captured. The final decision was a compromise in which units would hold positions as long as possible before falling back to disperse into small groups that would escape from the plateau.

A signal was sent to Algiers via London explaining that the *maquis* had only been expected to hold the plateau for three weeks but had held out for six. Another signal was taken by Lieutenant Conus to the *maquis* of the Drôme region to the south, asking them to help keep open the road to Die by attacking the German infantry and tanks advancing towards it from the east and west. Arrangements to evacuate the sick and wounded were changed early that Saturday morning, as the nuns in the hospital at Die feared for the wounded already there. The sick and wounded from the Vercors, including the American Chester Myers with an acute appendicitis, were therefore hidden in the network of caves 400m into the mountain near Rousset.

As soon as it was fully light German artillery renewed the accurate bombardment of those French defences on the south-eastern cliffs which had not been overrun the previous afternoon. This shelling had prevented rations being brought to the *maquis* here, and by 0830 hours more German mountain companies had been able to move westward. As they advanced they reached positions where they could cover the road up which German tanks were to advance from Die later the next day, relieving the airborne troops holding Vassieux.

They received their first supplies of fresh ammunition and rations, however, from Ju 88s, three-engined bombers converted to transports which put down on the airstrip. To the Allied officers on the Vercors this must have been a bitter blow, but they were not then to know that the Allied Command did not want to weaken the forces due to land three weeks later in southern France. The length of the runway or lack of it, therefore, seems to have been one of several excuses raised at that time to avoid sending regular forces to the Vercors. The arrival of the Ju 88s was reported to Longe. His signals officer Pecquet was still transmitting from the hay-loft of a cattle-shed near St Martin. Among his messages was one which became confused, probably in its encoding or decoding, for it reported that the French still held Vassieux near the airstrip. Allied airforces were therefore inhibited from bombing what was the German centre for the distribution of supplies from the incoming transports.

The Germans were better informed through their air reconnaissance, their aircraft succeeded in driving Hoppers' American and *maquis* units from the scrub south of the airfield back to their positions in the forests on the western part of the plateau. Any movement on the open roads or tracks had become dangerously exposed to air attacks, forcing the *maquis* to remain under cover of these woods. The woods on the eastern ridges enabled Prévost's men to maintain some cohesion, throwing back the first German attacks on the observation platform. But the Germans regrouped and after a whirlwind of mortar bombs had swept the French positions, it was followed by a determined German attack regardless of the mines laid in the woods. Chabal watched his forward positions overrun before a counter-attack drove the Germans back down the hill.

Huet planned several counter-attacks for that Saturday night, while the weary OG Section forced their tired bodies back across the hills to the scrub overlooking the airstrip. There they found the Germans firing illuminating flares to prevent anyone crossing the open ground around Vassieux without being seen. Nevertheless Hoppers led his men to the edge of the village but only six *maquis* stayed with them, probably because few had the skill in fieldcraft to use every fold in the ground or clump of grass that might give them cover. There was no alternative but to withdraw, for 20 men could not expect to dislodge the 500 or more Germans dug in around the village or in houses they had fortified. Back in the scrub, Hoppers deployed his men where they had a clear view after dawn of the Ju 88s' approach to the airstrip, shooting down three and firing on others during that Sunday.

The French held out on the south-eastern cliffs throughout Saturday, but by Sunday morning only one post had been overrun. This was manned by 10 or fewer *maquis* with firing positions in a cave, before a team of *Gebirgejäger* climbed above the entrance to lower a heavy charge of explosives into it—all the defenders were killed. To the north, the men around the observation platform were virtually encircled but fought on for four hours. Chabal himself killed 27 Germans before he fell, after the Germans had worked their way across a rockface overlooking the platform. The defenders were then pinned down by fire from above their positions but one of Chabal's runners got out through the woods with a message: these BCA sharpshooters would fight to the last man. This they did.

About midday Huet heard that Chabal's men had been overrun and the Colonel therefore ordered the rest of Prévost's companies to disperse. Orders were carried to the men covering the Die road, instructing them to destroy the road tunnel. Pecquet took one of the few cars for which there was petrol, loaded it with a transmitter-receiver, batteries and the cycle-pedal generator. He then set out for the tracks to Revoulat in the remote depths of the Sapine Forest where Huet intended to set up his new headquarters. General Zeller, Cammaerts, his courier Christine Granville and two SOE radio operators drove to the Rousset pass above Die. From there they climbed down through the beech woods to the ring road. Before they crossed this they heard *maquis* engineers blow up the Rousset tunnel high above the German column which was moving towards the pass. Later the agents and the General reached the Drôme *maquis* from where Zeller was flown to Algiers.

Some units on the plateau dispersed to various villages where men hoped to escape detention. Others remained as fighting units, as did Geyer's cavalrymen who withdrew into the Lente forest; Prévost moved into the cool caves above the thick woods east of La Rivière; Beauregard hid in the wild forests of the north-western ridges. Others were less fortunate: Conus was captured, tortured and taken out to be shot with five others, lined along the edge of a ravine. The big game hunter judged his moment as he knelt watching the others being shot one by one. Before the German executioner put a pistol to his neck, Conus jumped causing the German to miss his shot, giving the Frenchman that split second chance he needed to leap into the ravine. Fortune favoured the brave on this occasion with a tree that broke his fall, enabling him to make good his escape in the dusk. He reached the *maquis* to the south, sending from their radio a brief signal: 'Arrested. Tortured. Shot. In good health. Volume.' His code named 'Volume' is nicely descriptive of his size and sense of humour.

Shells had begun falling around St Martin at 1500 hours on the Saturday, when the Patron left his office to go into hiding. As was his custom, he moved only at night once he was clear of St Martin and able to stay albeit briefly in the ultra-safe houses of long-standing friends. Major Longe on the ridge overlooking St Martin had his second in command, Houseman and several maquis with him, but had lost touch with Pecquet. Huet had told the Major that he would send him orders before leaving the headquarters. These never came, perhaps because Huet moved westward while Longe was in woods on the ridge to the east. There the Englishman and his party spent a grim few days squeezing moss for moisture as they had no water, living off raw goats' meat as they dared not light a fire. Some of the French left for their homes and each time they did so, Longe moved camp. After three or four days, he decided to move his party to the west across the St Martin road in search of Huet. Such a move was fraught with danger. At one point the party came face to face with a German patrol at the junction of two walls, but Longe and his men escaped before these Germans could open fire. Later the party was fired on by machine guns, when the men were heard moving at night. Nevertheless they managed to reach the western woods. A patrol passed within touching distance of the Major but neither these men nor their dog noticed the British officer. Unable to find Huet, he and Houseman set out for Switzerland, despite the German patrols, their own physical weakness from lack of proper food and the difficult route through the Alps before they could reach the border. When they did reach it, a maquis soldier guided them to safety past the frontier posts.

The men who returned to their villages were betrayed by the Malice, a number of whom had been released on Huet's orders from their prison compound on the plateau. The former prisoners were led down the road by a pro-German night club singer, who had been brought from Grenoble as she was known to have betrayed several of the Resistance. A few collaborators who followed her were shot by maquis, not over zealous about the due processes of law. Others mingled with these former prisoners but when they reached the German outpost at Royans, the Malice pointed out the American shoes their late captors wore. Such evidence was all that the Germans needed to execute a man or woman, as they did to the 32 wounded maquis they found in the hospital caves. Only Chester Myers was spared, the seven nurses and the doctors being sent to concentration camps although Dr Ganimede escaped during the confusion in an air raid on Grenoble.

Huet's headquarters staff evaded capture, some 20 of them marching into the western forests with their colonel who carried his pack and a rifle. (The motorcycle he had used for a month or more was left at St Martin because there was no petrol.) After a week living on scant rations they were so weak that the colonel considered abandoning much of their equipment. Nevertheless they kept most of it and were in radio contact with London, as they dodged major searches by battalions of Germans. By the second week in August they were able to rebuild the organization of resistance in the Vercors. Some units had remained intact, as had Geyer's horsemen who raided only when the odds were in their favour. However Descour had insisted that they send two squadrons, in all some 120 men, back to the area of the airstrip and northwards towards St Martin. Those in the forest succeeded in evading German searches, once by scaling a cliff, but the squadron sent by Descour to the woods near St Martin were all killed or captured. Both Geyer and his regiment, 11th Cuirassiers, were awarded the Croix de Guerre for the cavalrymen's bravery and skill in the Vercors.

Hoppers' OG Section moved north when they received the order to disperse at the end of the battle. He had hoped to lead them off the plateau to the areas controlled by the Resistance but the Germans had the ring road heavily patrolled. Therefore the Americans spent 11 days '. . . in one spot while the German patrols scoured the woods and fired into the underbush . . .' Such searches Hoppers later described as frightening young maquis into making a dash for safer cover, only to expose themselves as easy targets. The OG lived on raw potatoes, a little cheese and scraps of food which they stole from a nearby farm. They never spoke in more than a whisper, nor moved more than one man at a time '. . . never more than 50ft away from where we lay . . .' Hoppers never was able to contact Huet although the Colonel sent men to look for the Americans. By the time a more general search might be made the OG Section had crossed the Isère after the Germans had withdrawn their regular patrols. By this time in the first week in August, Beauregard was able to mount several ambushes but the Germans began to leave the plateau the following week, after the Allies had landed in southern France.

Some 800 resistance fighters and sympathizers, had been killed, including Prévost. He had lost patience with hiding in caves, breaking out with several companions all of whom were shot before they could reach safety beyond the ring road. Many of those who were killed suffered needless brutality. Pecquet's young girl assistant was disembowelled so that she would die slowly, her tormentors throwing her entrails over her shoulder. Those who survived were left with little food for the Germans took away some 3,000 cattle, over 1,000 pigs, as well as wheat, hay and apples in great quantity. Retribution however came swiftly.

Zeller had been able to persuade the Allied Command to send a force up the Route Napoléon into the mountains, their advance from Nice, through Digne and

Gap being cleared by resistance forces. This enabled the leading regiment of armoured cars to reach the outskirts of Grenoble within a week. Huet met the column on the ring road when they were 10km south of the city waiting for their tank squadrons to join them. He was able to persuade their Colonel to move into the city, where the American insisted that Huet accept the surrender of men of the 157th Division who at first offered some resistance from their positions east of Grenoble.

Other Germans retreating north from the Allied advance, had to fight their way as often through ambushes as through Allied air-atttacks. *The Maquis de l'Ain* guided by Heslop, made no major stand against the Germans during July and early August but chipped away at their patrols with swift ambushes, sabotage and intelligence collecting on targets for Allied airforces. This *maquis* appear also to have provided some intelligence for OSS' 'Penny Farthing', the first of their SI teams parachuted into south-eastern France and based at Lyons. For nearly a year, from August 1943 until April 1944, the two senior organizers of this team set up a series of circuits with their own radio operators. The leader was captured in Lyons on 17 April, but by clever procrastination during his interrogations had contrived to stay alive until the Americans were nearing Lyons that August. Then two of his guards surrendered to him and he drove them to a *maquis* stronghold 40km from the city! He volunteered for further work behind enemy lines where SI had agents working to its Strategic Service Section (SSS) in the Allied headquarters of the Seventh Army. This Section had been created in April 1944 to co-ordinate intelligence reports and send agents into the field for both tactical intelligence (gathered often by local volunteers who went through the German lines) and strategic intelligence. During the preparations for the landings in southern France, SSS had received a great deal of information on rail shipments. Typically 'Penny Farthing' reported 'Movement 43 trains origin Bayonne. Destination Saintes and beyond. Rate at least 12 trains in 24 hours.' There followed details of the stations at which these would load men of an infantry division. Such signals were to be later passed to General Patch's command ship, but in order to avoid a sudden increase in signal traffic before the landings, a pattern of dummy messages was established in late July. Thus the Germans would not detect any change in the traffic flow when genuine messages replaced the dummies in the week before D-day in August.

As the Allies advanced Cammaerts' teams fought the Germans retreating through Lyons, for the bulk of the Germans had been bypassed in the Rhône valley. F Section's Tony Brooks, who had spent two years in the area as leader of 'Pimento' and whose Swiss upbringing had enabled him to talk his way out of a Gestapo interrogation, enjoyed the freedom to 'brew up' German vehicles with phosphorous grenades flung from a powerful motorcar. Cammaerts, however, was captured at a road block, but Christine Granville used her charms to persuade their captors that the Americans would be arriving at any minute. They were therefore released despite orders for their execution.

Heslop had become a hero in the liberated Alpine villages, although the villagers were probably among the only people at that time who realized his masterly understanding of guerrilla warfare, no doubt without fully appreciating its implications. De Gaulle's officers were less understanding when they took command, mistakenly fearing that the British colonel had some political influence or in some other way might undermine the general's authority. Whatever their reasons, Heslop returned to Britain within 36 hours of their arrival, scant reward for the considerable help he had provided for the people of France. His responsibilities had aged him beyond his years and he died not long after the war.

A NOTHER master of guerrilla warfare was Tito. At 49 years of age in 1941 he was a broad-shouldered, compact man with a pride and self assurance. His partisans were perhaps forced to be more ruthless than most, yet the heady mixture of communist 'religion' and the Slavs' natural fire of temperament led to fanatic devotion to their cause: if a female partisan became pregnant she was shot, and more than one senior

▼ This major supply drop in daylight was made by the RAF to Tito's partisans. By this time in the late summer of 1944, drops might spread over a wide area in remote parts of the Balkans without much risk of German intervention.

partisan took his own life for causing such a fatal pregnancy. SOE had no knowledge of such resistance nor indeed of Tito's activities in 1941, when these Southern Slavs (hence Yugoslavia) were by no means united. Behind this disunity lay the fact that the Serbs and Macedonians were nominally at least members of the Eastern Orthodox Church and used Cyrillic script, differing from the Roman Catholic Croats and Slovenes who wrote in the Roman alphabet of western Europe. All groups spoke Serbo-Croat as a common language, however.

The Royalist Colonel Mihailovič, as mentioned earlier, made contact with the British, and SOE's Bill Hudson was sent to contact him in the autumn of 1941. With Hudson were two majors of the exiled Royalist forces who, unbeknown to the British, carried secret orders for the colonel, which instructed the underground army, perhaps 2,000 strong, to avoid casualties and any actions which might cause reprisals. The Royalist Government in exile wanted to keep a force intact against the day when it would prevent the communists seizing power, after the Axis armies had been driven from the country.

Bill Hudson, a South African mining engineer who spoke Serbo-Croat, had worked as a British agent in the Balkans in 1939, and had been briefly imprisoned in 1940 by the Russian secret police after he reported to the Russian army in Poland, during a recce for Section D. He was not therefore likely to be surprised when Tito's communists delayed his mission in 1941, when he met the partisans. (A name associated with the Russian irregulars who had attacked Napoleon's army in 1812 during its advance on Moscow.)

Tito's force was based in the remote town of Užice near the head of the Detinja valley in south-western Serbia, 115km south of Belgrade. There they had made ammunitions, including 20,000 rifles in a local factory; and had access to the country's gold reserves lodged for safety in a local bank, the Germans having barely visited the town. After some difficulty, Tito agreed to Hudson's party moving across the Morava valley to reach the colonel's headquarters in the forests to the north-east of Užice. Mihailovič, a rotund and bespectacled staff officer wth a beard, was so reassured of British support by the Royalist majors that he decided against Hudson's protests to attack the partisans. He lost 1,000 men in the battle before the partisans drove his Četnićs back to their forest bases. This battle also weakened Tito's force to the extent that he had to move west into the Bosnian mountains when German and Italian battalions moved against him. The colonel also took to the Serbian mountains in the east where that winter Hudson had to survive among people with no more than potatoes to eat. His money, and even his compass, was stolen; but in the spring he recovered his

radio and reported the likelihood of civil war among other details.

Other agents were parachuted to both factions during 1942, but when the British decided to support Tito, the Americans initially remained loyal to the Royalists. Alan Dulles, OSS's senior officer in Switzerland, advised against supporting the Communists, although one of Tito's officers had visited him.

The major part of the OSS' operations in the Balkans, however, were controlled first from Cairo and later from Algeria, before moving this headquarters to Bari in Italy. In 1942 the hot climate of Cairo is claimed by one colonel to have bred the petty differences between the various secret agencies. Age old rivalries between American concepts of the British as imperialists, and the British fears of Americans outsmarting them, in fact caused many of the difficulties. For example, an OSS project to gain Arab support was seen in the words of an SOE report to be aimed at denigrating British diplomacy in the Middle East, '... hardly ... furthering our common efforts ...' On the other hand, the appearance of OSS Operations Groups in Greece was seen by the British as likely to provide unwitting support for communist factions there, who were fighting the British-supported socialist guerrillas.

Some individuals of OSS and SIS rubbed along in relative harmony, but incidents abound of secret misunderstandings and confusion. In retrospect many of these appear to be due more to the squabbles of cousins and misplaced enthusiasm, than to downright hostility. Yet harsher frictions did exist in some quarters, as several OSS officers discovered in operations. Major Louis Huot's smuggling is a good example of the 'get up and go' attitude of OSS officers in the field, more concerned with winning the war than with finer points of diplomacy. This liberal journalist had seen the spread of Nazi influence in Europe in the 1930s when he worked in Paris and believed it should be stopped by any means. Therefore on meeting one of Tito's officers in Algeria, Huot was willing to set up a means of smuggling arms to Yugoslavia using a fleet of fishing boats.

At the time Huot was putting together his fleet of boats and finding crews, the British Prime Minister sent a mission to Tito. Although not strictly an SOE operation, its leader, the 32-year-old Brigadier (later Sir) Fitzroy Maclean, and his aids were parachuted into Bosnia with the help of SOE. They spent September 1943 working out ways and means whereby the British might supply the partisans, although never officially recognizing Tito's claim to govern Yugoslavia or the part of it that his forces controlled.

While the Maclean mission was at the partisan headquarters, Huot landed his first shipment of supplies, and decided to visit Tito. However, when the American reached the partisan headquarters he was forced to hide from the British. Such a pantomime was necessary because the American had no official clearance to visit Yugoslavia or to send supplies to Tito. The affair might have had an unhappy ending before it had barely started but Huot was able to return to Italy with Linn Farish, OSS' official observer with the British mission. A few weeks later his smuggling was abruptly halted, although 400 tons of medical and other urgently needed supplies had reached Tito through Huot's fleet. (This was 100 tons more than had reached them from all other sources up to that time.)

Huot was posted to London apparently on the instigation of the British who connived with a senior OSS officer strongly opposed to the communists. Not satisfied with merely preventing the enterprise, some senior officers wanted to court-martial Huot and those who helped him. Bill Donovan intervened at this point: 'You will also have to court-martial me,' he is reported to have said, 'because I gave them [the smugglers] the freedom of action to do what they did.'

Donovan favoured helping both the Četnićs and Tito's partisans, with the aim of forcing the Germans to keep 15 divisions and some 100,000 pro-Axis local troops in Yugoslavia. However, in late August 1943 a number of officers from OGs who had parachuted into Yugoslavia had found that both irregular forces had their own experienced officers. Therefore the Americans became in effect intelligence officers, roles for which OGs were not specifically trained, limiting the value of their reports on political aspects of events in Yugoslavia. They were, however, able to provide useful details of the German order of battle which they trained some partisan intelligence officers to search out. Such information was important in planning Allied Strategies, dependent as they were on the disposition of German infantry regiments, artillery and other forces. Additional information of the greatest value was provided by two of OSS' Secret Intelligence teams which parachuted into Slovenia on the 26-27 December. In the following eight months they provided such details as the production serial numbers painted on aircraft, or stamped onto the breech blocks of artillery pieces, on engines of the tanks and on other equipment. Dr R. V. Jones in London could then assess the rate of output from German armaments factories. These SI teams were reinforced by 14 American operatives, one of which crossed the Hungarian border with two partisans on 23 June 1944. This team built a camouflaged log hide overlooking one of the main railway lines from northern Yugoslavia, radioing daily reports from the transmitter in an underground chamber below the hide. Forced to move after a railway man discovered them, they continued to radio reports until 5 August when their set 'went off the air', probably because the team had been caught and executed. No trace of their fate could be found after the war.

In December the German I Mountain, 114 Light and 775 Infantry Divisions cleared the Dalmatian coast of partisan units, but the island of Vis remained in Allied hands garrisoned by partians, British commandos and 211 men of the OGs. From Vis the Allies raided the coastal islands: on 27 January 1944 30 men of the OGs with three Troops of 2 Commando attacked an airstrip on Hvar 30km from Vis. They captured four Germans who no doubt were terrified of the partisans as no quarter was asked or given in this harsh theatre of the war. The prisoners, thankful to be in British and American hands, revealed where other garrisons were stationed on the islands. In later raids these garrisons were found to be well dug in with strong points blasted from living rock, defended with the tenacity of fear, for the partisans killed—if they did not always first torment—their prisoners. Such stubborn defence was put up by 110 Germans on Solta when 450 commandos with 150 men of the OGs made a landing on 17 March 1944. Crossing its steep and rocky hills in the dark, the raiders attacked the garrison soon after dawn when 36 RAF Kittyhawk bombers had strafed the enemy positions, before the garrison surrendered. The attackers lost two men killed, one from the OGs who also had five men wounded. Raiding from Vis continued until the autumn but the OGs were withdrawn from the island in July, when they were redeployed on the mainland in support of both Royalist and Communist partisans.

Although British supplies to the colonel—now general—and his Royalist force had ceased in 1943, they were continued by OSS. Tito meanwhile received major supply drops from both Allies, with the result that 76,000 tons of war stores, weapons, ammunition, explosives, rations and so on, were supplied to resistance forces in Yugoslavia from OSS and SOE sources. Allied drops provided 95 per cent of all the weapons sent there. The Russian contribution was small although Soviet influence remained very strong in communist resistance forces: Tito had only communist party members commanding units with 50 or more partisans. This caused concern to Bill Donovan among others, who is reported to have told two of his senior officers in the Middle East, Colonel Harry Aldrich, a regular soldier, and the financial lawyer Lawrence Houston, that in the early months of 1945, '. . . the main target for intelligence operations should now become [the discovery of] what the Soviets are doing in the Balkans'. He was not prepared to include this instruction in official reports, in part no doubt because many Allied airmen were dependent on partisans' help to evade capture by those Axis forces retreating through Yugoslavia, as well as those in northern Italy who held the line of the Po valley.

8
THE GREAT ESCAPE

IAN Garrow was weary after days without sleep in May 1940. His battalion had been constantly on the move, extracting its companies from the tangles of retreat, before he began what would be a long journey alone from St Valéry on the channel coast to reach the Mediterranean 800km to the south. He, like others in the 51 Highland Division, took the opportunity to evade capture when the Highlanders were encircled far to the south of the British Army's evacuation beaches at Dunkirk. Yet he had little more than his courage, a smattering of schoolboy French and probably a compass, to help him make the initial break from Normandy. Thereafter the journey was difficult enough, but in the confusion of their rapid victory the Germans had yet to garrison the towns of southern France and would not have troops in those of Vichy France until November 1942. Therefore when the tall young Scots captain in the Seaforth Highlanders reached Marseilles, he moved without interference from the local police although they knew he was a Scotsman. They also knew that Donald Caskie, a minister of the Presbyterian Church, was not running the local seaman's mission entirely for sailors: Caskie had lodged many an evader in this building and arranged some escapes to neutral Spain.

The two Scots worked together making friends with rich Americans on the Riviera who charitably provided some funds, while the neutral American consul no doubt also provided the names of people who might help. Through these Americans, Garrow received a letter from the British vice-consul responsible for refugees in Lisbon. He would have based himself in Spain but his work covered that of MI 9's agent with too delicate a job for the liking of the British Ambassador, striving to keep Franco's Spain out of the war. This agent, the young Donald Darling who spoke fluent French and Spanish, knew the eastern Pyrenees over which he established contacts in France. Darling was able to send money to Garrow and his successors using on occasion Nubar Gulkenkian, one of the world's richest men, unlikely to be suspected of risking his life—which he did—during holidays on the Riviera. Many other famous people worked for the Allied secret agencies: Greta Garbo provided Stephenson with details of Swedes who sympathized with the Nazis. Noel Coward worked for SIS in South America and 'wherever he could go' in Europe and Asia, meeting influential people whose opinions he reported to Stephenson.

SIS set up Darling's employers as MI 9 in December 1939 when the British realized that there would be a

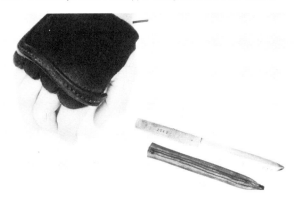

need for more than the provision of escape kits for men who had been captured. This was the responsibility of MI 1a, a World War I organization, revived in November 1938, but absorbed by Major (later Brigadier) Norman R. Crockatt, DSO, MC into MI 9 on his appointment as its first and only head during the European War. A man of front-line experience who had been wounded twice, the major was also a first class staff officer with great organizing ability. This MI 9 Section of the Intelligence Directorate—according to its 'charter'—was responsible '. . . for the preparation and execution of plans for facilitating the escape of British prisoners of war . . .' Crockatt divided this department into two branches: one branch dealt with the interrogation and vetting of enemy personnel, known from December 1941 as MI 19. The other dealt with escape and evasions, and continued as MI 9. The second branch included a school where the intelligence officers of units could be trained to teach others about evasion; and a sub-section dealing with tools for this trade.

We will return to the tools used in specific escapes but many of them were designed by Christopher Clayton Hutton, a man of infinite ingenuity. 'Clutty' has been described by Crockatt as eccentric, because he was no respecter of regulations when he needed materials for his escape tools. In 1940, however, there was no opportunity to distribute his tools to men already in occupied territories nor were there radio operators to spare for the nascent escape organizations like Ian Garrow's Marseilles 'line'. The Scots minister continued to help through his mission but eventually was

▼ Major C. Clayton Hutton of MI 9 had been on active service in World War I. He designed and developed many of the Allied aids for escape and evasion, like the silk map he is holding. Centre foreground is his dart pen with an escape radio to its right and the blanket from which a civilian coat might be made.

arrested, and later imprisoned by the Germans, but survived the war.

The formative years of the escape lines are full of coincidences which one doubts a good novelist would dare to invent, as they seem too far-fetched. One of these was the meeting of the tall, dark Ian Garrow with Pat O'Leary, a lively character who was held by the Vichy French as an escaping French Canadian airman. Yet nothing about Pat is what it seems: a doctor with a Belgian cavalry regiment in 1940, he escaped to England, disliked the squabbles among his fellow expatriots, and joined the Royal Navy Volunteer Reserve as an executive officer. In April 1941 he was serving as a lieutenant-commander in HMS *Fidelity*, a 1,500 ton merchant ship with a Free French crew, equipped with all manner of speed boats, Royal Marine commandos and facilities for clandestine raids. She had landed two agents east of the Spanish border from a boat that Pat commanded, but it capsized in a squall while returning to the parent ship and he swam ashore. On landing he needed a cover name and therefore acquired the name Patrick Albert O'Leary by which he was called throughout the war, although his real Belgian name was Albert-Marie Guérisse.

Ian wanted to recruit him into MI 9 and although

there was a reluctance in SIS to accept such expatriots as agents—because too many in London became involved in national politics if not civil war—Pat was accepted. Precisely how they created their line can be imagined. A friend of a friend would put up three evaders for a night, next day 'cousin Bet' would lead them to the station, buying their tickets to avoid the possibility of the booking clerk realizing they did not speak French—in the case of the Garrow line. This would eventually lead to a series of safe houses that ran from Lille, Rouen and several other towns in northern France, to Paris and southward along several routes which reached the Alps. But in October 1941 Garrow was arrested by the Vichy police who no doubt had decided that his work, known to them for some time, had become too obvious a breach of local laws. Pat took over the line, known to MI 9 as the 'PAO' line after his assumed initials but to his friends and most historians as the 'Pat' line.

A sergeant rear-gunner, bailing out of a crippled Wellington bomber near Lille might land far from the rest of the crew. He saw their beloved 'Whimpey' explode as it hit the ground, and knew that he had to follow the first rule for airmen evading capture: get away from the scene of the crash. Having done this, he buried his parachute and took stock of where he was. The navigator had no doubt given some indication over the intercom before the crew jumped, but in hurrying away from the scene the sergeant might cross a road or two, see a river and in the first streaks of dawn find a wood to hide in. On day one he could feed himself from his escape pack and might decide to make a fleece jacket sewn from the top of his boots, thus leaving him with a pair of walking shoes. These, although apt to get sodden because of their fleece lining, certainly were less conspicuous than flying boots. (They were not issued to aircrew after 1942 because the webbing join of the top to the shoes could not in the 1940s be sealed and the cold at high altitudes became unbearable.)

He thought back over the lectures he had been given on escape—'no picnic' he had been told—with help most likely in Toulouse or Marseilles. Where was he supposed to cross the Pyrenees? If he remembered correctly one lecture suggested '15 to 20 miles inland from Gerona'. Certainly if he could get to Toulouse he should find a cheap café, and hang around until something or someone turned up. But Toulouse was far away, maybe several months of footslogging even if he could steal the food he would need. Therefore, like most evaders, he sought local help, taking care not to approach a trio of farm workers that perhaps passed down the lane that morning. After lunch—three malted milk tablets and a boiled sweet—the sergeant watched a man get down from his bicycle and begin to clean a roadside drain, while the ditcher's dog began sniffing along the hedge, which prompted him to act before he

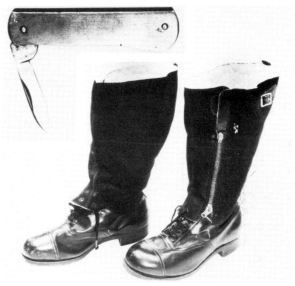

◀ A basic evasion kit provided for US airmen flying over Europe. The maps are printed on silk, the cardboard sleeve contained a saw blade, the miniature compass helped to orientate the map. The photograph of the airman in civilian clothes could be used in the making of a false identity card, if he was able to contact a resistance movement. Its organizer arranged the supply of such documents.

▼ A pair of RAF flying boots with the upper fleece lined portions that could be cut away from the 'shoes'. The fleece sections might then be used as a jacket; but these proved impractical boots in the cold of high altitudes and were not issued after 1942. The small knife (inset) was concealed in the top of the left boot, and easily withdrawn to cut the stitching between the fleece lined section and the 'shoe'. The small 2½-inch knife was designed specially for its purpose.

▼ A type-2 ration and escape pack, known as an 'escape box' was made of clear acetate in two closely fitting and waterproof sections. Curved to fit comfortably into a battledress or other pocket, the type-2 contained rations for 48 hours and various aids for survival when living off the country. The upper box shown here contained: malted milk tablets (in packet top left on box); a flashlight bulb; razor blades (magnetized to serve as a compass pointer); two packets of Benzedrine tablets (an amphetamine to ward off tiredness); matches in waterproof clear covers (bottom right); a rabbit snare with instructions on its clear envelope (right centre); water purifying tablets in bottom-left box; a small compass in sealed packet on a neck lanyard (top left); a heliograph (bottom left) that could be used to signal aircraft overhead; Needles and thread in a small packet (centre left); a magnifying glass (this might be used to start fires or for studying the detail of a map) seen here in the centre of the picture on its wrapper; a fishing line (bottom centre); and several items which have been used from this box. These include a rubber waterbottle to hold about a pint, chewing gum, a saw blade, and slabs of liver toffee. The lower box contained more liver toffee, boiled sweets, a razor, soap and a couple of bars of plain chocolate. The detailed contents varied in their combinations of concentrated rations no doubt due to the scarcity of, say, chocolate from time to time. The fishing line served also as a convenient length of line for improvising a waist belt or sling.

was discovered. The sergeant came out of hiding, trying to follow the instructions about slouching and not looking as if he had had military training. Yet the man was startled and cautious on catching sight of the uniform, quietened the dog, and made clear that the sergeant was to wait till nightfall.

A long, cold couple of hours passed in the November gloom, before it was dark and a car came slowly down the lane. The police? The ditcher had looked too understanding an old soldier to give away an English flyer, but ... the car stopped and someone got out, before he heard a woman's soft call '*Monsieur le sergeant*, Monsieur . . .' He stood up to cross the lane to meet her. A dangerous moment for both of them since he might be posing as an escaper, while she might be in the employ of the *Malice*. To his relief she helped him into the car and within 20 minutes he was drinking coffee in the kitchen of a small house outside Lille. This was the first time he had been in a French house or indeed in France. His host made him welcome. This railway worker perhaps had communist sympathies as he was proud of a picture of Lenin. A night's rest, a civilian suit and he was ready next morning to leave with the young girl who had brought him a bicycle. Many genuine evasion runs down escape lines began on bicycles, SOE providing a supply of French and other continental types of bicycle tyres which were scarce in occupied countries. The girl also brought him an identity card, a German permit for travel and for work, ration cards and other papers a man might be expected to carry if taking up work in Paris. There was also a ticket for a suburban station on the local line to the capital, which was his immediate destination. There he would be met by his new 'employer', a distinguished-looking man of 60 who—had the sergeant known it—owned a small factory. This neat handover was made almost before the sergeant realized what was happening, for as he left the train the man came forward to greet him.

From then on until he reached Perpignan in sight of the Pyrenees he was passed from one safe house to the next, sometimes travelling by train under the watchful eye of a courier, sometimes being left in a park to await the helper who would take him on the next stage of his journey. At Perpignan he was taken to a disused commercial garage to await the courier who would take him and three others to meet two smugglers who knew a way over the mountains to Spain. The man who organized these and the subsequent chain of smugglers was paid, through 'Pat' the equivalent then of £40 for an officer and £20 for other ranks (enlisted men), worth in the 1980s perhaps $1,500 and $750 respectively. The walk over the mountains proved less difficult than the sergeant might have expected. Although this crossing could be 'Hell on earth' as it was for Hugh Dormer whose guides took a difficult route, most crossings were less hazardous even if they were dangerous. Our sergeant's two guides led the party through the night across the frontier zone prohibited to civilians—the zone interdite—to a meeting with a second pair of guides who would lead them next day towards the frontier. These two provided meals with wine during the approach to the frontier, which was crossed in daylight after one guide had scouted ahead to be sure that the route was clear. By the evening the party had reached a rendezvous with Spanish guides, who took them after dark through the Spaniards' frontier zone, to reach a 'safe' farm before midnight. There the escapers could rest until the following night when they walked to '. . . a few kilometres outside Figueras to be met by a car which drove them to Barcelona'. The sergeant's troubles were not necessarily over when he reached neutral Spain, for many evaders were put in concentration camps at best, whilst others were returned to the clutches of the Gestapo. But with luck—he had needed a lot of this throughout his journey—he reached Barcelona safely, where he was taken in by the British consul's staff to be later driven by car to Gibraltar. Darling had moved there from Lisbon in January 1942, gently but thoroughly cross-questioning all who were brought out of France. In this way he was able to discover whose relations were helping whom, which friends' houses were used frequently and to learn the whole picture of what was happening in northern France and later in Belgium. Cross-checks had made him suspicious of Captain Harry Cole since no such name appeared in the army list of officers, and on investigation Cole turned out to be a petty crook. He was Sergeant Harold Cole who had deserted from his regiment in 1940, taking the mess funds. Pat already had his suspicions of this over enthusiastic helper who may well have diverted a few evaders through a loop so to speak, in the line. Along this route the houses were controlled by the Abwehr with bogus evaders whose conversation gleaned intelligence from unsuspecting escapers, before they were passed back to the genuine escape line.

Pat was smuggled into Spain, crossed it often hidden in the boot of an Embassy car to meet Darling in Gibraltar. There it was agreed that Cole should be shot on sight, but before he was seen in public, the Vichy police jailed him for some crime no doubt committed as a sideline. After the war, the British discovered that Cole had penetrated Garrow's embryo line through Belgium. He survived prison and the war to be shot by a Paris policeman in 1945 when he resisted arrest as a deserter while masquerading as an American sergeant. His betrayals, however, had not halted the Pat line which in 1942 brought out some 600 evaders, including several dozen aboard an armed British trawler. Among those reaching Spain was Ian Garrow whom Pat had rescued in December 1941, after Nancy Fiocca—Nancy Wake of F Section—had bribed a guard. She let her smuggle a German uniform to the Scotsman who then walked out of prison with the night guards going off duty. Ian was to have returned to France for MI 9 in 1944 but a serious car accident disabled him.

Radio contact with London or Gibraltar proved essential for escape lines. The young Australian, Tom Groome joined 'Pat' in October 1942. A fluent French speaker, his mother's native language, he maintained contact with SIS' communications centre for three months. Then he was caught by a routine D/F check, probably because he had no lookouts. The Cheramy family whose home he was using, and Edith Redde his courier, were inside the house when it was raided. They were all taken to Toulouse where Groome made a bold attempt to escape, jumping through a third storey window, only to be given away by a passer-by. In the confusion Edith slipped out of the building and warned Pat; SIS were also warned because when the Germans made Groome radio London, he omitted his security checks. The reply, at Dansey's behest, told the

Fig. V The organization for mounting escapes from a Prisoner of War camp was detailed, thorough and secret. Yet in any one camp there were many prisoners involved in this organization. The details are based on a document in the British Public Record Office, WO 208/3244.6 as reproduced in *MI 9* by Professor M. R. D. Foot and J. M. Langley.

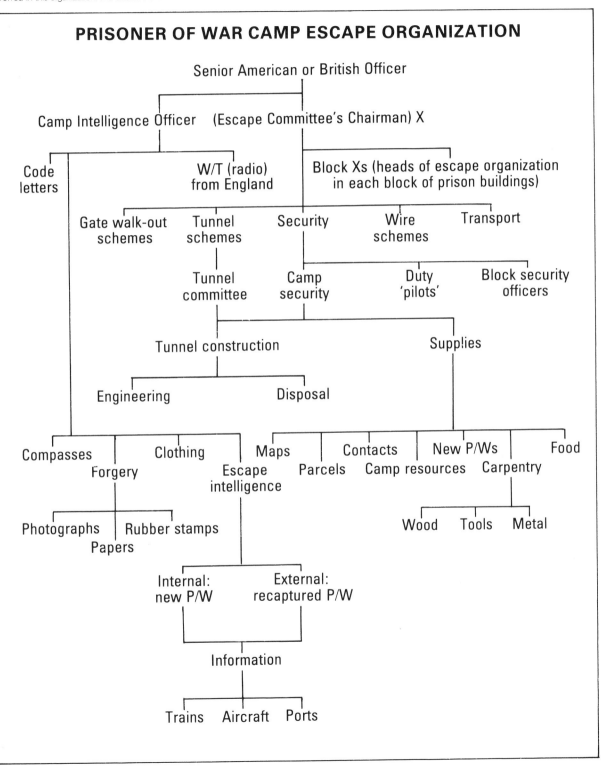

PRISONER OF WAR CAMP ESCAPE ORGANIZATION

Senior American or British Officer

Camp Intelligence Officer   (Escape Committee's Chairman) X

Code letters

W/T (radio) from England

Block Xs (heads of escape organization in each block of prison buildings)

Gate walk-out schemes   Tunnel schemes   Security   Wire schemes   Transport

Tunnel committee   Camp security   Duty 'pilots'   Block security officers

Tunnel construction   Supplies

Engineering   Disposal

Compasses   Clothing   Maps   Contacts   New P/Ws   Food

Forgery   Escape intelligence   Parcels   Camp resources   Carpentry

Photographs   Rubber stamps   Wood   Tools   Metal

Papers

Internal: new P/W   External: recaptured P/W

Information

Trains   Aircraft   Ports

controlled operator to arrange a pick-up of mythical escapers waiting under the protection of the chief of the Genoese police. (The deputy head of SIS had an old score to settle with this individual.)

The Germans sent a number of agents posing as escapers down several escape lines, usually to be conveniently 'arrested' just before they reached freedom. They also took control of safe houses from time to time, and inveigled agents to visit such *souricières*—mousetraps in French. Pat was asked to meet a man calling himself 'Roger le Neveu' who had been working as a courier guide for the Pat line in Paris, but he and a party of seven had been suddenly arrested in February 1943 while changing trains in a suburb of Tours. When he reappeared Pat wanted to know who had been betraying the line: his answer was immediate, for Pat was arrested. Le Neveu's description fits that of Roger Bardet, a known double-agent who was probably an associate of Harold Cole. MI 9 learnt of the demise of the Pat line within a few weeks, as Pat engineered the escape of one of his helpers from the train taking them to Paris. There and later Pat survived the rigours of interrogation and concentration camps, to be awarded a George Cross.

SOE's F Section anticipated the end of the Pat line by establishing communication circuits or lines, later run by the DF Section which from the spring of 1942 had several such organizations. These enabled packages, reports and agents to move in and out of occupied France, fortunately quite unknown to Déricourt and his air service. One route was established by the agent Eduardo V. H. Rizzo who had been landed by Pat from *Fidelity* just before the Belgian doctor swam ashore. This 'Troy' line used couriers and safe houses found by Rizzo, passing SOE agents to L. H. Mortimer, their anchor man in Spain who worked independently of MI 9's Donald Darling. Nevertheless MI 9 on occasion—more occasions apparently than SIS would have approved—allowed SOE men and women to use 'Pat' and other lines. Rizzo was in France from April 1941 until 1943 when he was brought out: the donnish Maltese schoolmaster had become a target for the Abwehr or so Baker Street believed. His wife continued to run the line but was arrested. Yet she did not betray the agents and sub-agents who worked for her and the Germans executed her. The 'Troy' line or 'Eduardo' line as it was first called, was therefore able to continue until Liberation.

Escape from a prisoner of war camp was far more difficult than evading capture. If the escaper was to make a 'home' run, he had to get the better of guards, hostile civilians and language problems. All these difficulties and more were considered by MI 9, whose activities were known to Bill Donovan. But the organization of help for prisoners fell to the American Army's Military Intelligence Section Escape and Evasion (MIS-X). We will come back to the broader aspects of the Section's work but in June 1942 General 'Tooey' Spaatz commanding the Eighth Air Force, got in touch with Crockatt. Together they set up the means whereby an American airman of World War I, the academic W. Stull Holt, would work with MI 9. The Americans then distributed Clutty's tools and the benefits of British experience to their aircrews in all three commands in the UK, bomber, fighter and ground attack. The aircrews also received British escape kits, maps, and purses which contained the equivalent of £12. This money was in French francs or other currencies appropriate to the countries they would fly over and perhaps worth £250 in the 1980s.

Holt's staff as 'P/W and X' took on many jobs similar to those of MI 9. Its officers corresponded in code with selected officers in prison camps. P/W and X also advised the American army on how to prevent escapes by the Axis prisoners it held. Once the Eighth Air Force moved to the mainland of Europe 'P/W and X' would collect 'int' from interrogations of captured Germans. These might have been jobs which Donovan considered could be taken on by OSS, but the army retained MIS-X in all theatres although at times joint teams of officers from both agencies worked in the field.

For many British, American and Allied prisoners in Axis camps during 1943 the fight was more against boredom than against the enemy. For Russians it was a grim fight for survival, as for all those in German prison camps in 1944 when starvation scythed through Europe just at the time when many prisoners were force-marched from eastern Germany. Each camp in 1943 had its escape committee (see Fig. V). What cannot be detailed here is the full range of prisoners' ingenuity in making escapes, for over 23,000 Allied prisoners and more than 10,000 evaders reached 'home' from occupied territories in Europe and the Far East up to June 1945. Many of them had help in one way or another from MI 9 and MIS-X, all had remarkable courage.

The escape agencies provided necessities for escaping prisoners but some items had to be manufactured, stolen or bartered from guards; a few were obtained by blackmail. The bulk of escape aids from MI 9 and MIS-X came in parcels from home, which were usually marked in such a way that the prisoners working in the camp mail room could spirit them away before the Germans searched the incoming post. MI 9 were in touch with camps through coded letters, often copied by a relation or friend at MI 9's direction with the result that the letter appeared innocent with its details of life at home. The Americans in Europe used MI 9 codes which were known to a few selected individuals; and distributed to other prisons by medical officers or in one case by a dentist visiting camps for other ranks (enlisted men).

Information was sent from the camps in such letters although OSS' knowledge of events in Germany was certainly detailed in some respects from other sources. An American instruction manual on escape included the comment that a bridge over the Rhine 'a mile south of Remagen' was likely to be unguarded.

The special parcels were usually sent from a fictional aunt or girl friend who provided 1,642 of these in 1941-42 among 7,815 sent to camps by MI 9 alone. None were Red Cross parcels but included gifts from the Lancashire Penny Fund who sent boxes of crackers to camps in time for Christmas 1943. Half were what they seemed, half contained money, dock passes and other novelties to aid escapers. Not all of these escaped the German checks on parcels but in several camps they reached the escape committee's supplies section. Clutty and the conjuror Jasper Maskelyne who had worked at Camp X, devised many clever hiding places for screw drivers in baseball bats, for maps and money in the double layer of special tins containing condensed milk, and even a camera which passed as a cigarette lighter. The Germans X-rayed parcels but the tins appeared only as a dark shadow on the screen; if they were examined individually the investigator appears always to have pierced the tin's top, never its sides.

Clutty's old school had a senior class analyse some 50 books on World War I escapes, which showed him the importance of maps. Therefore he arranged the production of several thousand printed on silk which aircrews could easily carry. He later learnt from a friend where he might get a Japanese pulp which made very thin, strong paper on which a map could be printed; and then concealed between the back and front of a playing card in a pack sent for the prisoners' entertainment. Compasses were another necessity for most evaders and escapers, and the British provided over 2,300,000 for their services. These ranged from the ¼-inch compass

that could be hidden in a pen or a smoker's pipe to those twice the size which were sewn into collars of shirts or more usually mounted in the base of a collar stud (a universal inconvenience for most men in the 1940s, who needed a front and back stud to attach a collar to a shirt). The evader had only to take out his front stud, scrape off the paint from its base and the tiny luminous pointer showed him in which direction he was heading from north. Magnetized razor blades were also provided, and by 1942 all blades sold in British service canteens were magnetized, so if a prisoner was left with his razor—by no means a certainty—all he needed was a thread from his clothing to suspend his improvised compass. North was where the maker's name started on the blade.

One of the most useful tools Clutty invented was a clasp knife which folded its lock breaking and hacksaw blades like any boy's pocket knife, but had wire cutters which were most efficient. The knives were probably sent to camps built into cricket bats in summer, or hockey sticks perhaps in winter. Hacksaw blades were sent in similar ways but MI 9 provided some men with a 4½×½in blade that had a hole at one end. A bit of string slipped through this enabled the owner to hide it down his trousers or in some convenient crevice in the prison buildings. One was even used as an improvised surgical saw after the British airborne troops were encircled at Arnhem.

Genuine Gigli surgical saws of strong wire with a serrated edge that also served as garrottes, were provided for escapers in the guise of boot laces, or rolled in condoms. No such saw was available, however, to a quartet who broke out of Colditz in October 1942 when nevertheless they cut the window bars, crossed some floodlit pathways, got into the castle moat and out

▼ A powerful radio for its size in the 1940s, the receiver on the left measured only six inches by five and a half inches by one and three-quarters. It had a range of 700 miles. To its right is MI 9's cigar case radio of 1941 with a range of 250 miles. On the far right is a so-called 'RAF cigarette case' radio receiver with its imitation leather covering. The cigar case radio measured 6 x 2½ x 1 inches, the cigarette case radio was 6 x 5½ x 1¾ inches. One of the latter was found by the German guards at Colditz on 16 March 1944, concealed beneath a floor in the castle's cellar.

▼ One of the small receivers designed by MI 9 in 1941. It had a range of 250 miles and could be tuned by the disc protruding from the body (seen here on right underside). It is the only example known to exist in the 1980s and suggests that this set might be passed off as a cigar case.

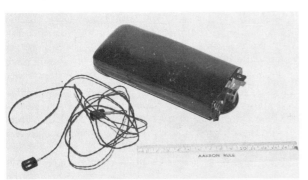

through a cellar flue. They reached Switzerland in a week as one of them, Pat Reid, tells in his book *The Colditz Story*. Some of their clothes had been made in the secret tailor's shop, with an overcoat perhaps from one of Clutty's blankets. These appeared normal comforts from home, but when soaked in water revealed a pattern which the tailor followed to cut the pieces for an overcoat. Other clothes were improvised from uniforms dyed with inks or even materials sent in by MI 9 or MIS-X. Both agencies provided a whole range of materials that often passed as educational supplies but were to be used for photography, map making or forging passes.

Forgery, not only of passes, was a difficult art requiring patience and a professional draftsman's skill. Engineers, commercial artists and architects possessed the skills as well as the patience to use them, often working under constant risk of being caught. Although the escape agencies provided inks and no doubt paper under the guise of educational aids, they never attempted to provide a regular supply of completed documents. This was not really such a shortcoming as some have suggested, for passes in a country with ever changing regulations needed to be up to date. Therefore they had to be forged if they could not be stolen, in the light of local knowledge. Papers borrowed from guards might be photographed with a matchbox camera, or in Colditz with the prisoners' home made camera that made use of binocular lenses. 'Official' rubber stamps were made by cutting their pattern in a piece of linoleum, to authorize identity cards, French workers' travel permits, passes to Danzig docks where boats left for Sweden, to name but a few documents. The signatures might be forged with the help of a hard-boiled egg which when shelled could 'lift' the impression from a genuine document.

Care was needed to ensure that the fakes looked genuine enough to deceive a man looking closely at them, although it would be wrong to say that the escaper's life might depend on it. Those caught in Europe were usually returned to their camps, provided the intelligence officers with useful local information once the prisoner came out of solitary confinement. The situation was different in the Far East, where prisoners caught in escaping were beheaded or bayoneted to death. Only one major crime of this sort was perpetrated in Europe, after 79 men broke out through an escape tunnel from Stalag Luft III at Sagan. This was a camp from which over 60 escape tunnels were begun including the one using a vaulting box (the wooden horse), and a tunnel in 1944 which was 6m under the ground and 110m long. Down this great engineering work 200 men were to escape, but after the 79th got out, the Germans began shooting, and those waiting to leave had to burn their forged papers and scramble out of their improvised civilian clothes. The escape was made on the night of 24 March 1944 and in the next few weeks all but three were caught: 50 of them were then shot on Hitler's orders, or at least with his approval, in order to discourage escapes. Three of the first men out of the tunnel reached home, two through Sweden and one through Holland and France, helped perhaps by those going to Scandinavia being Norwegians and the third man being Dutch.

ONE of the most remarkable series of escapes and evasions, the 'great escape' which gives this chapter its title, was achieved by the Americans in the Balkans. By October 1944 their Balkan Air Terminal Service (BATS) and the Air Crew Rescue Unit (ACRU) of the 15th Air Force, had rescued 3,870 American aircrew and perhaps half as many again of other nationalities from Yugoslavia and other countries in central Europe. BATS was essentially an airfield construction unit although they built their air strips in unusual places: mountain valleys held by partisans; or on coastal sites which might not always be so well protected. In August 1944 as the Russians fought their way towards Germany, Roumania surrendered and one third of the American escapers were from prison there. (They were encouraged to move, in part no doubt because there was a fiasco in Italy when Allied prisoners were told to sit tight, this they did and the Germans rounded them up.)

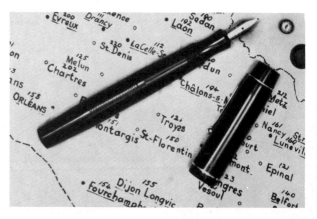

▲ This fountain pen had secret compartments that contained dyes for uniforms and five compasses. The first one (shown here after unscrewing the top of the pen-cap) was supplemented by magnetized components of the pen which might be distributed among several individual escapers or evaders. Also in the base of the pen were Aspirin and Benzedrine tablets. Holding the pen upright with its nib at the top the compasses were: 1. concealed in top of cap; 2. the pocket clip; 3. the nib; 4. the filler arm; and 5. a miniature compass in the bottom end of the body. This contained a small reservoir for writing ink, an ampoule of dye and one of dye concentrate. These were used to change the colour of the escaper's uniform possibly to a German field grey. The dyes in the pen were those appropriate to the escaper's likely need for a disguise. Also in the base of the body were the tablets referred to above.

▶ These escape maps printed on silk include on the left one titled 'Front-Stalags Locations'. It shows various prisoner of war camps in France north of the line of Allied-held territory in the autumn of 1944. The map on the right covers part of Germany and carries a number of instructions for evaders.

▼ This small heel knife—seen here extended for use—was intended for cutting wrist and other bindings of a fellow prisoner if not of the knife wearer. It was used early in the course of the wearer's capture, when his captors had left him tied up but were too occupied with other events to guard him properly. Other variations of heel knives include one similar to the above but fixed to the face of the heel at the instep. The hook heel knife proved unsatisfactory and was replaced by a longer serrated insole blade, this fitted tightly—possibly too tightly—to pivot from the insole. It was plated with a copper 'wash' to protect the steel and then blackened.

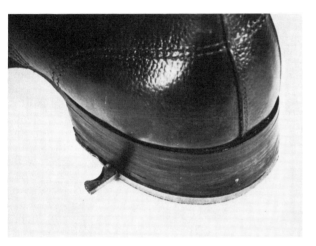

▼ A Mark IV RAF escape box designed as a single container which could be used as a waterbottle. It contained an appropriate map for the airman's flight, Ovaltine tablets, a bar of chocolate, and other survival aids. The stopper unscrewed to provide a compass behind which was a tiny watch. These boxes reportedly leaked once the side had been removed to empty them and replaced to form a bottle. The map in the box illustrated includes the Sea of Azov and the southern Ukraine. The survival aids included water-purifying tablets, adhesive tape, matches and a needle with thread. There was also a tube of what may have been condensed milk or other nutritious food concentrate. The Ovaltine tablets were 'A Concentrated Extraction, containing Malt, Milk, Cocoa, Soya, Eggs and Flavouring'—according to the label on the tin.

▲ A series of easily concealed mini-compasses and magnetized objects to serve as compasses were devised by MI 9. Among these were uniform buttons that many Allied servicemen were taught to unscrew to find a compass. Other designs included the ultra-small compass that might be hidden in a cigarette. The black comb (top centre) needed to be broken apart to release the compass concealed in its handle. The service buttons (top left and top right) with their compass components were opened by left-hand threads in the RAF button. The RN button had a right-hand thread which MI 9 introduced as a variation to confuse the enemy. Its compass component has two dots marking north. The RAF button on the right had the third type of concealment fitting, with a pressure fit closure. Some miniature compasses were supplied in boxes of a dozen from the makers (second from top in centre). Many special compasses were made by Blunt Brothers of London and included no doubt the magnetized pencil clip (seen below the compasses in a box). This clip might be balanced on the point of its pencil. Seen below the clip is the tiny compass concealed in a cigarette and which is only a few millimetres in diameter. It was a third of the size of the standard escape compass seen below it. The three items in the centre of the illustration are (on left) the compass from an escape box, the underside of a magnetized battledress button and a magnetized fly-button. The pair of dots on the buttons indicated north when the item swung freely on a thread. In the case of the fly-button this pivotted on a second fly-button. Below these three items is seen another variation of a compass with two dots for north, it could be concealed possibly in a collar stud. The belt buckle (lower centre) has a small component which could be detached to form the pointed pivot for the magnetized component of the buckle. After use it was reassembled into the buckle. Bottom right is a British issued service razor with its compass that screwed into the handle. Bottom left is the escape box compass in its waterproof pouch on a lanyard. The pouch was necessary because many small compasses failed after a day or two when moisture penetrated their cases. Bottom centre ia an OSS compass worn on a wristwatch strap and which could be concealed without its strap. Also probably of OSS or MI 9 origin is the signet ring (centre left) the top of which pivots to reveal a compass.

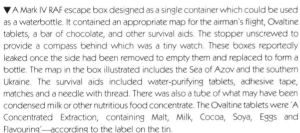

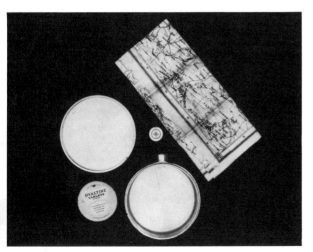

The 15th's ACRU was commanded by the energetic Colonel George Kraigher, a strong minded officer who acted when he thought things needed doing and then told higher authority that he had done whatever was necessary. His teams were each led by a captain, with a doctor, a radio operator and an OSS officer whose duties involved some liaison apparently with local forces. In Yugoslavia he would also liaise with OSS teams deployed by the Strategic Balkan Service to help round up—if that does not sound too casual an expression—escapers and evaders and guide them to BATS's airfields. Many of these airmen had little more instruction on evasion than to '. . . contact the partisans if you are shot down'. This may well have been all that they might be expected to do in the rough mountain country of central Europe, and certainly it was an order which brought many of them later into contact with an ACRU, sometimes quite soon after being shot down. One crew of a B-17 Flying Fortress were back on their own airfield within four days of crash-landing in Croatia. Other collections took longer, as did that of a medical team whose Dakota got lost before crashing in Albania. Its nurses and stretcher bearers were hidden by partisans for nearly two months in the hill town of Berat, until SOE's deceptively mild mannered agent, known to the nurses as Sandy, came to their rescue. 'Peering benignly from behind a large pair of spectacles' he must have seemed an unlikely man of daring, yet he led the party 65km over the mountains to a disused airstrip where they were due to be collected on 29 December 1943. As they huddled in a ditch on one side of this field, a German armoured unit pulled up, probably by chance, at the other side. Therefore when the Wellington bomber leading the rescue flight flew over, its pilot was not given the pre-arranged signal to land. The intention had been to use the Wellington's rotating machine-gun turrets against any infantry force which might interfere with the evacuation of the nurses by the Dakota which the Wellington protected. Such a tactic could not be used against armour, even though 36 USAAF Lightning fighters covered the rescue aircraft from any attack by the *Luftwaffe*. They had to fly home and the girls were rescued a week later by a motor gun boat taking them from a coastal base of BATS. Three had been left behind in the mountains, not having received the message to move down to the coast, and they were only rescued after an OSS officer had acquired both German and partisan passes, to get them through the many road checks during the drive to the coast. They were safely back in Italy by 22 March. All the girls had survived the ordeal with little more than the bites of body lice picked up on their first night in an Albanian hut.

George Kraiger's teams sensibly did not pick up everyone who presented themselves for evacuation by

▶ This button-making kit from MI 9 was used to make plaster of Paris moulds for German insignia. The lead for these was obtained by melting down toothpaste tubes. The moulds were made in shoe polish tins in which the die's impression could be set in soft plaster. Once this hardened the lead could be poured to form a casting.

▼ The escape knife (top) was designed by Clayton Hutton and is considered by many to be his masterpiece of escape aids. Below this (to right) is a Gigli surgical saw concealed in a condom. The OSS 'frisk knife' (bottom) was flat enough to be taped behind the biceps muscle of the forearm. There it might be overlooked during an initial search when the knife was beneath the wearer's clothing. The MI 9 escape knife was about seven inches long but could be concealed in a cricket bat handle sent to a POW camp. At one end was an efficient pair of wire cutters. The blades (seen from right to left) were: a lock breaker; a conventional knife blade; and three hacksaw blades. On the far side, not seen in this illustration, was a stub screwdriver. There were two concentric metal fixings for a lanyard, the larger of which might get broken or distorted in using a bar with this knife in breaking a lock. The steel of the Gigli saw was of high quality and strength. The OSS 'frisk knife' could be used possibly to break a lock or as a thumb knife.

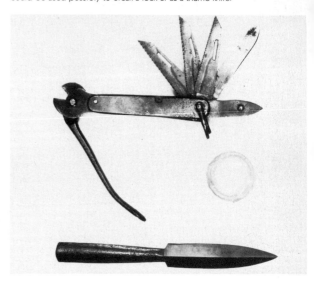

sea or air, a matter of selection which MI 9 had faced since 1940. Its officers, later as members of MI 19, handled arrangements to interview all escapers and evaders, as Skinnarland had been interviewed on his arrival from Norway in 1942. They used two main interrogation centres. One took up a floor of the Great Central Hotel at Marylebone and the other was a hutted camp in the north London suburb of Cockfosters. The brass bedsteads and Victorian wardrobes of the station hotel had been replaced by 1941 with trestle tables and filing cabinets, while in the hutted camp German and a few Italian aircrews were interrogated. Here also their mail from home was checked before distribution to prison camps. A third very secret reception centre was run by SIS in the forbidding Latchmere House, which had been used as a mental hospital, near Ham Common in south London. It would intimidate most men, and since the Abwehr agents sent to England were not adequately trained, many were easily 'turned' at Latchmere House.

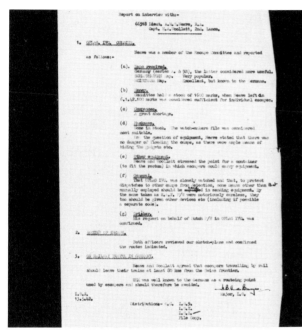

▲ This report of an interview on 13 May 1942 was made by a major of the escape branch of military intelligence 'ISX' with copies to IS 9 (known more usually as MI 9) among others. It shows the care with which successful escapers were debriefed. In this case they—Lieutenant A. M. S. Neave RA and Captain H. A. Woollatt 2nd Lancs—had travelled together for part of their escapes and reached Spain with the help of the 'Pat' escape line. Neave had escaped from Colditz and Section 1 of the report refers to this Oflag IVc. The detailed answers read as follows: (a) *Maps received*—Germany (series A. & 9B), the latter considered more useful . . . [comments on other maps] . . . (b) *Money*—Committee held a stock of 1600 marks when Neave left on 6.1.42, 100 marks was considered sufficient for individual escapes . . . (c) *Compasses*—A great shortage . . . (d) *Hacksaws*—None in stock, the watchmakers file was considered most suitable . . . (e) *Other equipment* . . . (f) *General* . . . (g) *Driiber* [sic] . . . Comments under (d) and (e) include references to Colditz's adequate number of hiding places for gadgets, and the need for some form of rectum container for escapers' aids. There is also under (f) a request that the RAF aircrews be given a separate code as 'RAF P/W were notoriously careless'. Driiber was a Dutch POW whose request 'was confirmed'. Section 2 deals with 'routes of Escape' on which both officers confirmed routes indicated on 'our sketch maps'. Section 3 was titled 'On Railway Travel in Germany' about which both officers agreed that escapers should leave their trains ' . . . at least 80 kms from the Swiss frontier . . .'. They also stated that Ulm should be avoided as it was known by the Germans to be 'a routing point used by escapers . . .'. Airey Neave subsequently worked for MI 9 and after the war became an MP.

OSS' X-2 also vetted 1,844 potential agents during July and August 1944 before these men and women were employed by SI or SO staffs in Europe. X-2 had been set up for counter-intelligence work, using techniques suggested by BSC in New York. Most of the work involved liaison with other Allied clandestine agencies, cross-referencing information and carrying out some special investigations. One of these was set up by the Insurance Unit of X-2, whose experts' knowledge of insurance policies and related routines, enabled them to trace details of installations in the Far East. Some of these could be of help to the Japanese war effort, although they had been insured before the war in London. Another X-2 unit investigated the looting of art treasures, and other German attempts to salt away resources against possible defeat when senior Nazis intended to go into hiding.

O N the Pacific west coast of America there were a number of Japanese agents whose activities by 1941, had drawn the attention of the FBI and American Military Intelligence services. One such agent criss-crossed the Hawaiian Islands in the autumn of that year, posing sometimes as the playboy Ito Morimura, who enjoyed flying light aircraft, and at other times working as a Filipino labourer or fisherman. When he was eventually caught, he was found to be a 29-year-old Japanese naval lieutenant, Takeo Yoshikawa. Signals sent to him from Tokyo were intercepted by Military Intelligence and found to contain questions on the defence of Pearl Harbor, including details of which vessels were double berthed. Other decrypts showed that the Japanese intended to attack British and Dutch territories but there was no clear indication that they might also attack American ships. Without such direct aggression against American interests, Congress might have been slow in declaring war, although the President had promised Prime Minister Churchill that America would help the British if they were attacked by the Japanese.

The President may have decided to create an incident that would move Congress to act, when on his orders three small United States warships were sent to the Indo-China (modern Vietnam) coast. Two of these were hastily requisitioned yachts, and the schooner *Laniakai*, commissioned into the US Navy on 5 December 1941, was the flotilla leader. Her single .5-in machine-gun seems as inadequate for defence as was her low powered radio to report movements of Japanese convoys. Yet the small ships were to trail an American coat-tail across the convoys' invasion routes. But on 7 December the Japanese attacked the American battle fleet at Pearl, and Congress were then not slow in supporting the President's declaration of war.

9
AGENTS IN THE JUNGLES OF ASIA

THE explorer, Captain Freddie Spencer Chapman, hidden in the Malayan jungle, watched hundreds of Japanese soldiers heading eastward to the Perak river during the last week of December 1941. They travelled light in stolen trucks and on bicycles with their rifles tied to the crossbars. The variety of their uniform—some in rubber boots, some in gym shoes—suggested that the force was equipped with what they had picked up since landing in Thailand as much as with issued kit. There was nothing casual, however, about their determination to reach the river, as they pedalled four abreast through the afternoon rain, each man wearing the one standard piece of uniform which they all possessed: a hooded mackintosh cape. A major was seen to threaten a Malay with his sword, in a gesture which to Chapman suggested that there might be some local people who would come to resent the Japanese. The British, however, were by no means sure that they could expect the loyalty of many Malays or other eastern peoples of their Empire. Having seen that the Japanese were able to move comparatively quickly in their advance towards Singapore 600km to the south, Chapman withdrew with his two companions, Sergeant John Sartin, a Royal Engineer attached to SOE, and Battery Sergeant Major Ian Patterson of the Malay Volunteers. Patterson spoke the local language which no doubt helped the trio to find a boat—albeit a leaky one. In this they had a wild passage down the fast flowing river, risking possible shots from alert British sentries as the boat neared the rearguard of the retreating army.

There would be no opportunity to establish parties left behind to report by radio on Japanese movements in northern Malaya. Yet such a scheme had been suggested by Valentine Killery, when he was sent in May 1941 to head SOE's Oriental Mission based on Singapore. He was a World War I veteran who had lost a leg in action before joining the chemical company ICI as an executive in the 1930s. His senior staff officer was a regular Royal Marine, Lieutenant-Colonel A. G. Warren, a tactful and experienced officer who had served in MI R. Neither of them in the summer of 1941 could persuade the Commander-in-Chief Malaya, of the need to train 'gangs of reliable natives' to carry out sabotage in the Malaysian jungle should the Japanese occupy the country. The British governor, like his C-in-C, was convinced that such training might cause the local people to believe that the British doubted their own ability to defend Malaya. Nevertheless, the

Mission established a training school where a group of Danes were trained as instructors for Chinese guerrillas. All had some experience of China; and while, technically at least, Denmark was not at war with the Axis powers, these volunteers were willing to fight for the Allies. They reached the Nationalist Chinese capital, Chunking, 2,400km from the sea, in October 1941. There they were frustrated by the intrigues of Chinese politics which prevented them training any guerrillas. Several of the Danes died during the four months which they spent on inadequate rations, before the survivors reached India in February 1942.

In the early winter of 1941 the Japanese broke a secret wireless code used by British merchant ships, enabling them to intercept several vessels during the second week in December. On one of these was a detailed assessment of Singapore's defences. This probably did not include any reference to 'left behind' parties, as the first of these were not trained until late December after Killery and Warren were given permission to train six parties of Europeans. This permission was granted only on the day after the attack on Pearl, and another fortnight would pass before the Mission was allowed to train the first parties of Chinese who had been living in Malaya. By January there were 163 of these and other Asiatics trained for sabotage and in basic intelligence work, forming some 10 'left behind' parties. Another 15 were formed by Europeans with Asiatic radio operators, the majority of the officers having the rank of lieutenant or second lieutenant but considerably more experience of the world than such junior ranks usually possess. Many of them were planters in their thirties or mining engineers, some of whom were over 40.

Early in January sites had been found for several parties, including Chapman's headquarters party which would co-ordinate the work of six others. Communications, however, would be difficult because the only transmitter was with Chapman and had to be moved by six porters carrying the bulky set, its batteries and a generator. The other parties only had radio receivers but knew where they might be picked up on the coast should Singapore fall. This RV was some 100km from their bases which were stocked with three months' rations and seeds from which to grow fresh vegetables. Their weaponry was less comprehensive although a wide variety of explosive devices was available. Chapman's 10 men had several Thompson sub machine-guns, but there was only one in each of the other six parties. The rations were in tins which meant that 15 coolies were needed to carry the headquarter's stores to a secret base eight kilometres off the road running south from Kuala Lumpur and east of a range of hills known as Main Ridge. This could take several days to cross in visiting other parties: one 35km to the southeast, another across a couple of valleys east of the headquarters, with the remaining four well to the south of the HQ. From these positions each party could overlook natural features which formed bottle-necks on the line of the Japanese advance.

The Chinese parties were sent to the area of the Perak river, their stores being carried into the jungle by coolies from Singapore. This prevented any local porters knowing more than was advisable about the location of the secret bases. Indeed the local men who carried in the HQ party's stores must have told others if they did not come back themselves to steal 2,000 Malay $, Chapman's whisky and tobacco, thefts which forced him to relocate the HQ caches of explosives. This was barely accomplished before the Japanese broke through the defences along the Slim river. They then advanced 40km down the road past the HQ base some seven days before they were expected. Therefore, a few days later, after Chapman had recovered from a bout of malaria, he moved the HQ deeper into the jungle. The other parties were all scattered within the next few weeks and even the Chinese parties had difficulty in keeping in touch with each other. This was not known to Chapman who set out with Bill Harvey and John Sartin to visit an observation post set up by three others from the HQ and to search for the radio operator who was among several of the HQ party who had not reached the new base. This first trek was to prove how difficult movement could be in a jungle, even if—in the title of Chapman's book—it later became 'neutral'. On this first march it was decidedly hostile. Harvey, a local planter, had some knowledge of the country, but none of the three had any experience of cutting a trail through the trees. Something which they found surprisingly difficult on the first afternoon, particularly as the maps showed paths which turned out to be overgrown, the steep sides of river banks being impossible to follow, being an impenetrable tangle of bamboo thickets, thorns and a type of palm. Every swing of a man's *parang* bumped the butt of his Thompson against his hip, their loads although only 11kg (25lb) snagged in the jungle creepers, and by the time they made camp they had covered only a couple of kilometres. Bloated leeches fell from their bodies as they bathed in the river that evening. Lighting a fire

took half a dozen attempts, but being fit they did not seem downhearted. Chapman's broad grin and Sartin's cheerful banter no doubt making light of a difficult day.

It was the first of 11 days which they needed to cover 24km, one night huddled in the freezing cold on top of a 1,000m high ridge, by day toiling in temperatures of 30°C. The leading man cut a path, the second man widened it and the third checked that it followed their intended compass course. They stopped widening the trail after a week, but pressed on although by the tenth day the yellow skin of their bodies was covered in purple marks from leech bites, Harvey had also taken in three notches on his belt and Sartin was unusually silent. On the eleventh day they came to a pipeline, one of many in Malaya supplying water to tin mines and other workings. At the foot of this pipe was the village of the Chinaman who had provided coolies and was to prove a good friend. He, Leu Kim, did not recognize the starving Chapman as the European who a few weeks earlier had hired the coolies, but the Captain was able to establish who he was by recalling earlier conversations. Leu then hid them in the jungle because his seven wives did not want them in the village, in case the Japanese took reprisals against the villagers for helping Europeans.

The Chinaman had previously cached some explosives in their jungle hide and this Chapman decided could be used against the rail and road traffic passing down the valley. They had no detonators but Sartin adapted explosive from grenades to serve the purpose, cutting up the cases with a hacksaw—the others taking care to be out on recces whenever he did this! These explosives probably came from one of the Chinese parties for they had been issued a selection from 54 different types of sabotage devices including incendiaries. Each man in a party carried a pistol or a revolver, as well as a fighting knife, a jack knife and a *parang* when he went into the jungle in mid-January. Every three men had a rifle and a Thompson for ambushes.

Chapman's first ambush of the railway was made with one of Leu's villagers, who guided three saboteurs through a rubber plantation clear of any houses to a small bridge over the Bernam river. Here they put 4.5kg of gun cotton under 2m of rail on the outside of a curve, linking this to PE charges on the bridge girders, a job which took half an hour although all the charges had been prepared in their jungle camp. Dawn was breaking and the job nearly finished when they heard a train's whistle. There was only time to connect the instant-

▶This page from the OSS Weapons manual of June 1944, shows several blows which might be struck with a smatchet. The knife was carried on a thong around the wrist when drawn for action with the 'knot on top of the wrist and the [fully sharpened] edge downwards'. When properly used the knife could cut through an 'ordinary steel helmet' according to the manual.

▲ The three smatchets on the left were made for OSS, the one on the right is a British design with a webbing sheath. These blades are sometimes referred to as bolo fighting knives or matchets. The most common was probably the knife second from the left with its leather-covered wooden sheath. This blade was sharpened its full length on one side (to left in illustration) and for half its length on the opposite side. A press stud on a leather strap—the fastening is on the top right of this illustration—held the knife securely in its scabbard. The knives at left and third from left have blackened blades. The second from left was 16½ inches long and weighed 1 lb 9 oz. The blade was of tempered carbon steel. The scabbard weighed 2 lb 3 oz.

aneous fuse on the bridge charges to a fog signal before the train neared the bridge. The saboteurs ran down the embankment to find themselves waist deep in a stinking riverside swamp. Momentarily they were caught in the lights of the engine cab as they held their Thompsons over their heads clear of the mud, before the charges (in all 21kg of PE) exploded. The engine dragged to a halt, Japanese soldiers jumping out of the cab as swirls of steam hissed from the damaged boiler. Fortunately, the enemy did not search the swamp and the raiders got back safely to their jungle hide.

In the next fortnight they ambushed more trains, finding that four metres of track needed blowing if the engine was to come off the line. They put a kilogram of explosive between the crank case and clutch on each of six unguarded trucks, linking these with instantaneous fuse as the drivers slept in their cabs. The whole job took a couple of dangerous hours but after Chapman lit the long fuse, giving himself a couple of minutes to crawl clear, the explosives went up leaving '. . . neither the trucks nor their drivers of much further use to the Japanese war effort . . .' to quote Chapman. In later raids they used a few 'clams' and a home made road mine of bamboo containing sticks of very sweaty gelignite. One of these, about half a metre long, would be placed in the road with other bits of bamboo, to be exploded by Sartin yanking a piece of string to the mine's switch fuse. As it exploded under the first vehicle in a convoy the other two agents each tossed a couple of grenades at the following vehicles. At the same time they shouted at the tops of their voices to give the impressions of a large party. Not every ambush went to plan and one night Sartin was laid out by one of his own grenades. Only the fact that the Japanese themselves had 30 casualties prevented them mounting an immediate search of the roadside before the sergeant could be carried to safety.

At times they placed a series of small charges to hamper railway repair gangs. They also filled bamboo strips with PE to form grenades set off by one of Sartin's special igniters in a small piece of copper tube. These were fused to explode at varying times after they had left an ambush, and helped to create the impression that many more than three agents and their Chinese helper were in the area. The Japanese stopped using the road and the railway at night, sending maybe as many as 2,000 troops to search the area before Chapman was ready to move back over Main Ridge. On 15 February he set out with his companions for the original head-quarters camp, having caused between 500 and 1,000 casualties among the invaders. They used bicycles on part of this journey from Leu's village, and found them a good means of transport. They decided therefore to use these for their next move, when they left the HQ base to travel north to join the Chinese parties. By February several other officers had reached the HQ from outlying positions, after the main Japanese forces had passed through the area. In all eight of the original 'left behind' parties were therefore to set out for the north, after they cached two tons of stores.

They left in pairs, to cycle by night and lie up by day. Harvey, Sartin and Pat Garden were caught at one of the checks where arc lights lit the road. Chapman had been fortunate to coast through one of these as it was on a downhill stretch of road. He and Hayward had also seen others in time to skirt around them through the jungle. When the five surviving cyclists reached the Perak river they found that the Chinese 'left behind' parties had

CUT AT INNER ELBOW, OR SLASH JUST ABOVE WRIST.

PLUNGE DEEP INTO STOMACH.

SABRE SLASH TO RIGHT OR LEFT LOW ON NECK.

SMASH UP UNDER THE CHIN WITH THE POMMEL.

joined the communist guerrillas. The British were then taken to the headquarters of 5 Independent Regiment of guerrillas with whom the British would work from time to time.

Colonel Warren had played a part in the landing of two agents whom the Chinese communists knew had taken one of their officials back with them by ship to Ceylon. All but three men of the other European parties left behind the Japanese advance in Malaya, were killed or captured in January before Singapore fell to the Japanese on 15 February. By coincidence this was the day Chapman had left Lue's village.

While Chapman was stirring up trouble in central Malaya, Warren was working from Sumatra. From there he sent John Davis, a former superintendent of the Malay police, and a colonial civil servant, John Broome, to recce the Malay coast. They had a crew of Chinese 'pirates', as Warren described the CIPs because of their usual fighting dress, and their evil-smelling Chinese

coaster, the *Him Lee*. They used her for recces until she was sunk as a blockship in Sumatra on orders from the Dutch garrison's commander. SOE also organized through Major (later Colonel) Ivan Lyon, Gordon Highlanders, the so-called 'Tourist Route' across this island. Many were able to evade capture by using this route as SOE could pay for the trucks and train journeys over the 400km to safety. MI 9 also planned to set up escape lines but these would not be established by what became their 'E' Group until later in the war. Davis, Broom and Lyon escaped to India but Warren was captured when the Dutch surrendered Sumatra. He survived the war by assuming the identity of a Colonel Warren in the Indian Army, although the Japanese interrogators produced a list of SOE agents, captured from one of the colonel's 'left behind' parties.

Once captured very few Europeans escaped from the Japanese and only 50 did so by June 1945. One of them was Lieutenant-Colonel Leslie Ride of the Australian

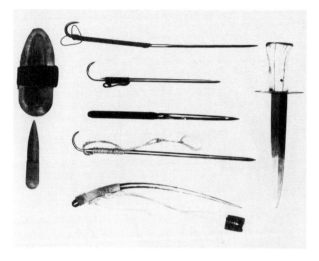

▲ This series of knives was designed for concealment by Allied forces in Asia and other tropical theatres. On the left is a lapel knife in a rubber sheath or scabbard. Its design was intended to minimize the effects of damp on blades carried in the jungle. Top centre is a single-hook thrust blade that could be concealed in the equipment and below it is a small blade of similar design. The hook enabled the wearer to withdraw the weapon from its concealment, the loop slipping over the little finger as he made a fist to thrust the knife at his enemy. Their cord wrapped handles provided a means of grip. The fourth item from top is a more robust variation of the same design, its binding has been varnished to further improve the grip. Third from the top is a thrust blade with a cord wrapped handle and which was supplied in a leather sheath. It could be concealed or worn on a belt. The curved knife (bottom of illustration) has a small scabbard attached to protect the point when the knife was concealed, and was made from the tine of a pitchfork. On the right is an Indian wrist dagger, reportedly designed for escape and evasion by Chindits of Brigadier Orde Wingate's 77th Infantry Brigade of 1943. The wrist dagger was purchased in Calcutta in 1944 from a reputable cutler who called it an 'Orde' knife. It is 7¹/₁₆ inches long with a 4¾ inch carbon steel blade, a cross-guard of 2¼ inches and a horn handle. It was held by the thumb against one side and the first and second fingers extended beyond the grip, the thumb pocketting the handle firmly in the palm. Slightly larger knives of this type were made in 1955 for the CIA. The 'Orde' knife was carried in a 'shortened Fairbairn sheath' on the left forearm or leg.

Army medical service who walked out of a prison camp near Hong Kong. He and four companions, dressed immaculately in suits smuggled into the camp when all prisoners were in rags, were not challenged by the sentries. Ride reached Chiang Kai-shek's Nationalist capital only to be thwarted in his attempts to help the Allied cause. For he, like SOE's Danes before him, fell foul of General Tai Li who headed the Chinese secret service and was ardently anti-British, having been deported from Hong Kong for trying to set up a private 'Gestapo'. The colonel later returned to southern China where he ran the British Army Aid Group (BAAG) which from May 1942 was financed by MI 9 with SOE radio operators, to provide not only escape lines but also medical services to the Chinese. By that date the days of improvisation were over and SOE operated as the wide-ranging Force 136 (see Appendix 3.12). Its organization grew to over 2,400 personnel of whom 1,000 were in

Burma, Thailand and Malaya, and over 200 in China by the summer of 1945. There were also four training schools: one for Eastern Warfare at Poona (modern Pune in India); for Jungle Warfare in modern Sri Lanka; for Eastern Interpreters near Calcutta; and Air Despatch Training at Jessore from January 1944, after SOE courses in parachuting were taken over from the RAF's Air Landing School. A Psychological Warfare Division—not an SOE role in Europe—handled propaganda by making films for cinemas in the Far East and spreading selected news. Some of these news stories gained credibility because they were distributed by the *Sidney Morning Herald* under a secret agreement. This led to items being regularly accepted by 60 American newspapers and magazines, among the many publications worldwide that used these articles. Much of the Division's work was later passed to an offshoot of the Political Warfare Executive but SOE continued to provide clandestine presses for printing leaflets in occupied territories. These small presses were similar to OSS' Press X which came in a suitcase weighing 38lb and included duplicating stencil plates, inks and other accessories. OSS also provided a contact paper printer, the 'Gilhooley' weighing 12lb.

In 1944 SOE's Psychological Warfare Division began spreading rumours through 220 agents. These items of black propaganda included such simple untruths as: 'The Japanese are enrolling Burmese women in Batttalions of Comfort and Relaxation'. Another implied that so many left-wing Japanese prisoners were willing to join the Allies that they were being trained in battalions. In April 1944 SOE formed the Globe News Agency which blended, or perhaps more correctly, bent the truth in issuing propaganda items to reinforce the rumours. The Executive also formed the Indian Field Broadcasting Units (IFBUs) that spring, to bombard enemy defences with loudspeaker messages suggesting the Japanese soldiers should desert their posts. At one time Royal Navy motor launches carried IFBU equipment, broadcasting the screams of Japanese women being chased by jabbering monkeys. This was one of several recordings calculated to demoralize Japanese soldiers moving through the tidal swamps of the Arakan (Burma) coast.

Other IFBUs showered leaflets from special mortar bombs fired into enemy positions, although more urgent military necessity could lead them to fire smoke bombs which covered a tactical retreat. The Units also recruited rumour mongers during visits to villages where they set up medical clinics (a forerunner of one SAS practice of the 1950s and 1960s) which gave the Units the confidence of local people. This enabled the IFBU to recruit guides and river boatmen for the Fourteenth Army.

All SOE India's operations benefitted from the

availability of aircraft in Special Duty Squadrons formed in June 1943, although the previous year only seven successful missions had been mounted by air. The RAF's No. 1576 (SD) Flight with Hudsons was being used almost exclusively for SOE and OSS operations by late 1943 and was expanded to 357 Squadron in 1944. Its pilots flew Dakotas, Hudsons, Liberators and Catalina flying boats (from a lake near Madras, India); a Lysander flight was added to the Squadron from April 1945. Long distance flights were made by the Liberators which were supplemented in November 1944 by those of 358 Squadron and in the following January by 160 Squadron. These aircraft were capable of remaining airborne without refuelling for over 20 hours, as a Mark VI did in dropping containers to a DZ in South Johore (southern Malaya). There the

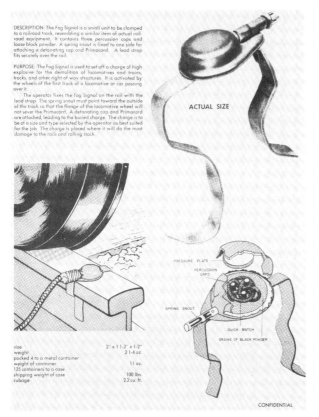

▼ The fog signal device shown here in a page from the OSS weapons manual, looked like a common railway warning device of the 1940s. This made a loud report to warn signalmen that a train had reached a particular point on the track. The OSS version had a pressure plate and three percussion caps surrounded by instantaneous fuse. This ignited black powder surrounding the fuse which fired a detonator usually fixed to more instantaneous fuse leading to a rail cutting charge of explosive. A number were issued in OSS' China-India-Burma theatre. The device weighed 2¼ oz and was 2 inches in diameter. It had to be set with the spring snout facing outward from the track, otherwise the rim of an engine wheel would cut the Primacord connection to the charge. The lead metal strap fitted over a rail and was pressed home to ensure a secure attachment to the track.

DESCRIPTION: The Fog Signal is a small unit to be clamped to a railroad track, resembling a similar item of actual railroad equipment. It contains three percussion caps and loose block powder. A spring snout is fixed to one side for attaching a detonating cap and Primacord. A lead strap fits securely over the rail.

PURPOSE: The Fog Signal is used to set off a charge of high explosive for the demolition of locomotives and trains, tracks, and other right of way structures. It is activated by the wheels of the first truck of a locomotive or car passing over it.

The operator fixes the Fog Signal on the rail with the lead strap. The spring snout must point toward the outside of the track so that the flange of the locomotive wheel will not sever the Primacord. A detonating cap and Primacord are attached, leading to the buried charge. The charge is to be of a size and type selected by the operator as best suited for the job. The charge is placed where it will do the most damage to the rails and rolling stock.

ACTUAL SIZE

PRESSURE PLATE
PERCUSSION CAPS
SPRING SNOUT
QUICK MATCH
GRAINS OF BLACK POWDER

size   2" x 1 1-2" x 1-2"
weight   2 1-4 oz.
packed 4 to a metal container
weight of container   11 oz.
125 containers to a case
shipping weight of case   100 lbs.
cubage   2.2 cu. ft.

CONFIDENTIAL

massed jungle trees, often 30m high, made the job of spotting a DZ extremely difficult, especially as neither S-phones nor Eurekas worked satisfactorily from a forest floor and were not apparently used from jungle canopies. Smoke from fires could also prove ineffective as markers for DZs, being easily dispersed by the trees. This accounted for some villagers being surprised to receive a batch of containers dropped to their cooking fires. Yet aircrews were particularly sharp eyed on occasion, one spotting a DZ marked only by candles in small pits! Others supplied one DZ with such accuracy that a Japanese outpost only 3km away never discovered the site although it was used for five months. There were, however, few Japanese air reconnaissance flights during the last nine months of the war when the Allies had overwhelming air supremacy. DZs could therefore be marked with white cloths panels: one 'I' requesting a replacement radio; two requesting a radio operator; and three for a doctor.

A Mark Vc Liberator once spent 85 minutes searching for a DZ in a jungle but saw no reception committee's signals. The aircraft had used nearly all its 16,000lb of fuel when it returned with the 1,984 load of containers to reach India after being airborne for more than a day. Such flights were hazardous not only because the aircraft took off when grossly overloaded with fuel, but also because the monsoon of May to October could make flying conditions dangerous in the turbulence at low altitude. Many of the 27 aircraft lost from the SD Squadrons, crashed in these conditions. Only one of them is known to have been lost through enemy fighter attacks: a Liberator, caught during a daylight drop over Thailand. All its crew, two OSS agents and their conducting officer survived the forced landing. Some, including the OSS personnel, were rescued by the reception committee, but four of the ten-man crew were interned by the Thais.

Other drops, especially those made 'blind' could be hazardous because the clearing chosen as a DZ was strewn with *panjis*. These sharpened bamboo stakes hidden in long grass might spear through the foot of a parachutist. Indeed anyone stepping on these stakes could be injured and seven Karens were lucky to avoid injuries when they were dropped several kilometres east of their intended DZ. The seven men left the aircraft with their leader jumping as fourth man in the stick, following the drill which should place him in the centre of the team as the men landed. He then organized the collection of containers which had been dropped from their Liberator's second pass. Next day when they reached the intended DZ they found it was sown with *panjis* firmly planted with points upwards in the grass. The containers which they collected carried similar weapons to those dropped to European guerrillas. In Asia, however, they might include 'Stingers' and

'Liberator' pistols not normally distributed in Europe. They also contained several months' rations for radio teams in remote areas where there were few if any sources of local food.

Despite the great efforts to supply guerrilla forces, these in south-east Asia (see Appendix 3.12) proved difficult to co-ordinate. This was because of their uncertain loyalties which also bedevilled secret intelligence work. Few details of these cross-loyalties are available, but perhaps to protect such secrets SOE used explosive devices in some brief cases. These could also be used as booby traps for the inquisitive, one accidentally injuring an SOE officer in Thailand. Exactly why he opened an 'armed' case is not known. Nor are any official records available to explain if consideration was given to merging the resources of SOE and SIS (known in the Far East as the Inter-Service Liaison Department [ISLD]), as one senior SIS officer once suggested. Such divisions of responsibility were spread even wider over clandestine agencies in the Pacific, where OSS was replaced by the Australian Intelligence Bureau.

I N the southern Pacific the Australians had established a coast-watching service, as suggested by Captain C. T. Clarke, RAN in 1919. It was supplemented in 1941 by men of the Australian Army's Independent Companies which had been trained as commandos by Chapman among others, when these companies were intended to serve in the Middle East. When war threatened in the Pacific, however, these 'commandos' manned a series of observation posts stretching over 1,600km from Manus in the Admiralty Islands, through New Ireland, Bougainville, the New Hebrides and to Tulgai in the Solomons. Although these were uni-formed troops, they carried out similar work to SOE's 'left behind' parties, those on Amboina continuing to radio reports until overrun, with only two men of the company surviving. This company's reports were radioed 800km to Darwin in northern Australia where the intelligence was sifted for reports to Allied Head-quarters. Other reports came from the coast-watchers who by the nature of their peacetime work often as planters or traders on the islands, were better able than the 'commandos' to evade the Japanese invaders. On Guadalcanal, for instance, was D. S. Macfarlan who had lived on the island for many years. His Observation Post was hidden on a ridge overlooking the flat ground where the Japanese cleared the tall *kunai* grass to build an airstrip. Mac's Melanesian helpers went into Japanese camps, reporting to him the length of the queues for meals. These 'boys' as Mac called them, also pinpointed beach strong points and camouflaged coast batteries, valuable intelligence

which 1 USMC Division used in planning their landings on the island in November 1942.

Other intelligence provided by coast-watchers, included movements of Japanese ship convoys and of aircraft. These reports were at times difficult to act upon, because the distances in the Pacific are so great: Hawaii is 2,200 miles from the US west coast and 3,000 miles from Guadalcanal, several weeks' passage by slow convoys. The Pacific and Indian Oceans were also divided into several theatres of command: the British Admiral Lord Mountbatten commanding the South-East Asia Command (SEAC) from 1943; the American General, Douglas MacArthur commanding the South-West Pacific theatre in 1942; and two other theatres the South and the Central Pacific commanded by Americans. MacArthur refused to allow Donovan's OSS to operate in his theatre, as he later refused to allow its successor, the CIA, to work in Korea in the 1950s. Instead he created from Australian intelligence, a clandestine agency working to his command.

When the general arrived in Australia in 1942, the existing Australian intelligence services included elements set up along the lines of SOE some two years earlier. Its propaganda division was not hived off; Americans joined the service which became the Australian Intelligence Bureau (AIB) commanded by the Director of Australian Army Intelligence, Colonel C. G. Roberts. He set out the Bureau's purpose in his first directive of 6 July 1942: '. . . to obtain and report information of the enemy in the South-West Pacific Area; and in addition where practical to weaken the enemy by sabotage and destruction of morale; and render aid and assistance to local efforts to the same end in enemy-occupied territories.' This organization (see Fig. VI) later became the Service Reconnaissance Department with a semi-autonomous section working in the Philippines.

Donovan, shut out by MacArthur, built OSS' Far East operations from bases in China, but the intrigues of General Tai Li—'. . . more a Himmler than a Canaris' to paraphrase one official report—caused problems, until money and plenty of it sweetened the General's attitude to co-operation. He became head of the Sino-American Co-operation Organization (SACO) for which OSS provided from April 1943 both the training and equipment for Chinese agents. But the intrigues continued in a puzzle box of plots within plots in China. For instance in 1944, 20 of Chiang Kai-Shek's best Nationalist Divisions were fighting Mao Tse-Tung's communist army, pitting more Chinese against each other than against the Japanese. Not surprisingly, therefore, attempts by OSS to work with Mao met many setbacks at the hands of the Nationalists, while SOE—curiously arguing that communist areas were not 'China'—had some contacts to Mao's forces. But later

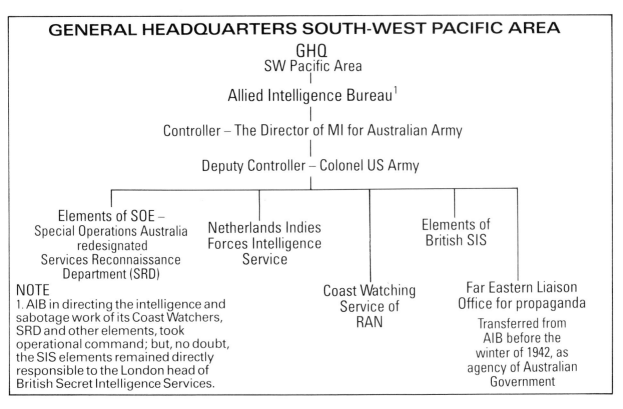

GENERAL HEADQUARTERS SOUTH-WEST PACIFIC AREA

GHQ
SW Pacific Area

Allied Intelligence Bureau[1]

Controller – The Director of MI for Australian Army

Deputy Controller – Colonel US Army

Elements of SOE –
Special Operations Australia
redesignated
Services Reconnaissance
Department (SRD)

**Netherlands Indies
Forces Intelligence
Service**

**Elements of
British SIS**

**Coast Watching
Service of
RAN**

**Far Eastern Liaison
Office for propaganda**

Transferred from
AIB before the
winter of 1942, as
agency of Australian
Government

NOTE
1. AIB in directing the intelligence and
sabotage work of its Coast Watchers,
SRD and other elements, took
operational command; but, no doubt,
the SIS elements remained directly
responsible to the London head of
British Secret Intelligence Services.

Fig. VI The Allied Intelligence Bureau (AIB) was commanded by the Australian Army's Director of Military Intelligence, with an American colonel as his deputy. Other Australian and American personnel served in the Bureau which provided OSS-type services for General MacArthur's forces in the Pacific.

when American missions were sent to Mao's headquarters, SACO became anti-OSS to the extent that Tai Li probably had some of OSS's Chinese agents murdered, although OSS could never prove this. Most of the wrangles between American and Nationalists were largely a matter of words, if bitter ones. However, the sticks wielded by some thugs brutally injured the 31-year-old Rosamund Frame after she had helped to expose the treachery of two senior Nationalists, who were sending information from India to the Japanese. This was by no means the only case of double-dealing exposed by OSS, but there seems little doubt that associates of the traitors arranged the attack from which Rosamund died within the year.

Other OSS operatives were physically attacked by Nationalist soldiers posing as bandits, as when Captain Robin North's road convoy of OSS supplies was looted, and he was stripped of all but his trousers and shoes. The stolen goods were later only recovered because the local Nationalist war lord realized that among the items were heart pills for General Chennault. He commanded the 'Flying Tigers' who had been flying in support of the Nationalists since before 1941. His squadrons were redesignated 14th Air Force and by 1944 integrated with the USAAF. Donovan created a separate organization,

5329th Air and Ground Forces Technical Staff (Provisional) (AGGFRTS—rudely known as Agfarts to other OSS staff) which undertook from April 1944 all intelligence services for Chennault's headquarters. This was at Kunming in the mountains of western China, a couple of hours or less from the Burmese border.

SOE in 1942 was able to recruit Chinese agents for work in Malaya, through Li Bo Seng, a university graduate whose family had contacts, probably commercial ones, with Chiang Kai-Shek, as the little general at 55 had several business interests. However, the Communists rather than the Nationalist Chinese were the principal resistance force in Malaya. Davis returned there in May 1943 landing from a Dutch submarine to contact the Communist Party in Malaya. He and five Chinese landed 'blind', avoided the Japanese coast patrols and made contact with the Communists, before Davis came out to report that these resistance forces were well disciplined but short of arms. He was back with their headquarters in July, as the senior representative of the British South East Asia Command authorized to organize the supply of instructors and arms to the Communist regiments. Broome followed him in September as did others who would be SOE's liaison officers in the various Malayan states. At Christmas Freddie Chapman appeared at the headquarters, remarkably fit considering he had spent two years in the jungle. Chapman had lost touch with Pat Noone, the ethnologist who later SOE learnt had been living with a tribe of aborigines, taking one as his wife. Chapman set out to find Noone but was captured by the Japanese. He avoided execution, however, by claiming that he was the younger brother of the Colonel Spencer Chapman whom his interrogators believed commanded all the Communist forces.

The reality was that the SOE liaison officers were able to provide radioed intelligence on the strength and disposition of Japanese forces in Malaya. But at first these forces caused SOE some set-backs, capturing Davis' generators in March 1944, leaving him out of touch with India until December. Then—a bicycle generator providing the power—Davis was back on the air. Air drops from Liberators provided arms and other supplies; more agents were landed and each communist regiment had an SOE officer to help co-ordinate its operations in the overall Allied plans, but not to command it.

Such liaison work led SOE's Force 136 to be more concerned with intelligence in 1943 and 1944, than with sabotage in the South-East Asia theatre. But several 'Jedburgh' teams were dropped to provide 'a more professional intelligence service' than SOE's Chinese agents could provide for the Fourteenth Army in its advance south through Burma. These 'Jeds' usually consisted of two British officers and a sergeant radio operator, with a Burmese agent who could act as an interpreter. However, on one occasion at least the interpreter was given the title 'Head of the Military Mission to the Anti-Fascist Organization', in this case in the Arakan. One of the most successful 'Jeds' was codenamed 'Reindeer' led by the resourceful Major D. J. C. Britton. He landed west of Toungoo on the Sitang river where an SOE radio team had established contact with India late in January 1945. The Fourteenth Army were due to cross the Irrawaddy 300km north-west of this 'Jed' on 11/12 February when the Japanese were bringing up reinforcements by rail at night. The troops detrained by day to hide from Allied air-attacks along the 1,000km of railway and road from Rangoon to the Irrawaddy defences.

Britton worked with the headmen of villages who had the loyalty of the local people, '. . . simple folk with no particular knowledge of politics . . .' These villagers, trained by the 'Jed', provided an intelligence network which by the second week in April covered a radius of 30km from their base and eventually employed some 300 Burmese. They also carried out sabotage for which SOE had a standard container load providing for every hundred guerrillas: 54 carbines, 42 stens, 240 handgrenades, two PIATS, four Brens and a Welrod. These weapons had to be returned once the war moved on from the villagers' area, before they could be paid. Explosives and demolition devices were also dropped, including those used to booby-trap Japanese bivouacs when these were unguarded because the men were on patrol. An agent hidden nearby in the jungle would light the fuse to these charges after the soldiers returned, ensuring that the explosions occurred when the men had turned in for a night's sleep. (This drill underlines one of the limitations of time-delay pencils, which proved unreliable in the hot and humid atmosphere of the jungle.)

Britton's men could also mark targets for Allied airforces, which were quite invisible from the air as they lay under the thick canopy of jungle trees. The technique made use of the cloth panels, as used to mark a DZ, two of which formed an arrowhead pointing towards the target, with additional panels 'each representing 1,000 yards' to form a tail to the arrow that showed the distance from the target. By this or other means such as radioed directions to aircraft, the RAF were directed to ammunition dumps, motor-transport concentrations and other targets of significance from 19-27 April, as the Fourteenth Army neared Britton's area of operations. Parties of his guerrillas also cut the railway to Toungoo in several places, with marked success. Maybe they used the technique for this which OSS had developed, because the SOE practice of placing '. . . two ¾-pound charges of PE one metre apart . . .', had failed to overturn trains '. . . on 50 per cent of the occasions it was used . . .' The new technique put the explosive under, not beside, a rail taking out over 2m of track and creating a crater which toppled nine out of ten trains from the rails. The Burmese also attacked Japanese patrols but avoided any set-piece battles. Major Britton was killed in action late in April on the day Major R. A. Rubinstein's 'Chimp' Jedburgh joined 'Reindeer'.

These two 'Jeds' had a remarkable run of success, to which General (later Field Marshal Sir) William Slim paid particular reference in the Fourteenth Army's report on the campaign. In expressing his appreciation of the value of the guerrilla forces he wrote especially of those '. . . delaying . . . the 15th Japanese Division . . . enabling IV Corps to reach Toungoo first'. After the Army reached 'Reindeer's' area on 27 April, the guerrillas helped regular forces for several weeks in tracking Japanese units which had moved to the east into the Karen hills.

In Thailand SOE had more political than military operations (see Appendix 3.12), but the quality of agent and equipment is typified by the three officers dropped 'blind' into Thailand on 14 March 1944. All were from the 23 Siamese nationals who had been in England when war broke out, and were trained by SOE as the 'White Elephants'. This might seem to the English to be an unusual choice as a codename, because the agents proved anything but unwanted. However, it relates to the sacred white elephants of southern Asia. Captain Pratan Pramekamol, a post-graduate science student of Liverpool University, and expert radio operator; Captain Samran Varnbriksha who had been in his final year as a veterinary student, and Major Puey Ung-phakorn who had 'a long string of academic successes' formed this team for 'Appreciation I'. Their drop was followed by seven containers one of which fell outside a village temple as they had been dropped 25km east of the intended DZ. There is no record of the villagers' reaction although their dogs made enough noise to deter any rash endeavour to recover the container. No doubt it proved a bountiful gift for the village since the stores in the seven containers included: light weight blankets, battery acid, groundsheets, quinine, shoe-laces, 'hussifs' (needles and thread to repair clothes), pencils and socks, not to mention ammunition and weapons.

The three each had an L-pill and no doubt wore jungle clothing with rubber-soled boots that were 'light, silent and absolutely leech-proof' which was the standard dress for SOE's agents in tropical countries. Having landed, they set up their radio but for three days could only hear the home-station at Calcutta, not contact it. However, Major Ungphakorn was caught by the Police which directly led him into contact with the political leader, Luang Pridi, for whom he had a letter from Mountbatten. OSS also had contacts with this leader of a free-Thailand movement and were more convinced than the British had been that it was a guerrilla force for anti-Japanese operations. However, OSS did not want to become enmeshed in the politics of exiled Thais, nor did they approve of the sentiment expressed by a British diplomat that '. . . south east Asia was not ready for independence . . .' He also suggested that the kingdom of Thailand—never a colony—should be '. . . under some sort of tutelage . . .' Whether or not this was the official Foreign Office view, it was certainly not Mountbatten's assessment, but the State Department's political guidance to OSS aimed at a free Thailand.

Before looking at other OSS operations, there is one unusual if not unique operation which brought more money into the coffers of the Bank of England than the entire cost of SOE operations world-wide. It was a remarkable coup by the gargantuan Walter Fletcher, who traded in China for SOE. Originally this buccaneer merchant had been allowed to spend considerable funds trying to buy rubber smuggled from Malaya but achieved for SOE quite a different return on the British Treasury's investment. He sold diamonds and Swiss watches to Chinese warlords at such inflated prices that

many millions of rupees were smuggled with other currencies from China. Although the Nationalists had fixed an arbitrary set of exchange rates, Fletcher's black market netted perhaps the equivalent of £1,000 million in terms of 1986 value for the Treasury, in what the official history of SOE describes as '. . . the biggest currency black market in history . . .' Seven per cent of the profits on those goods was also paid to Tai Li's secret service.

'Blue' Ride's escape lines provided a more savoury contribution to British operations in China. Through his contacts with Mao, SOE were able to send agents to the Communist-held region of Yenan. Ride's BAAG were handling some 30,000 Chinese patients a year in clinics at Kweilin 350km north-west of Hong Kong, where his staff's honest publication of news on the war's progress and general straight dealings with the people, brought remarkable rewards. His agents near the coast provided twice daily weather reports for the 'Flying Tigers', but the Nationalists ensured that he had no long range radios. His weekly 'int' reports were therefore brought out by couriers; they or other guides also led to safety 38 American airmen, spirited away from crashed aircraft by Communist guerrillas who operated within sight of Hong Kong. Escapes from POW camps were few but BAAG brought out 52 skilled dockyard 'mateys' from the shipyards of Hong Kong. However, as the total labour force in these yards was 10,000, any scheme to bring them all out was quite impractical. AGFRTS took over all aircrew rescue from Ride in the autumn of 1943 and OSS agents joined the organization. 'Joined' is perhaps misleading here, as these operatives apparently tried to bribe the couriers for sight of the weekly 'int' reports.

OSS' operations in the Far East began in Calcutta in the spring of 1942 with the closest co-operation. The

▲ This view of the OSS radio room in Kunming, China was taken probably in the spring of 1945. The operator is tuning an American AR-88 receiver. From this capital of China's south-western province of Yunnan, OSS ran a number of operations. These all required the approval of the American theatre commander. After November 1944 all clandestine operations including those by SOE in China were subject to this general's approval.

burly Major Carl Eifler commanding Force 101 found that '... no file was considered too secret...' for his American eyes. His mission was to recruit men from the 150,000 Kachins living along the Burmese border with China. But '101' did not begin operations against the Japanese facing General Stilwell's Chinese Army until September 1942—delays endemic to Chinese politics that year. The force carried out a series of successful operations over the next 18 months but in the summer of 1944 Chinese troops looted nine Kachin villages. This provoked a counter-terrorist operation by a battalion of Kachins led by officers of Force 101, which crossed into China to avenge what turned out to be more than an act of banditry. There is no positive proof of the Nationalists' reasons for the original raid, but there was a suggestion at the time that Tai Li had authorized it. Certainly Chiang Kai-Shek demanded $25 million in compensation for damage to Chinese property, a claim that was dropped when an investigation laid the blame equally between all commanders involved. Although the Americans' methods were criticised by some Koren officers who accused Force 101 of the 'forceful conscription' of local people.

Of the 121 other operations mounted by OSS in south-east Asia (see Appendix 3.13), one example showed clearly the difficulties and dangers in this theatre. In 1944 the Allies were seeking intelligence on potential air landing strips from which the gradual advance of their armies might be covered. Therefore SOE and other clandestine forces like the Small Operations Group, mounted recces in which airfield engineers studied and photographed potential sites in Japanese-occupied territory. Two of these engineers from the RAF with an OSS guard of OG personnel landed from HM Submarine *Truculent* on Sunday 7 May 1944, to recce Simalur Island west of Sumatra.

They came ashore in two boats with the intention of using the landing party as sheet-anchors to steady them as they passed through the surf. Stripped of their clothes, the men were to go into the water before they reached the breakers, carrying their clothes in waterproof bags so that they would be dry for their march across the island. But the leading boat was capsized by a great roller of a wave, Flight Lieutenant Malcolm Bunting grabbing the equipment bags and surged ashore with them on the next wave. Sergeant E. Eckhardt tried to swim ashore but lost his life jacket and had to be supported by First Lieutenant R. Peterson, USN who commanded the OSS team. Lieutenant Donald Lowe, RAF and the photographer, H. Martin, USNR, got into the water from the second boat. Their radio operator, Sergeant M. Flaherty, was to follow them, but he was pitched out of the boat, disappearing in a smother of surf while the others struggled to hold

the life lines as the waves pounded them. All the men were exhausted when they eventually got ashore and Flaherty, badly shaken but unhurt, was washed onto the beach some distance away along the tide line. In the stress of the moment the others forgot to signal their safe if uncomfortable arrival, which caused concern aboard the submarine as the crew could not see the beach beyond the breakers.

Having dried out and dressed, the landing party hid the boats and set off for the airfield site to be recced. During Monday and Tuesday they made reasonable progress despite the heavy rain storms, and the need to make a detour from their route to avoid villages. On Wednesday they carried out their recce taking photographs, while making notes of the problems that would have to be tackled in clearing the ground for an airstrip. They then had seven days to cross the island to Sibabo Bay by way of a track that they had been told crossed a ridge of hills. These only rose to a little over 300m but this made the jungle floor steep and slippery in places, under the early monsoon rain. Peterson had been carrying the radio, Flaherty the generator and both were beginning to feel the effects of the continuous wet. Pete's feet were raw and from Saturday each man took it in turns to carry the 20kg radio.

They had been ashore a week, without finding any sign of a trail going westward over the ridge and therefore Lowe led them on compass bearings across the island. Starting out at 0600 on the Sunday they made slow, painful progress. Both the photograper Harry Martin, and Flaherty had their feet bandaged over socks, their blisters being too painful for boots, even if their boots had not disintegrated in the constant wet. On Monday morning when they came to charge the batteries, they discovered that Flaherty had left the winding handles of their generator at the previous night's camp. They might not be able to contact their submarine, 'much feeling'—in the words of the official report—was expressed by most members of the party and the generator was thrown away. They continued their jungle march throughout Monday and Tuesday when at 1600 hours they caught sight of the RV bay on the coast below the hills. Reaching it was another matter, for although they had come only 10 to 15km from the airstrip site, every metre was a struggle of willpower over painful, exhausted bodies. They were forced to skirt round a village, floundering into the stinking mud of a mangrove swamp. This bordered the beach which they reached within a couple of hours, just before sunset. Lowe took a bearing which gave him some check on their position before dark and they found a place to sleep. Flaherty had been walking barefoot for the past 12 hours or more. Harry Martin was in such a bad way that he crawled to their camp some time later, unable to speak.

On Wednesday, 17 May, Lowe kept them in camp until 0800—one suspects that none wanted to move far—but then they staggered 200m along the beach to the place Lowe thought was the pick-up point. His navigation had been faultless and much more difficult than in open country. Late that afternoon the submarine surfaced, her lookouts seeing the recce party's signals; after dark she sent boats in to collect them. Once aboard they received the medical treatment all of them needed while she sailed back to Ceylon. Their hard won report on this possible airfield was one of many which in the event was not used, as the war ended before the Allied armies had to force a landing in Sumatra.

The sudden end to the war in August 1945 produced many unforeseen difficulties for the Allied staffs in Asia, who for security reasons could not be advised of the atom bombs' likely effect on 6 and 9 August. Although the Allied governments feared possible reprisals against Allied prisoners in Japanese hands, since they had always been considered expendable in the Japanese ethos of military valour, which called on

▲ A number of agents were trained by OSS in Kunming. This trainee has a Liberator pistol in his belt but carries no other weapon apparently. The photograph was taken in 1945 or possibly late in 1944.

▼ The SSTR-5 was used by OSS mainly in China during the last year of the war. Advances in the design of radio valves (vacuum tubes) by this date had reached the stage where some were described as 'pea sized'. The SSTR-5 was therefore small enough to fit into an eight-inch cube, but had a range at least equivalent to the SSTR-1. The key, the crystal, the aerial load and trim switches were on the pack (seen on left) of this set. The second pack or section (on right) had the tuning dial with its concentric tuning knobs. The volume control was positioned towards the right front of this pack and top right were the other controls including an on-off switch. One of the small valves carried as a spare is clipped in the top right corner of the lid in the foreground.

soldiers to die in battle. Such an attitude made escape not only dangerous but foolhardy in most circumstances. This had been known to MI 9's E group and the American MIS-X since they first briefed crews flying in Asia. Both agencies worked closely together on briefing these aircrews and the design of escape equipment, or more correctly, evasion kits. MIS did not, however, become deeply involved in the Far East war until late in 1943 when a headquarters was set up in Australia with American, Australian and British personnel. Their work, like that of E group in India, was mainly directed at briefing crews on jungle survival: what to eat, the tender shoots at the top of palms being quite a delicacy; how to use bamboo for spears, to make water-carriers, rafts and makeshift shelters; and how to keep healthy in treating leech bites. Maps were provided from Australia and India showing relatively safe areas where the local people might help the crew. The airmen were also warned that in Malaya, for example, some Indians were known to be helping the Japanese and therefore all were to be avoided. Aircrews were issued with evasion kits with cookers, amongst the other kit which was more sophisticated than their European equivalents. The RAF issued the Beadan suit which ensured that aircrew did not fly without their evasion kit, but apart from such survival equipment and training, there was little that could be done to establish escape lines for prisoners of the Japanese, until the tide of war turned. The suit contained a box of concentrated rations, a machete, small compass and other survival aids. The American E vest was somewhat similar, but with a smokeless cooker and other refinements.

E Group's only attempt at landing agents in the spring of 1942 put a team on Sumatra, the large jungle island over 1,500km long with an area greater than four times the size of England. They disappeared and thereafter the Group used air reconnaissance to establish the location of prison camps, a means also used by MIS-X's headquarters set up in the central Pacific theatre early in November 1944. This headquarters, like other MIS-X HQs, was also involved in establishing air-sea rescue services with the complexities of positioning seaplanes and high-speed craft where they could best effect rescues.

When the war ended suddenly that August, E Group, OSS and SOE/Force 136 mounted a major series of rescues for the 100,000 Allied prisoners scattered in camps across five countries of south-east Asia. These were delicate missions in most cases as any approach to the camps was forbidden until 26 August, 12 days after the Japanese Government's surrender. A precaution taken because the Allied commands feared reprisals if rescuers appeared before all the Japanese and Korean guards knew of the Emperor's orders to cease fighting. During this fortnight 50 four-man teams of SOE officers

were briefed and the SD squadrons were joined by four others to provide 100 Liberators and other aircraft in SEAC alone, ready to drop containers of food and medical supplies to the camps.

SOE's 62 radio stations in occupied territories provided communications for these rescues, but 1,500 miniature Communications Receivers (MCRs, similar if not the same as the MCR I but possibly with features to keep out the insidious damp of the tropics) were distributed to camps. The former prisoners were persuaded by broadcasts and rescue teams, that they should wait for an orderly evacuation. Meanwhile, the Japanese continued to administer the camps under the supervision of Allied repatriation teams. In Burma this caused relatively few problems because Allied forces were in the country in strength, although Major R. G. Turrall was unable to convince a Japanese commander in the Koren hills that the war was over. He was held prisoner despite his attempts to escape, until the last week in August when leaflets dropped by Allied aircraft finally convinced this officer that his Emperor had ordered him to surrender. Nor were there any major difficulties in Thailand, Malaya and Indo-China (modern Vietnam) where understandably some guerrillas attacked the Japanese. These actions may have discouraged any suicidal atrocities by camp guards, and fortunately did not provoke them.

Conditions in Java and Sumatra were far worse, with only three teams from SOE on Sumatra before the surrender. Therefore the arrangements for rescuing prisoners could not begin until one of the repatriation teams arrived in mid-September. Commanded by Captain A. W. Fordyce, the team's nine officers, four signallers and two medics, began evacuating 3,000 former prisoners. A rescue mission here as elsewhere in the Dutch East Indies that was complicated because there were also many civilians who had been in camps. They were evacuated despite the local peoples' hostility to the Dutch administration, which led to the SEAC command allowing some Japanese to retain their weapons for the defence of former prisoners. The repatriation of prisoners from all the theatres of war in the Far East, the redeployment of Allied armies after Japan's surrender and feeding the many peoples of India where famine had led to four million deaths, all placed heavy demands on the available Allied shipping. These ships took weeks rather than days to make passages from the Indian and Pacific Oceans. This time factor is sometimes overlooked in considering World War II naval operations, and in particular the use of small ships by SOE and OSS. In north-west Europe use was made of high-speed motor launches, while in the other theatres the clandestine services used local boats relying on deception rather than speed to escape the attention of the enemy.

10

SABOTAGE FROM THE SEA

AT midnight on a dark night early in 1942, Ben Cowburn began flashing a regular Morse signal out to sea. He was standing at the water's edge on the shingle of Moulin-de-la-Rive bay, where only a few outcrops of rock might make a landing difficult on this stretch of Breton beach. Yet no boat had come in after half an hour, and Ben realized that it was Friday, 13 February. Then he saw a dark figure approaching him along the tide line. He gave the challenge, receiving the correct reply before he walked with the man to a dinghy beached not far away. A seaman had rowed it inshore so quietly, without a single splash of oars to attract attention, that Ben had not seen this cockle of a boat. In it an agent had been landed, as well as the Royal Navy lieutenant who had walked along the beach. Such a load for a pram-dinghy a mere 3m long was a risk in calm weather, but the wind was getting up, as a second dinghy brought in another agent. Such moonless nights with a rising tide were ideal times to make such landfalls but on this night the wind rose with the tide, capsizing both little boats before Ben and his party could get aboard.

They spent a wet half-hour righting the boats and emptying them, before the seaman launched them again into the surf. This was now breaking some distance from the shore, with five lines of white rollers surging towards the beach. The lieutenant signalled the skipper of the MTB from which the boats had landed, and a larger dinghy came to the outer edge of the surf. But when Ben waded towards her, he realized that the water was too deep and rough for him to reach the plunging boat and he half swam, half waded back to the shore. On further signalling to the MTB, the naval officer told the seamen to swim the dinghies out, an essential precaution if the Germans were not to find the prams on the beach next morning. Ben saw the two men enter the surf, each pushing a dinghy which was capsized a few metres from the shore, but doggedly pushed on out to sea. The larger boat no doubt took them in tow for there was little time left before the MTB must put out to sea. She had to be clear of the coast at dawn before German aircraft might patrol it. The men and one woman left on the beach had no choice but to go inland and resume their secret war, although at this time it was less secret than Ben would have wished. For the woman in the party, peering through shortsightedness as much as weather conditions, was on her own admission a double-agent. Voluptuous, plausible, Mademoiselle Mathilde-Ley Carré was known to many as *La Chatte*

(the 'Darling') perhaps because of her selfish ways. After being captured she had gone to live with Sergeant Hugo Bleicher of the Abwehr's counter-intelligence section, one conquest of the several she made among the officers and NCOs in the occupying forces. For this 30-year-old law graduate had been looking after her own interests since she married in 1933: through Bleicher she had arranged that no patrols would intercept Ben's party. This would enable her to escape to London where she had promised to keep in contact with the Abwehr. (How this was to be done presumably depended on agents already in England, who unbeknown to Bleicher were controlled by the XX Committee, as we have seen.)

After the fiasco with the dinghies, she went to the local German headquarters and arranged for their patrols to continue their discreet surveillance of the SOE party without arresting any of its members. They were to split up and lie low the next day. Several took a room in a local hotel, but the naval lieutenant preferred less restricting hides in woodlands. There he was seen and had to be arrested—the Germans told La Chatte— because he was in uniform. They also collected the luggage thrown out of the capsized dinghies which included a radio. Nevertheless they were quite prepared to let Ben, La Chatte and another agent, Pierre de Vomécourt, try a second time to get off the beach. She told the Germans that the two agents landed the previous night, would also have to go back to England. So a second night was spent on the beach, a calm night in which the Germans watched but did not interfere with the agents. No boat came, therefore Ben made his way south. He was followed by a sequence of Abwehr officers but managed to give one the slip. This German was not quick enough to realize that having rounded a corner, Ben had slipped into the side door of a busy café. Free of this 'tail' Ben was able to reach the Pyrenees, which he crossed possibly with the help of the 'Pat' line and reached England. La Chatte arrived there with de Vomécourt who had chaperoned her return to Paris and on a later evacuation by sea. He handed over the double-agent for interrogation, after which she was imprisoned in England. After the war she was tried in France, sentenced to death but later reprieved. Bleicher never knew that she had double-crossed him, until after the war when the Allies called him as a witness in several treason trials. Bleicher, in his early forties, had remained a sergeant in the Abwehr throughout the war. His thinning grey hair, average build and sad mouth which drooped at the corners, belied his abilities as a counter-intelligence agent even though he may later have exaggerated these. He never used torture, but his urbanity had an appeal to women, if not to his superiors.

When Ben Cowburn returned to France in 1942, he was brought in by Lysander, in general a more reliable route for SOE agents than sea passages from southern England, because SIS took priority on the sea routes. This had been especially the case in 1940 and 1941 before the Germans had established their coast defences. Yet even these could not seal the thousands of kilometres of bays and inlets from the Spanish border to Norway's North cape. Therefore SOE's agents were trained in landing from dinghies which could be launched from a small flotilla of airsea rescue 'crash' boats. These were based on the Helford river in Cornwall for use by SOE. The Executive also financed a most successful recce of the Gironde by a Free-French crew in a tunny boat that fished with other boats, while noting the procedures of U-boats passing in and out of the river.

This technique of posing as a local boat worked well in France, Norway and the Mediterranean until the Axis powers took a tighter control of these fleets. Then many boats in 1943 had embarked a German soldier or two to prevent the crew making contact with any Allied ship. This did not prevent all use of local boats as we will see, but few were as successful as SIS' flotilla on the Dart River in Devon. In its early years this was commanded by Captain Frank Slocum, RN who had been with SIS since 1937, and was a descendant of the nineteenth-century small boat sailor who made some of the first singlehanded ocean passages. The captain's staff acquired in 1940 a Concarneau trawler of the type used by Brittany fishermen. She was given new engines which pushed her 50ft hull at a steady 6kt, while her Boys anti-tank rifle could put an armour jacketed .5in bullet through most inshore patrol vessels. She sailed to the Scilly Isles remote from prying eyes, 45km south-west of Land's End, where her naval grey paint was replaced with green, blue, brown and orange, colours favoured by fishermen. Her number—N51 in British registration—was changed to CC 2682, painted in the distinctive lettering of a French registration. Her crew dressed in replicas of French canvas trousers and brightly coloured smocks, but they had their naval uniforms aboard in case they had to hoist the White Ensign and repel borders with the sten guns and grenades she carried.

Her first operation after several false starts was the collection of 'Remy' a French intelligence officer who was to be one of de Gaulle's best agents. Colonel Gilbert Renault-Roulier to give the gentleman his proper name was due off Lorient on the afternoon tide, when the SIS trawler approached the port. Three German mine-sweepers came towards the fishermen just when they expected the colonel, but the German crews took no notice of CC 2682 although passing within 500m of her. Behind these ships was a sailing smack which came out from the shelter of a small island, her crew responded to the fisherman's hail with the password and the smack tied alongside CC 2682. The first passengers to be lifted across to the bigger boat were Remy's three children, all under 11, followed by his wife and an aide to the colonel carrying the luggage. Then the colonel appeared with his six-month-old baby on one arm and a bulging brief case in the other. A Heinkel flew over as CC 2682 hauled her nets, a German armed trawler passed her as did three of their destroyers as she sailed back to the Scillies. None of these made any attempt to prevent the fishing boat making a safe passage home, a pointer to the value of such vessels for clandestine work, not only in the English Channel. Here by 1944 the Germans had sea patrols, coast defences and had also restricted the movement of the few civilians that had not been forcibly evacuated from the coast to 25km inland. SOE's DF Section nevertheless continued to land agents finding the Germans were less alert, even unsuspecting, if the dinghies and dories landed near to strong points. One organizer took advantage of this in making six landings on different nights only tens of metres from the same pillbox.

The SIS flotilla moved from the Dart to join SOE's 'crash' boats in 1942 on the Helford River. They then formed the Inshore Patrol Flotilla, although the shores these boats visited were not confined to the south coast of England as the title suggested. A purpose-built craft was added to the flotilla in 1943, built in a British yard to look like a French Douarnenez crabber. Her mast and deckhouse were made of veneered balsa wood and were therefore extremely light. In addition to the small engine she used for fishing, she had two 650hp Hall Scott engines, giving her the power to lift on her flat-bottomed hull to 'cream' out of trouble at 25kt; other French boats were added. The 15th Motor Gun Boat Flotilla with four craft capable of 27kt, and also in April 1944 a flotilla of US Navy 40kt PT boats, joined this clandestine ferry service.

The flotillas landed agents and some stores, usually working in the moonless period of each month. They put ashore agents for Remy and for other circuits operated by de Gaulle's secret services (they were brought together as BCRA in January 1942). One of these had been set up in October 1941 as 'Overcloud' with several undergraduates in Brittany whose enthusiasm outweighed any sense of security. The circuit was penetrated by a double-agent and its radio set controlled by the Germans, as the Allied services quickly realized. More successful were the French 'Mango' missions which in 1943 led to the formation of the 'Var' line that brought agents by sea from Brittany in

1943 and 1944. MI 9 used the craft to evacuate 128 Allied airmen during these years, when techniques were improved with the use of S-phones in craft. The British had also improved the small boats which ferried agents to and from the beach, with a double-bowed dory able to land through surf, her stern being the same shape as the bow.

These boats proved seaworthy enough to survive even in the rough weather off Norway, where SOE was able to operate without the restrictions that gave SIS priority on the French coasts. This was one reason why Norwegian crews, supported by SOE, could run a regular fishing boat service from the Shetland Islands to Norway with such methodical regularity that the service was known as the 'Shetland Bus'. By November 1943 the 'Bus' had landed 84 agents and brought out 135 people, mainly volunteers for the Free Norwegian military services. However, the Germans began much closer surveillance of the fishing fleets from July 1943 in the Channel, and elsewhere later that year. The British made it known that any German-controlled shipping would be attacked as part of the war against U-boats. In Norwegian waters this forced the fishing fleets to work among the islands rather than far offshore during the summer months when the weather was more favourable to fishing. Indeed most of the eight boats lost on the Shetland service were probably sunk in bad weather rather than by enemy action. In high summer the long hours of daylight made such operations all too easily intercepted by German aircraft. Both the problems of weather in winter and long summer days were answered by 1944 with 110-ft American submarine chasers, provided through OSS and manned by Norwegian crews. They landed 135 agents in the seasons of 1944 and 1945, being able to operate for a longer period each year before the nights became too brief.

A less usual operation for SOE was set up in Sweden in January 1941. At this time their organizer George (later Sir George) Binney found volunteers to 'cut out', in the buccaneering phrase, five interned British ships loaded with special steels and ball-bearings used to make armaments. They broke out of Göteborg and reached a naval escort in the North Sea, which drove off German aircraft that had somewhat belatedly taken up the chase. This delay was not accidental: a Swedish police officer had helpfully cut telephone lines by which squadrons in Norway and Denmark might be alerted. A similar attempt with ten ships in April 1942 was intercepted by the Germans before all but two ships reached safety; six were sunk and two returned to Sweden. There the anti-aircraft weapons smuggled onto the ships for the breakout, caused a diplomatic rumpus at such a breach of the Swedes' neutrality. Thereafter the smuggling of ball-bearings from Sweden had to be

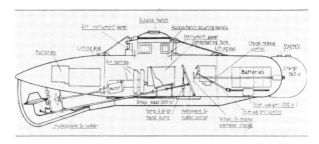

▲ The Welman one-man submarine designed to place a 560 lb charge while submerged beneath an enemy ship. It was launched by derrick from a transport ship or towed by a ship to the enemy's coast. The craft was 20ft 2in overall including the bow charge. Its surface displacement was 4,600 lb. The 2½hp electric motor gave it a speed of 2.5 knots when submerged at its operating depth of 75ft, with an endurance of 10 hours. This could be extended to 20 hours if the speed was reduced to 1.7 knots. In an emergency the crewman dropped the 630 lb keel in order to surface, even if the boat was partially filled with water. The design and prototype came from the Welwyn Laboratories of SOE.

▼ A Welman submersible recovered in 1980 from 70 feet of water off Scapa Flow on the north Scottish coast. Many training exercises for all manner of Allied submersibles were carried out in these waters during the last two years of the war. This craft does not have its explosive charge fitted and the keel appears to be still in place. It may have been lost because the heavy glass ports imploded as they did, on at least one other craft. The access hatch is missing and therefore the crewman probably escaped but no report of the sinking has been traced.

reorganized with a few motor gun boats, but that is not part of SOE's story.

Before leaving Scandinavia for warmer seas, the operations of the one-man Welman submersible need unravelling. This craft was the Army's answer to the Royal Navy's Motorised Submersible Canoe. The only record of operational missions by Welman pilots relate to a raid on Bergen in 1944. A team of Norwegians with both these craft and the submersible canoes, infiltrated onto the south-west coast of Norway in a fishing boat towing the Welman craft. There is no firm evidence that they managed to place charges on or under any craft in the harbour, and in all probability this daring team were all drowned.

T HE Italian MAS boat (submarine chaser) was perhaps 4km from the French coast when her Italian skipper cut the power of his main engines. The boat, slowing from the 30kt at which she made the passage from the Special Forces' base on Corsica, was switched to silent running as she neared a secret landfall. The 'pinpoint' in OSS jargon, where she was to put two agents shore. Typical of several Italian ships in the Allied service since October 1943, she also had aboard a Royal Navy officer who no doubt felt he had a 'square number' of an easy job as SOE's representative on this mission. He continued to think so until, without any warning, one of the Italian crew shot him. It is possible that there were lingering pro-Fascist sympathies among the men, but more likely they just wanted to quit the naval service, so they shot their own officer, the SOE representative and the two agents. Then with all four dead the crew sailed for a German-held port in northern Italy. Such treachery was an extreme example of the violence that seemed endemic to operations from Corsica.

USN Squadron 15 of PT Boats and a flotilla of Royal Navy MGBs had operated out of Bastia since October 1943, with the five MAS attached to them until March 1944 when the above incident made the Allies wary of using Italian crews for clandestine work. Bastia was 140km from the French Mediterranean coast. Also within a few hours' passage were the islands of Capria north of Elba, Gorgona 30km from the German-held port of Livorno, and Elba although it was strongly garrisoned; all made useful places for coast-watching observers from OSS' OGs. However, after six weeks the teams on Elba, closer to the Italian mainland than to Corsica, were detected by the garrison and had to be withdrawn.

By 1945 the OGs in the Italian theatre, '. . . tough little boys from New York and Chicago with a few live hoods mixed in . . .' to quote one of their training officers, were considered almost as dangerous to their Allies as to the enemy. Therefore when Groups returned from operations they were confined to their billets in a castle near La Spezia, with retraining exercises and refresher courses. There were brawls and several murders, unpopular officers were threatened; while Donovan's staff became concerned that several members of Murder Inc and the Philadelphia Purple Gang would never become disciplined soldiers in OGs. The undisciplined were therefore sent back to the States and others, the vast majority, returned to operations. These members of the OGs, like the British SAS, were well disciplined if hard men who fought in Greece, Yugoslavia and elsewhere in the Balkans. More often they were inserted on a mission by local boats, like SI operatives in this theatre, than by other means.

The US Balkan Airforce seldom had aircraft to spare for OSS who were refused permission to raise its own Middle East air unit. Therefore OSS ran a fleet of 36 caïques, the Mediterranean fishing boats that ranged from large vessels of 80 tons or more to smaller ones of 20 tons. Several of the larger craft ran from Alexandria in Egypt to Karovostasi in north-west Cyprus where OSS built up a large depot. From there 20-ton craft ran operatives and later OG parties to the islands near the Turkish coast. (SIS had arranged with neutral Turkey to allow Allied craft to carry stores and personnel through their waters, although caïque skippers carried an emergency supply of gold sovereigns for any hand-outs needed to quieten local officials who might want to inspect a caïque's cargo.)

The Germans garrisoned many of the Aegean islands which were raided by British Commandos, the Special Boat Squadrons of the SAS, the Greek Sacred Squadron and OGs. These operations were controlled latterly by Raiding Forces Middle East in concert with SOE at Cairo which controlled its own agents and those seconded to guerrilla operations from the OGs. SI had its own operations separately run from those of the British SIS but in the early days (1943) SIS provided gold, ships and other support until OSS had established its fleet of caïques. The Germans also used these local wooden-hulled fishing boats and schooners. Many of them were destroyed by the Allies when raiding island garrisons, others might be sunk by attacking OSS' 'pin up'. When they could intercept these supply vessels' convoys, however, commandos or other special forces were put aboard them from naval launches and the captured prizes sailed to Allied ports, their cargoes often providing some welcome variety in the rations.

One of the most successful OSS operations supported by seaborne operations was run by a former British agent in Crete who joined the American Army. His 'Horsebreeders' circuit by 1944 had some 500 agents and sub-agents providing 'int' from the port of Volos, where it appears that SOE had not been able to establish a reliable circuit. The organizer was established in a village not far from Volos, with his radio operator and a courier. From the village the network of agents spread northward across Thessaly. A second radio operator on Skiathos island reported movements of shipping between Piraeus and Salonika. Two local sub-agents were trained as relief radio operators, no doubt recruited as were many Greek sub-agents through the Communist National Liberation Front, which controlled a military force known as ELAS partisans.

The Communists, not only in Greece, had been used to keeping their secret organizations secure from penetration by their enemies. They therefore readily adopted, if these did not already exist, the organizer's scheme for a series of chains of separate cells numbering between 10 and 20 people. Only one of these knew a courier from the neighbouring cell in the chain. Then if anyone was arrested in the first cell this courier reported the fact to his contacts and dropped out of touch with his or her cellmates before they could be compromised.

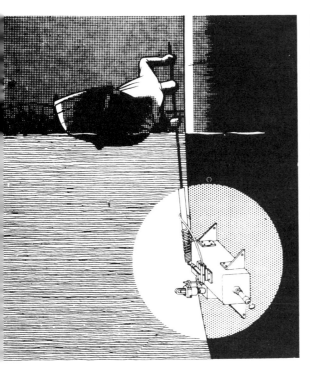

▲ Conventional limpet mines with magnets could not be used against wooden hulls. Therefore OSS produced the 'Pin-Up Girl', a device for pinning a limpet mine to a wooden hull. Its case of Torpex explosive had four extended brackets to steady its hold on a ship's side five feet below her waterline. A fitting below this case took the pinning device with its steel pin fired by a small charge. The main charge was fired by two AC time delay fuses. The pinning device was 5½ inches long, weighed 8 oz and was supplied ready for firing. The steel pin was driven into a hull once the pull ring on its line had been pulled free by the agent. The manual suggests that the sound of this small explosion would not be noticed by anyone aboard the ship. Two types of pin were available, one marked with a green band for use against wooden hulls and others for use against steel. The main charge in its plastic case blew a hole 'about 25 square feet in the hull'—to quote the manual from which this page is taken.

Such a system of cut-outs ensured that the Germans could not work from one cell to the next in a town.

After a cell had been penetrated a different courier, the 'reconnecting agent' worked with the help of one of the neighbouring cells. He or she would try to re-establish contact with any survivors from the penetrated cell. If this sounds complicated, the annotation on agents' field reports is even more so. Each carried a reference, say 1706b5619: cell 17's agent 06 whose helper 'b' had seen with his own eyes (5) whatever was reported as occurring on June (6) the 19th. The organizer commented on such reports, asking for further information when necessary. Needless to say there were also less elaborate means of reporting German movements. There were five OPs in direct telephone contact with the organizer, although whether these phones were part of the public system is not clear. Whatever the connection, he was kept informed of ship

movements and all German traffic on important roads, details of which could be radioed to OSS Cairo. Several of the most valued agents worked outside the chains of cells, including interpreters working for the Germans. Being close to the enemy they were able at times to give warnings when the Germans began to be suspicious of certain agents. At other times the interpreters provided safe houses for cut-out couriers and others, including no doubt the sabotage teams which worked separately from the 'int' cells.

The saboteurs '. . . put sand and emery dust in grease boxes of trains . . .' but from April 1944 OG teams were landed by caïque, as were British commandos, to provide the 'know-how' for more elaborate sabotage. The OG teams varied from three-man parties to complete sections each of 15 men. By the time the main operation 'Smashem' was mounted in Greece from 8 September 1944, there were 190 men of the OGs mainly in southern Greece. In the 10 weeks before they were withdrawn they had destroyed 15 bridges and many sections of railway track, totalling some 10km, ambushed 14 trains and caused over 2,000 German casualties.

All three Allied agencies—OSS, SIS and SOE—kept agents in Greece during the civil war which broke out as the Germans withdrew that December. Even before then as OGs and Commandos were attacking the retreating German lines, ELAS' 20,000 partisans had units fighting EDES, the 6,000-strong Socialist guerrillas. These Socialists would have been totally overwhelmed had not SOE arranged for the Royal Navy to evacuate many of them. The British had political commitments to the Royalists, but both OSS and SOE found that the Greek monarchy had few supporters in Greece. There was also the feeling among some Americans that the British were interested not only in stemming any spread of Communism, but wished to maintain some diplomatic influence over Greek politics. Be that as it may, an OSS team negotiated the release by ELAS of 965 British soldiers whom the guerrillas had captured during fighting in Athens. Such hostilities had led to criticism at the time, not only from some OSS officers. Yet by defeating ELAS in Athens, the British enabled the Greeks to remain free in later years. The OSS also had operatives in Greece that December, providing invaluable information for the State Department.

Once Greece was freed of German forces, even if other battles were being fought, the Allies moved their military Special Forces into the northern Adratic. The islands there were well defended, however, and the successes of the Aegean were not repeated. In the southern Adriatic OSS' Maritime Unit had 15 schooners which helped to supply Tito's forces, while along the Italian east coast that summer a small detachment of D

Company worked with the British Eighth Army. After being landed from naval craft or OSS *caïques* they operated in small teams. Each had an organizer who liaised with Italian partisans and at least one radio operator. Some teams gathered intelligence from as far north of the battle area as Venice. Others worked much closer to the German front line, two of them being able to direct artillery fire onto targets not far from the main battles. This action and the high quality of information which the teams provided, was appreciated by the British. The Eighth Army therefore issued orders which concentrated '... all clandestine line penetration ... under the [Company D's] detachment instead of SOE ...' in those sectors where OSS teams operated. (These details were noted in the OSS War Report.) OSS' Maritime Unit also took command of teams of Italian swimmer-canoeists from the elite San Marco Battalion. They brought with them to the east coast such Italian equipment as the two-man inflatable 'mattresses', each powered by a pair of silent electric motors. In June 1944 these swimmers destroyed a railway bridge 150km north of the battle area; in July they brought out the first of many Italians working for OSS. One of these brought out in late April 1945 provided invaluable details of the German 'Gothic' line around Pesaro, which was to be attacked four days after his intelligence reached the Eighth Army's headquarters.

In April also Allen Dulles, heading OSS' offices in Switzerland, had been able to enter into secret negotiations for the surrender of German armies in Italy and Austria. The negotiations were drawn out until 2 May 1945, a week or so before the final surrender.

One of the last waterborne operations in Europe was the infiltration of two OSS teams across the Rhine on 'waterlilies'. Two others parachuted to DZs across the Rhine, from the OSS detachment with the American Ninth Army, but were overrun by its advanced units '... before any intelligence of real value ...' could be transmitted.

W HEN the war came to an end in Europe that May, many OSS and SOE agents were transferred to the Far East, as the Allied junior staffs anticipated a long campaign. They envisaged Singapore being recaptured in the winter of 1945-46, and an invasion of the Japanese mainland in the following winter. However, by May 1945 the US Marines were fighting to clear Okinawa, an island 550km from the Japanese mainland; the American army was fighting in the Philippines; the Australians preparing to seize Lubuan Island off the north-west coast of Borneo; and the British landed unopposed at Rangoon in Burma, before the end of May. (The Russians, however, did not invade Manchuria until 9 August.)

Something of SOE's and OSS' land operations in the Far East have been described but SOE also had some swimmer-canoeists based in Australia. There the Executive was known by various titles: Services Reconnaissance Department (SRD); the Inter-Allied Services Department; Force 137; and by Baker Street as 'SOA' (Special Operations Australia). These canoeists were trained to use limpet mines in anti-shipping raids and other methods of sabotage. Six of them provided teams for a series of operations from submarines in January 1945, when small ships, coastal railways and other targets were attacked. Targets which were either not worth the cost of a torpedo or too risky for the submarines to attack by surfacing to use their guns. Other SOA canoe teams worked with the American submarine command in the south-west Pacific theatre, but when this headquarters moved to the Philippines the canoeists were not allowed to go there. MacArthur disliked SOE as much as OSS, hence the reason for his support of AIB.

The coast watchers we left on Guadalcanal in 1942 were at the eastern end of a chain of observation posts on several islands including those manned by W. J. 'Jack' Read and Paul Edward Mason at opposite ends of the jungle-covered mountains of Bougainville, at the western end of the Solomon Islands. Jack was an experienced administrator who had worked in the Solomon Islands for many years. Edward Mason was a planter with mild blue eyes behind spectacles giving no hint of his ability to endure great hardship. Each had a small band of Solomon Islanders they had picked for the men's common sense and reliability, before the Japanese landed. When they came ashore Mason did not have time to cache any stores from the coconut plantation which he managed. Despite this setback, he established an observation post overlooking a bay on the southern tip of the island, which became a major Japanese anchorage. Both coast-watchers would be re-supplied either by submarines or air drops. The first parachuted supplies for Mason fell 110km from the intended DZ. He set out therefore on a three-day journey dodging Japanese patrols, only to discover the stores had been stolen before he could collect them.

Jack Read, in the north of the island, had been able to cache some stores. His 'teleradio' was the type of radio-telephone used by the Flying Doctor service in the Australian outback but it could also be used for continuous-wave (Morse) transmissions. His coded messages by the summer of 1942 passed first to the radio station 1,100km to the south-west on New Guinea, from there another 1,300km to AIB's communications centre at Townsville and then a like distance down the Queensland coast to AIB headquarters in Brisbane. But in July 1942 terse voice messages were used with crisp call signs, Read's was 'Jer'. It was used by him at the time of the 1 Marine Division's landing 800km to his south-east on Guadacanal, with the brief comment, '40 bombers headed yours' (your way), which became a catch phrase. The American Task Force was therefore ready and waiting when the bombers arrived. Only eight of them returning later over Read's look-out station. In the next seven months Read, Mason and other coast-watchers including American Marines trained by the Australians, maintained a steady stream of such warnings.

The Japanese landed dogs to search for Mason on the south-east tip of the island but they were killed in an air-raid laid on by the RAAF at the request of AIB. This was only a temporary respite, for Mason had to bury his radio and send some of his Melanesians back to their villages. He later recovered the set but was then forced for six weeks to dodge the Japanese after four 50-man patrols were sent to search for him, before he reached Read in the north of the island. From there in December 1942 Read organized the evacuation of women and children in the USS *Nautilus*, a 3,000-ton submarine. A second evacuation the following March enabled the USS *Gato* to carry to safety most of the remaining Europeans and Chinese when she crammed 51 passengers below her hatches before diving. The evacuation had become necessary as the native population was by this time being dominated by the Japanese, and Europeans could no longer hide safely in the mountains. *Gato* had brought in supplies, including precious petrol for the generators which recharged the 'wet' batteries, and some experienced coast-watchers among whom was Captain E. D. 'Wobbie' Robinson of the Australian army.

The Japanese no doubt heard of these reinforcements as their patrols became particularly active early in April, when Read and Robinson had their observation post on the escarpment edge of a high ridge overlooking the sea. This look-out could only be approached up a single track through the jungle. It was guarded by an outer ring of defence posts with an inner one closer to the palm-leaf hut in which Read had the radio. Pieces of dry bamboo were laid on the trail between the inner and outer defence posts, so that they would break with resounding cracks should anyone step on the pieces. The inner defences' automatic weapons were set to fire along the trail, and manned by some of the platoon of Australian infantry who had been put ashore by *Gato* to relieve the soldiers she took off the island. Also in the inner defences was Sergeant Yauwika of the island's police who had been Read's companion since the beginning of the war, and took charge of the few Melanesian islanders who helped the coast-watcher.

One afternoon in April an old man came up the trail to trade some edible taro roots for calico cloth, a routine piece of barter. Yet this exchange almost subcon-

sciously gave Read some concern for he put several items in his pack, after the old man left. Almost immediately a runner came to the hut to report a large party of Japanese climbing the trail. The radio was therefore quickly buried before the brief tropical twilight became night. A single shot reverberated across the ridge, followed by the chatter of machine-guns fired from the inner defences. Realizing that the attackers would soon be at the hut door, Read dived through the palm leaf side, closely followed by Robinson. Grenades burst inside the hut as they rolled clear to see the enemy on all sides but the one facing the sea. They went over this escarpment edge, finding the steep slope became a precipice as they clung to the matted undergrowth over a sheer cliff. When daylight came they worked their way to the left before reaching a gully which they climbed down to the valley floor and the safety of the jungle.

A couple of days later they reached one of Read's caches of rations for such emergencies. They also joined soldiers and Sergeant Yauwika who no doubt had a pre-arranged rendezvous in anticipation of the post being overrun. When they later visited its site to recover the radio they found the body of the old man with the calico. He was lying on the bamboo strewn path, from where the sound of his return must have warned the inner defences. There seems no doubt that he led the Japanese to the hut, a sign of their growing dominance over the islanders.

Some time before Read's camp was raided, Mason had gone back to the south-east shore of the island, but here he was again attacked and several of his companions killed. Yet this boyish looking planter with his quiet manner and round face had powers of endurance beyond those of many a trained soldier. Once again he took to the island's jungles with a small party of survivors, and his radio. It withstood the damp, the bumps as the Melanesians carried it over mountain trails and the days buried in the ground when Mason had to hide it, wrapped no doubt in waterproof sheeting. As the party moved along the southern shore, perhaps 130km from Read, he found enough petrol to run the generator and recharge spare batteries, for those at the camp had been destroyed. He then transmitted a coded message to AIB who replied that a submarine would pick up Mason's party in four days.

USS *Guardfish*'s skipper must have been surprised at the size of this group, for when he rendezvoused with Mason there were 60 passengers to take aboard. These included soldiers, Chinese traders, loyal Melanesians and two airmen who had survived a crash in the mountains when resupplying Read. (Some of this crew had been injured in the crash and were subsequently killed by the Japanese.) The submarine ran her passengers south of the island to transfer them to a surface ship, before *Guardfish* returned to

Bougainville's north-west shore to collect Read and his party. Jack Read had been 17 months in the jungle surviving its hot and fetid climate, laid low at times by malaria but always inspiring the loyalty of his men. They were all to be evacuated by *Guardfish* but as Read suspected when he briefed them, a number of married men stayed on the island.

Others would be back six months later in November 1943, guiding American Marine companies in their recapture of the island. By that date AIB had raised and supplied a number of guerrilla bands from these Solomon and other islands, with sabotage teams and other clandestine forces led by officers who had served as coast watchers in 1942.

AIB's most extensive undercover operations were in the Philippines, too distant from the Bureau's bases to be reached by air in 1942. A plan was considered to use a stripped down Liberator, but submarines were to prove a more reliable means of crossing nearly 2,000km of ocean to reach these islands. In 1942 several American and Filipino officers had evaded capture to lead guerrilla bands with marked success, but there was little information in AIB about their activities. Four men escaped in small boats from the islands early in 1942, others were drowned in such attempts. The survivors' reports and a somewhat bizarre series of transmissions from a clandestine radio which berated the Japanese, provided the first hard intelligence of conditions on the islands. No European could expect to move around undetected, therefore AIB recruited men like Captain (later Colonel) Joseph McMicking, the highly educated son of a wealthy Spanish-Filipino family. He was the only junior officer MacArthur had included in his party, ordered out of Corregidor after the Japanese invasion of the Philippines. He intended to use the young captain's abilities and contacts to re-establish an Allied force in the islands, as he had helped to set up 'left behind' parties. Few others escaped, but Major Jesus Villamor was ordered to fly out on one of the last American planes to leave the islands, as he was a national hero in the Philippines, decorated for flying his obsolete P-36 fighter against overwhelming forces of Japanese bombers.

The son of a well-known judge in the islands, Villamor's family were close friends of the McMickings, and Joseph recruited him for AIB. The young major was allowed to pick his team for what would be the first reconnaissance, with important questions to answer. Were the Filipinos resentful of the Americans' failure to defend the islands? Which of the bands of fighters on the island were attacking the Japanese and which were no more than criminal gangs? There seems little doubt that some could be more aptly described as bandits than guerrillas. Yet several of the parties left behind on the island proved responsible agents, later radioing brief reports which were more informative than the radio transmissions attacking the Japanese.

In training, Villamor's team had to chop wood and plough land after hard days in surf training, judo, and the many skills needed for clandestine operations. The ploughing was cover for the story that these Filipinos were hill farmers being resettled in Australia. Their night training included more warlike practices, like caching stores brought ashore through heavy surf. By the winter, the 'summer' season in Brisbane where they had trained, they were physically hardened and their knowledge of radio procedures, map reading and recognition of Japanese military vehicles, honed sharp before they boarded USS *Gudgeon*. She put them ashore 'blind' on Negros an island of over 2,500km^2 and within a day's sailing of the much larger island of Mindinao to the south. Their intention was eventually to establish an intelligence circuit stretching from this major island, where guerrillas were known to be operating, to the north on the other large island of Luzon with the Philippines' capital of Manila. If this could be done among the many islands' population of over 20 million, MacArthur would have sound information on the situation before his army landed to re-conquer the islands.

Villamor, like Ben Cowburn, was prepared to take infinite care to ensure that his mission would succeed, although he had not bargained for his picture, cut from newspapers of the previous year, appearing on the walls of many homes whose families honoured him as a hero. This and other necessities for caution delayed their first transmission until 26 January 1943, when the powerful 50-watt radio built in Australia by the American Signal Corps began a series of transmissions which provided AIB with hard intelligence. Included were reports on the successful delivery of a high grade cipher to the guerrilla leader on Panay Island. Known as 'Peralta' this young graduate of the Philippine Military Academy had been a member of one 'left behind' party, his radio operator first contacting the American 'comcen' in San Francisco when by chance the duty officer knew of Peralta. The less understandable transmissions came from Cebu, east of Negros, where the mining engineer, James Cushing, ran a guerrilla force. The radio had been built by a former announcer of the Philippine Radio Company, Harry Fenton, who was in the habit of making somewhat inflammatory broadcasts. Cushing, however, was more concerned with Fenton's violent habit of using firearms if any of his companions annoyed him—he had shot a local priest in some dispute. Villamor's sub-agents on Cebu had already reported something of these difficulties, and when Cushing visited Negros he had left Fenton under arrest. The mining engineer was to become one of AIB's principal agents in the islands, but early in 1943

Villamor had some difficulty in persuading the Bureau that these guerrillas should be provided with supplies, weapons and ammunition from the submarines. Fenton's broadcasts had not only inflamed the Japanese but also angered the Americans, aware that such vilification was bound to bring Japanese forces to attack the guerrillas.

The broadcasts ceased only when, in Cushing's absence on Negros, the Filipino officers of the guerrillas tried and executed Fenton for the murder of the priest. Cushing and others were later provided with transceivers, including the ATR 4A which was reliable and no larger than a British 18 Set, but far more robust. Villamor's agents set up a series of radio networks which reported to Negros, intelligence that was then sifted and relayed to AIB. These operations, code named 'Planet', were supplemented in later months by seven other major circuits, all supplied by submarine before the autumn of 1944. The following year many more missions were landed and supplies were parachuted to guerrilla forces, which made a major contribution to MacArthur's recapture of the islands, after the American Sixth Army landed on Leyte in October 1944. This campaign would last through the winter when 360,000 Japanese fought battles of attrition as the Americans reconquered the island.

A IB carried out 264 missions besides those in the Philippines, two of which highlight the need for good luck in such operations, and the high price of failure. Both were led by the ever cheerful Ivan Lyon who had organized the 'Tourist Route' across Sumatra in January 1942. Long before the Japanese invaded Malaya he had sailed through Riau archipelago of which Singapore island was the most northerly one. These many uninhabited pinpoints of land could provide secret bases, from which shipping lanes to Singapore might be watched, but there was no opportunity in February 1942 to leave any coast-watchers so close to the Japanese shipping routes. In the late summer of 1944 Lyon had a different purpose in mind for these islands which could provide a secret base for raids against ships in Singapore.

The techniques for such raids had been developed by the Special Boat Sections of British Army Commandos in 1941, mainly for operations in the Mediterranean. Other uniformed canoeists—if a swimmer's waterproof suit counts as a uniform—of the Royal Marines 'Cockleshell heroes' in the RMBPD and the SAS troopers of the Special Boat Squadrons, also used the technique. A two-man canoe, usually launched from a submarine, was paddled into an enemy harbour, went alongside a ship and the canoeists then placed limpet mines below the waterline of the hull, using a special

rod or a hook on the end of a paddle. Time fuses would give the paddlers the opportunity to be clear of the harbour before the mines each blew a hole two metres in diameter in the plating of a merchantman.

Lyon, as we have seen, had reached India safely in 1942. That year the small Japanese trawler *Kofuka Maru* reached Ceylon, after the Australian Bill Reynolds, with a scratch crew had sailed her from Singapore to evade capture. She was renamed *Krait* (after a particularly venomous small Indian snake), and SOE found a crew to sail her to Australia. However, her worn-out engine failed and she was shipped as deck cargo to Broken Bay where in December 1942 Lyon was training AIB's canoeists of Force Z. In the next nine months he and his second-in-command, Lieutenant Donald Davidson, RNVR, trained the canoe teams in launching their Folbots from submarines, landing in surf after paddling long distances. They also learnt to use astronavigation, to supplement their dead-reckoning. The frail canvas canoes with their light wooden frames proved remarkably seaworthy in the hands of experienced paddlers, but the training was prolonged as *Krait* had to be fitted with a new Gardiner engine.

Her skipper, Lieutenant H. E. Carse, RANVR, worked up his small crew of seven to a high pitch of efficiency by the summer, before she sailed on 2 September 1943 from the American submarine base in Exmouth Gulf,

▲ A limpet mine with its magnets that could hold to a metal hull or other metallic structure such as a bridge pier. It could blow a 25 square foot hole in the hull of a merchantman and was fired by a time delay fuse. The ship might have left her berth before the explosion, but the magnets were strong enough to hold to her side against the pressure as she moved through the water. Always provided that the fouling on her underwater hull did not prevent the magnets obtaining a proper grip. On a steam vessel the limpet should be placed opposite the boilers. The OSS limpet case measured 9¼ x 8 x 3 inches (including the magnets). The AC fuse was activated by crushing its ampoule of solvent with the butterfly nut (seen on left). A second AC fuse might be inserted by removing the cap (on right end of mine illustrated) and replacing this with a second fuse holder with its butterfly nut. The standard OSS charge was Torpex but the plastic cases were also supplied for charging with PE. (PE reacted with the plastic of the case and therefore had to be inserted just before use). The raised centre bracket on the case allowed the agent to use a placing rod to position the mine five to six feet below a ship's waterline.

▼ A 'Sleeping Beauty' submerging during training, cruising at a depth of 30 ft. The canoe was intended for underwater approaches to ships in harbour. On reaching his target the diver-pilot might ground the canoe on the sea bottom. He then swam with his limpets to place these on the ship's side before returning to the canoe and withdrawing from the harbour. The 13-foot canoe weighed 600 lb, had an endurance of about 12 miles when submerged but over 30 miles on the surface. Its submerged speed was over two knots and on the surface 4½ knots even when riding through small waves.

▼ The joy-stick controlled the MSC's hydroplanes and rudder. To vent the main ballast tanks, the diver used his right thumb on the control extended to be near the right-hand grip. To the right of this are controls for venting the trimming tank in the bow and another which 'blew' this tank by opening a valve to the compressed air supply. The depth guage can be seen at the top left.

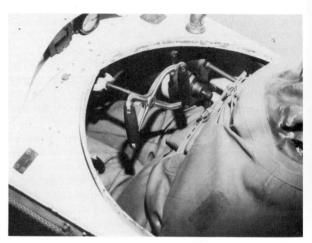

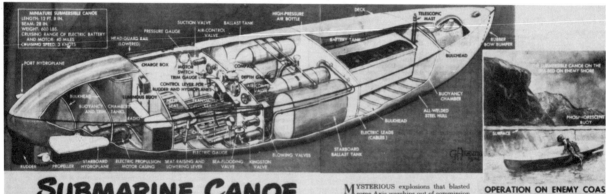

SUBMARINE CANOE

CRUISING ON THE SURFACE

CRUISING UNDER SURFACE

PADDLES OR SAIL MAY BE USED TO SAVE MOTOR POWER

Drawings by the British artist, G. H. Davis, show the intricate equipment that enabled submersible canoes to float or go under water. Sketches at the bottom reveal how the versatile craft attacked enemy ships. At right, an enemy coastline is the target

MYSTERIOUS explosions that blasted some Axis warships out of commission were set off by a weapon the existence of which was one of the most closely guarded secrets of the war.

This potent weapon was a British-designed submarine canoe, a 13-foot 600-pound craft that carried one man wearing underwater breathing equipment.

Powered by an electric motor but also outfitted with sails and paddles for emergencies, the submersible canoe would be driven on the surface until there was danger of being spotted from an enemy vessel.

Then the operator would nose his craft under water and proceed until he made contact with the target. With his canoe resting under the enemy ship, the "frog man" would attach delayed-action charges to the bilge keel. Climbing back into his canoe, he would speed away toward his "mother ship."

Another use for the fishlike canoes was to transport fighting men to enemy shores for meetings with members of the resistance movement or for raids on Axis installations near the seashore.

OPERATION ON ENEMY COAS

PILOT LEAVES SUBMERGED CANOE AND WADES ASHORE ON MISSION IN HOSTILE TERRITORY

SUB CANOE ATTACKS AN   ENEMY VESSEL ANCHORED IN HARBOR ◆ ◆ ◆

TARGET CONTACTED BY HOLDING. PILOT SWITCHES OFF AND SLOWLY SINKS

CANOE RESTS UNDER ENEMY SHIP AS PILOT ATTACHES EXPLOSIVE CHARGES

DELAYED ACTION CRAFT WITHDRAWS

RENDEZVOUS WITH MOTHER SHIP AFTER ATTACK

Western Australia. Abroad were three canoe teams and an RAMC corporal, R. G. Morris, as medic. There was no sign that she had been converted from her intended purpose as a fishing boat, as she was to sail several thousand kilometres north on operation 'Jaywick', through Japanese-patrolled waters. Once she had passed through Lombok Strait east of Bali Island in modern Indonesia, with luck no patrolling Japanese ships or aircraft would think one of 'their' fishing boats was worth a close inspection. Her luck held and 30km north-west of Singapore she hove to under the lee of a small island. There the canoes were launched by Lyon, Davidson, Lieutenant R. C. Page of the Australian Army, Able Seamen F. G. Falls, F. W. Marsh and A. W. Huston. The seamen would provide more than the muscle power for the long paddle to Singapore harbour, for while the officers placed the limpets the second man in each canoe had to steady it. Both men worked equally hard on the approach run for officers and men worked as a team, checking the distances covered with 1,000 paddle strokes equal to perhaps two kilometres (each team knew its own rate of strokes per kilometre).

They slipped into the harbour unnoticed, partly by skill in that they moved the canoes quietly over the water avoiding phosphorescent splashes from the double paddles' blades. No doubt they also used the single half of each paddle when in the harbour to move with even greater stealth. Part of their success was due to luck, for an inquisitive lounger on the quays or chance meeting with a harbour motorboat could give them away. As it was they had placed limpets on seven ships and were clearing the harbour when the first of these exploded. It had clung firmly to the ship's side, an indication not only that it had been properly set but that weed on the hull had not prevented the magnets holding fast. As more explosions awakened the garrison to action, Japanese submarine chasers began searching for an Allied submarine which they believed was still in the harbour. A confusion which must have helped the canoeists make their escape at no more than four knots, however hard they paddled. They reach Krait, sailing on the return passage without a serious incident, to reach Exmouth Gulf on 19 October. She had been at sea 47 days, steamed nearly 9,000km two-thirds of them in Japanese waters—AIB later confirmed that her canoeists had sunk 37,000 tons of shipping.

This was a small tonnage by comparison with Japanese losses from air and submarine attacks, but canoe operations were considerably less expensive in both the cost of training and of equipment. This point

◄ The Motor Submersible Canoe was known as the 'Sleeping Beauty'. This cutaway diagram shows the cockpit with the ballast tanks forward of the diver-pilot and the electric batteries towards the bow. These powered the half horse-power heavy duty motor in the stern. This illustration was drawn by G. H. Davis in 1946 when the MSC was described as a 'Miniature Submersible Canoe'.

was no doubt discussed by Lyon with SOE and others when he visited London after the raid. There he studied the Motorized Submersible Canoe (MSC) which had been invented by Colonel Quentin Reeves (at Welwyn) and issued to Royal Marine swimmer-canoeists.

Sub-Lieutenant Riggs, RNVR attached to AIB went to Portsmouth, Hampshire, where Marines were training on the MSC which had been dubbed the 'Sleeping Beauty'. This relatively short canoe of 4.2m had an alloy hull with a series of air tanks that enabled her pilot in a diving suit to dive the canoe some 10m (see Appendix 3.14). She could cruise at 4.5kt for 60km on the surface but submerged at her maximum six knots—she had a third of this range. Her cockpit was equipped with simple controls, principal of which was the joystick with hand grips each side controlling the hydroplanes and rudder, as the pilot nosed her gently below the surface. Fifteen of the Mark II MSC were taken by Riggs to Australia where Lyon was training AIB's Group X of swimmer-canoeists for operation 'Rimau' (Malay for 'tiger').

In this operation Lyon's teams and a back-up party would be based on one of the Riau islands, from where they could mount raids against Japanese shipping over a period of several weeks. They sailed for the islands, known in the 1940s as the Rhio islands, on 11 September 1944 aboard the mine-laying submarine HMS Porpoise. The submersible canoes were stowed in her racks, normally used for 're-load' torpedoes. There were 32 officers and men of Group X aboard in addition to her crew of 64, making conditions not only cramped but also, after long spells under water, the men found breathing difficult as the oxygen became exhausted in the boat's air supply. Nevertheless after two weeks she reached the islands, surveyed Pulo Merepas in a periscope recce before landing Group X's detachment on this totally deserted island. The stores brought ashore included a number of items specially made for this raid, such as the stockinette masks worn with rubber skull-caps that could be garnished with seaweed. These were more suitable camouflage than the shark's fins used to disguise the swimmers' heads in training. (These would surely have attracted any lookout's attention.) The swimmers also had 'collapsible observation posts' with imitation grass camouflage which could be set up to hide a man after he had crawled ashore. All that Lyon needed to complete his plans was a suitable junk which would carry the canoes from their island hide to within striking distance of Singapore. Therefore, once the six weeks' supplies were ferried ashore from the submarine, Lyon set out to capture a junk. The good fortune that had favoured the expedition to this point now deserted them: the submarine took five days, cruising along the 10-fathom line before a junk was caught. She proved not entirely suitable as she had no engine and was painted an eye-catching white, but was taken to Merepas before the submarine sailed for Australia.

In the next week or so the raiders may have carried out at least one operation, as intercepted Japanese signals from Singapore reported slight damage to a cruiser. This might have been caused by limpets which were never totally effective against heavy armoured plate of warships. Certainly on 16 October Lyon's white junk was anchored 20km from Singapore when it was approached by a Malayan police launch. These policemen, Lyon must have realized, might radio the raiders' position to the Japanese ashore. He ordered his men to open fire, killing the launch's crew before the junk was scuttled '. . . with its cargo of fifteen "Sleeping Beauties" '. The men took their Folbot canoes and began the island-hopping paddle back to their base on Merepas. They were disguised as local people, having dyed their hair black, using a chemical to crinkle it, and a die on the exposed parts of their bodies which appeared a light chocolate brown, according to Japanese reports. Such disguises, however, might only deceive a distant ship's lookout during the next few weeks as they avoided Japanese search parties. The canoeists hid on various islands, moving camp when the searchers seemed likely to corner them, in the hope that they could survive until picked up by a submarine due at Merepas on 4 November. They almost succeeded, but after four weeks Lyon and several others were killed by Japanese patrols which captured nine others. One man reportedly reached Timor in his inflatable, a remarkable feat of endurance as he must have covered some 3,000km in passages from island to island. His luck ran out when the inflatable became tangled with barbed wire on a Timor beach and he was captured by two Japanese soldiers.

All the canoeists and their support party in 'Rimau' were killed or were executed just a month before the end of the war. Plans for similar raids against shipping by SOE India's paranaval N Section came to nothing, because there were few large Japanese ships in harbours which offered any reasonable prospect for the canoeists to escape. This seemed a wise decision when the Japanese were almost certainly going to execute any raiders they caught. Royal Naval charioteers riding the so-called 'human torpedoes' sank two ships at the time Lyon was near Singapore in September 1944, but no further anti-shipping raids were made. N Section had a large collection of small underwater craft: 29 Welman one-man submarines; 12 chariots each ridden by two divers; 48 'Sleeping Beauties'; and 24 Welfreighters. These last were submersible, with a crew of one or two able to carry a ton of stores which could be landed after a submerged approach to a beach rendezvous. The section also had 12 Mobile Flotation Units (MFUs) on order but these did not reach India before the end of the war. They were built with a boat's hull around '. . . a cylinder four feet in diameter and forty feet long', in which a swimmer's rations and combat stores might be sealed. The MFU carried two canoes and their four swimmer-canoeists to the area of operations, where the canoes were floated off and the MFU's hatches closed before it was submerged without crew. A mechanical timing device was set before the MFU submerged, its machinery later blew the flooded tanks hours or days after the canoeists had left it. They could then return at a pre-arranged time to pick-up the MFU which had surfaced, ready to carry them out of the area.

Less sophisticated craft like *Krait* were to be used for long range missions such as a recce of the Mergui Archipelago off the south-west coast of Burma. A 70ft lugger, the *Island Gold*, was acquired for this reconnaissance but here fitting out by an Indian shipyard proved so badly completed, with a lorry's engine among other faults, that she had to be written off. Most of the other local craft gave equal cause for concern, although like *Island Gold* they had been bought because they were types in common use in different island groups. There were four 150-ton dhow-like buggaloes, a 40ft Akyab sloop and six small '. . . native lighters, which had no operational value of any kind'. Indeed only one of these craft made any long voyage: one buggalow making the round trip of 4,800km across the Indian Ocean to the Cocos Islands even though her fitting out had been given to an 'incompetent and inexperienced' firm.

A FTER the dropping of two atom bombs in 1945 had led to the Japanese surrender neither the British Prime Minister, Clement Atlee nor the American President, Harry Truman wished to retain such secret organizations as SOE and OSS. Therefore steps were taken to disband them swiftly, if not in haste. SOE's worldwide radio networks were closed down within days of the Japanese surrender, and the Executive closed officially on 15 January 1946. OSS had already ceased operations on 1 October 1945, and even prior to the final victory some of the wartime activities had been closed down. Harry Truman wrote to Donovan that October, thanking him for this work '. . . to liquidate those wartime activities [of OSS] . . . which will not be needed in peacetime . . .' Other activities were to be conserved with the Research and Analysis Branch and the Presentation Branch transferred to the State Department. The remaining activities were transferred to the War Department. Truman intended these transfers to begin '. . . the development of a co-ordinated system of foreign intelligence within the permanent framework of the Government . . .' This led to a number of OSS officers forming the nucleus of the Central Intelligence Agency (CIA) in 1946.

11
ACHIEVEMENTS AND DISAPPOINTMENTS

THERE is no doubt that SOE and OSS provided hope for many a resistance fighter unsure of the Allies' final victory in 1943. That the agents also provided the channels by which arms, food and a thousand other necessities reached these guerrillas is beyond dispute. Such organization led in Europe to the national revolts that these agencies were created to foster. If such national revolts were less prolific in Asia, their delay was more a matter of the war's abrupt end, than of national spirit, as events have proved since 1945. Therefore the intentions of Allied governments were justified in establishing SOE, OSS and AIB. They had also provided an invaluable distraction for Axis forces, since every battalion searching for some band of saboteurs or division trying to contain a guerrilla force, meant that fewer men were available for the main battle fronts. The need for guards to protect key points from Normandy to the German border, or on the many Japanese-held islands of the Pacific, absorbed legions of men and often good soldiers at that: for a resolute clandestine force could not be stopped by the faint-hearted.

The sabotage of bridges, railway tracks and other heavy installations proved of particular value in delaying German reinforcements reaching Normandy in June 1944. But the value of other sabotage and ambushes often lay more in their boost to the morale of local allies, than in the loss of a railway train or the blocking of a road which delayed the movement temporarily of the Axis troops. Air bombing caused much greater damage to these roads and railways. Yet the intelligence provided by agents serving with guerrilla forces or specifically inserted into occupied territories for such work, led to many hidden targets being exposed to Allied bombing. Other intelligence from the espionage of men like Erickson, to the purely military intelligence provided for Allied armies by agents working close to the battle fronts, had a cumulative value which made a major contribution to local victories and to the wider strategies of Allied governments.

These successes in fostering revolt, in sabotage and collecting intelligence, were achieved for the Allies by perhaps 30,000 individuals. No detailed figures have ever been revealed and probably have never been calculated. Professor Foot has estimated that there were 13,200 personnel in SOE at its peak in the summer of 1944, OSS had some 13,000 by the following December and AIB was 'several thousand strong'. The number in

SIS is not known but probably was considerably fewer than in SOE. All the agents and operatives in the field, including the OGs fighting in uniform, probably never numbered more than 12,000, 5,000 of whom were from SOE. The other personnel were required to provide the recruitment, training and logistic support for operations. The casualties among this 12,000 were not particularly high by wartime standards, when it is considered that a bomber crew statistically was due to be shot down after their twenty-fifth mission, a life span of three months' regular flying. In some fields, however, an agent's life could be equally short, 117 of Section F's 470 agents being killed or dying in captivity. Many died extremely bravely, as did Michael Trotobas of F Section. He had led a most effective sabotage circuit near Lille in northern France, where he was surprised by 200 Germans at 0630 hours one morning in 1943 setting up machine-guns around his 'safe' house. He came out of the front door firing his pistol for the few seconds before he was killed. Many others suffered a slower death whether they were in the British or American special forces or were working for them.

There are often no clear distinctions regarding who was considered an SOE or OSS employee and who was regarded as a sub-agent paid or unpaid by these agencies. If they worked for SOE they paid no income tax, one advantage at least of the close security with which their activities were hidden. Yet, when they told friends quite correctly that they worked for the Ministry of Economic Warfare, this sounded anything but a dangerous job. OSS officers in the OGs did not need to be so reticent, since they fought in uniform but, Secret Intelligence agents of either service—OSS,SI or the SIS—usually had plausible reasons for their absence from home.

Dusko Popov, an SIS spy and the son of a wealthy shipowner, travelled from his home in Yugoslavia to London with Ming vases ostensibly for a friend, although this 'friend' had been invented by the SIS. Popov's visit to London, his subsequent work as a British agent infiltrating the Abwehr, and his various missions in Europe were carefully planned. For in the words of his SIS controller, the barrister, the Honourable Ewen Montagu, OBE, '. . . spying is too serious and dangerous . . .' for derring-do, whatever authors may write about it. Such dangers linger on after the time of many wartime missions, since the turbulent political cut and thrust in many countries could and at times did lead to former Allied agents becoming enemies of their home governments.

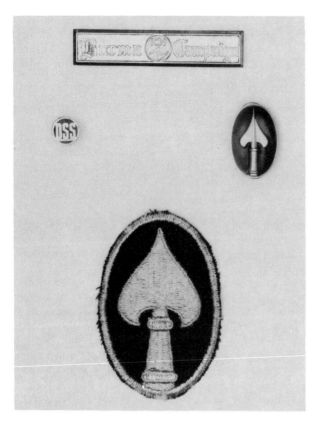

◄ These four badges include post-war emblems and the OSS insignia worn as a lapel badge on uniforms or as a shoulder flash. Top centre is the sterling silver bar worn by members of OSS Detachment 101 which fought in Burma. Top left is the OSS veterans' lapel emblem in gold lettering with a gold edge to a red enamelled background. Top right is a factory made insignia worn by OSS personnel on both lapels of a uniform jacket. It is a gold spearhead with gold edging to a black background. This authorized insignia differs from some made in various theatres of operation. At the bottom of the illustration is an authorized form of the cloth shoulder flash worn by OSS. It is made of yellow-gold thread on a black cloth ground.

▲ Detail of the OSS lapel badge in gold on black manufactured in Europe.

▼ This cloth badge was worn on the left shoulder by personnel of the Special Forces HQ. It was formed late in 1944 to provide liaison between OSS and SOE. The letters 'SF' are in white and 'HQ' in red thread sown on a roundel of dark blue cloth. This flash is known to have been worn by OSS personnel but was probably not worn by SOE personnel.

▼ This second-lieutenant's uniform jacket, known as an 'Ike' jacket carries three different winged badges. The OSS lapel insignia are of European manufacture, with a spearhead of slightly different design to the authorized pattern. (The bars of rank on this uniform were also manufactured probably in Europe, as they have a similar fastening device to the lapel insignia.) On the right shoulder is the Special Forces winged badge. On the left breast above the pocket are parachutist's 'wings'. The metal badge on this pocket flap was worn by those personnel who had completed a special course for agents.

▼ These cloth badges were worn on the right upper arm about four inches below the shoulder seam. They were designed by the British for personnel who had completed certain special forces' training. Americans who served in 'Jedburgh' teams wore these 'wings' after completing SOE courses. They were referred to by Americans as 'Jedburgh wings'. The centre roundel is in red cloth with the letters 'S.E.' embroidered on this in light blue thread. The feathers of the wings are embroidered in gold coloured thread. The whole design is on a black cloth ground.

Other reasons for secrecy long after events, include the political need of governments to appear trustworthy, or at least not to reveal that their nations have been involved in double-dealing which could have diplomatic implications bearing on present times. That said, there appears to be an element of secrecy for its own sake without any clear reason, for example, as to precisely how the Double-X Committee was successful. Did the German Admiral Canaris meet the head of SIS in 1943? There is a possibility that he might have done so on visiting an Abwehr radio interception installation in Spain. Was Colonel Ellis of the USMC as blatant a spy as was suggested by the role he played, or was he a decoy? Ellis was highly intelligent, an able strategist and unlikely to have been allowed to 'bum' his way around the north Pacific if American intelligence agencies were not privy to all he was doing. Guessing at the answer to such secrets is no more fruitful than speculation over the possible outcome of OSS missions against mainland Japan. Yet one of these had an intriguing purpose in attacking the two road tunnels under the sea between Honshu and Kyushu. A fleet of PT boats, carrying 50,000lb of explosive were to be steered by remote control using TV cameras aboard the boats, with the 250 OSS personnel involved no doubt operating from aircraft. The boats were to be exploded over the tunnels cutting the islands' communications.

Fortunately the cloak of secrecy and the mirror of speculation can be set aside, in showing the manner of men and women who performed feats of great daring, running calculated risks, not giving way to hot-headed flurry. Such behaviour points to the motivation of patriotism and love of freedom, rather than any yearning for adventure. No single agent can be nor would claim to be typical of the breed. Yet the tall American red-headed newspaper correspondent from Baltimore, Virginia Hall, with her sense of humour, her dedication and organizing ability, typifies all that was best in those working for secret services. When her artificial foot, known as 'Cuthbert', was giving her trouble, London signalled: 'eliminate Cuthbert'. This was an understandable confusion between the controller in London and the agent in the field, yet plainly an error that was only possible when those sending instructions into the field had no intimate knowledge of the agents there. In the summer of 1942, however, once the services had expanded, and Virginia was working for F Section in Vichy France, one suspects that all those who needed to know of her activities were aware of that artificial foot. She kept most of her fellow agents in touch with London and steered them out of trouble, until the German occupation of Vichy France. Then she was forced to flee from Lyons in November 1942, only reaching the UK after diplomatic intervention saved her from internment in Spain. She returned to France by

Lysander in May 1944 with a roving commission to visit *maquis* units in an area of central France '. . . to see what sort of sabotage work she could get going . . .'. This she was still carrying out when the Allied armies arrived the following September.

What would not have amused her or her controller in SOE, was the fact that while she was out of France in 1943, another British Secret Service—MI5 or MI6?—told the Germans her real name and the purpose of her work in France in 1942. The revelation was made as part of a wireless game when, as was not unusual, the British gave away certain secrets to cover the misleading facts that they sent from their XX agents. Such mishaps are symptomatic of what appear to be unnecessary and dangerous errors, yet they were probably inevitable since the secret war is just that: separate from the knowledge of others. Therefore not only were agencies of different Allied nations likely to work at cross-purposes but those of one country could trip each other up. Less excusable were the needless delays, short-sighted differences and petty squabbles between some staff officers and their counter-parts in other clandestine services. Yet experience suggests that the full details of such differences have not come down to us, and the pettiness arises in the playing down of the facts. Anyone consulting the few histories which are available of the individual actions of the Allies' clandestine agents, can only be convinced that most were sensible, level-headed people. What they also had in common was a strong will, essential in steeling oneself for a night raid or to face an interrogator. This strength of character, however, made them unlikely to bend in less crucial moments confronting colleagues or Allies.

In total, the disappointments did not amount to more than relatively minor setbacks, even if these loomed particularly large for individual agents. For example, the 61 from SIS and SOE who were captured as a result of the Germans' 'North Pole' wireless game played on the Netherlands Country Section of SOE in 1942 and 1943. By the summer of 1944 these losses had been made good in the way clandestine agencies have to swallow their disappointments. Far greater were the achievements by both SOE and OSS in fulfilling the promises to resistance forces. First and foremost was the agents' encouragement for those weary of facing what were formidable odds against efficient and well-armed Axis armies. The clandestine services then provided the arms and reassurance of proper organization which enabled the underground armies to achieve substantial victories, as their contribution to the Allies' overall strategy. Yet in providing this encouragement and the close support to the resistance forces, many agents paid with their lives for the freedom of other people; and to those who made this supreme sacrifice, this book is respectfully dedicated.

APPENDIX 1
LIST OF ABBREVIATIONS

AFHQ	Allied Forces Headquarters		**HMS**	His Majesty's Ship or Submarine
AFO	Anti-Fascist Organization (Burma)		**IAMM**	Independent American Military Mission (to Tito)
AGFRTS	Air & Ground Forces Resources & Technical Staff		**ICI**	Imperial Chemical Industries
AI	Air Intelligence		**IFBU**	Indian Field Broadcasting Unit
AI 10	cover name for SOE		**IO**	Intelligence Officer
AK	Armia Krajowa (Home Army in Poland)		**IRA**	Irish Republican Army
AMF	SOE Section working into France from Algiers		**IS 9**	Intelligence School No 9 (an SOE cover)
AN	Army/Navy		**ISLD**	Inter-Service Liaison Department (cover name for SIS)
BAAG	British Army Aid Group			
BATS	Balkan Air Terminal Service (USAAF)		**ISRB**	Inter-Services Research Bureau (cover name for SOE)
BBC	British Broadcasting Service			
BCRA (M)	Bureau Central de Renseignements d'Action (Militaire)		**ISSU**	Inter-Service Signals Unit (cover name for SOE)
BDA	Burmese Defence Army		**JIC**	Joint Intelligence Committee (of British & Americans)
BNA	Burmese National Army			
BRAL	Bureau de Recherches et d'Action Londres (Free French)		**JPS**	Joint Planning Staff (British)
			JSP	Joint Staff Planners (of US COS)
BSC	British Security Co-ordination—cover for SOE and SIS in America		**M**	Symbol for head of SOE's operations
			MCP	Malayan Communist Party
C	Symbol for Executive Head of SIS		**MCR**	Miniature Communications Receiver
CAS	Civil Affairs Section (of OSS)		**Med TO**	Mediterranean Theatre of Operations
CBI	China-Burma-India (American theatre of operations)		**MEW**	Ministry of Economic Warfare
CD	Censorship & Documents (OSS)		**MFU**	Mobile Flotation Unit
CD	Symbol for Executive Head of SOE		**MI**	Military Intelligence (branches of War Office)
CIA	Central Intelligence Agency		**5**	for counter-intelligence—part of SIS
CIC	Counter Intelligence Corps (US Army)		**6**	for intelligence—part of SIS
CinC	Commander-in-Chief		**9**	for escape and evasion—part of SIS
COI	Co-ordinator of Information		**19**	vetting refugees—part of SIS
COPP	Combined Operations (Assault) Pilotage Parties		**R**	research
COS	Chiefs of Staff		**MID**	Military Intelligence Division (American)
CP	Command Post		**MIS**	Military Intelligence Service (American)
D	Section of SIS		**MO**	Morale Operations (of OSS)
DF	West European Section of SOE		**MO4**	Section D and later SOE's office in Cairo
D/F	Direction Finding (radio)		**MOI**	Ministry of Information
D/R	Director of Region (SOE)		**MPAJA**	Malayan People's Anti-Japanese Army
DZ	Dropping Zone		**N**	Netherlands Country section of SOE
EDES	Ethnikos Dimokraticos Ellinikos Syndesmos		**N**	Naval section of SOE in Burma
EH	Electra House (offices of FO's propaganda branch)		**NDRC**	National Defence Research Comittee (US)
ELAS	Ellenikos Laikos Apeleflherotikos Stratos		**NID**	Naval Intelligence Department (British)
EMMFI	État-Major des Forces Françaises de l'Intérieur		**NID(Q)**	cover name for SOE
ETO	European Theatre of Operations		**NORSO**	Nowegian Special Operations (Group)
EU/P	Country Section of SOE for Poles outside Poland		**NKVD**	Narodny Kommissariat Vnutrennich Dyee (Peoples' Commissariat for International Affairs —Russian)
EWS (I)	Eastern Warfare School (India)			
F	Country Section of SOE for non-Gaullist French			
FANY	First Aid Nursing Yeomanry		**OELR**	Office of European Labor Research (OSS)
FBI	Federal Bureau of Investigation		**OG**	Operational Group (OSS)
FEB	Far Eastern Bureau (of MOI)		**OM**	Oriental Mission (SOE)
FED	Foreign Exchange Division (OSS)		**ONI**	Office of Naval Intelligence (USA)
FETO	Far Eastern Theatre of Operations		**OP**	Observation Post
FFI	Forces Françaises de l'Intérieur (Free French)		**OSS**	Office of Strategic Services
FN	Foreign Nationalities (OSS Division)		**OVRA**	Organizzazione di Vigilanza e Repressione dell' Antifascismo
FO	Foreign Office (British)			
GC & GS	Government Code & Cipher School		**OWI**	Office of War Information (USA)
GSI (k)	Cover for SOE in India		**PE**	Plastic Explosive
HF/DF	High Frequency Direction Finding (radio)		**PIAT**	Projectile, Infantry, Anti-Tank

PRC	Portable Radio Communications
PWD	Pschological War Division (SEAC)
PWE	Political Warfare Executive (British)
PWJC	Political Warfare Japan Committee (British)
PWO	Psychological Warfare Operations
R & A	Research and Analysis
RAF	Royal Air Force
RDX	type of explosive
RF	Country Section of SOE working with Free French
RMBPD	Royal Marine Boom Patrol Detachment
RSHA	Reichssicherheitshauptamt
RSS	Radio Security Service (British)
R/T	Radio/Telephone
SAC	Sandeman Club (Division 19 of OSS)
SACO	Sino-American Co-operation Organization
SAS	Special Air Service (for OSS)
SAS	Special Air Service (British Rgt)
SBS	Special Boat Squadron (British)
SD	Sicherheitsdienst
SEAC	South-East Asia Command
SEI	School of Eastern Interpreters (SOE, India)
SHAEF	Supreme Headquarters Allied Expeditionary Forces
SI	Secret Intelligence (OSS service)
SIS	Secret or Special Intelligence Service (British)
SLU	Special Liaison Unit (British)
SO 1, 2, 3	Special Operations: 1 Propaganda; 2 Operations; 3 Planning
SO	Symbol for Minister of Economic Warfare as political head of SOE
SO	Special Operations (branch of OSS)

SOA	Special Operations Australia (cover name for SOE)
SOE	Special Operations Executive
SOM	Special Operations Mediterranean
SOU	Ship Observation Unit (OSS)
SR	Service de Renseignement (French Intelligence Section)
SS	Special Service (British Commandos)
SS	Schutzstaffel
SSS	Security Services Section (of US Military Intelligence)
SSTR	Special Service Transmitter-Receiver (OSS radio)
STS	Special Training School
T	Belgian & Luxemburg Country Section of SOE
TRE	Telecommunications Research Establishment (British)
USAAF	United States Army Air Force
USMC	United States Marine Corps
USN	United States Navy
V-E	Victory in Europe (day)
V Force	Force from Assam Rifles administered by SOE
V-1	Vergeltungswaffe (pilotless aircraft)
V-2	Vergeltungswaffe (ballistic missile)
W	Inter-Service Committee for most secret intelligence
WAAF	Women's Auxillary Air Force
WRNS	Women's Royal Naval Service
W/T	Wireless Telegraphy
X	German Country Section of SOE
X-2	Counter Intelligence Branch of OSS
XX	British Committee controlling double-agents
Y	Radio Interception Service (British)
Z Force	formed Hong Kong July 1939 for covert operations and later known as GSI (z) in India

APPENDIX 2
EXAMPLES OF OSS RESEARCH PROJECTS

Abalone: methods of attaching limpets (3)

Adams Plan: use of bats carrying incendiaries (6)

Adhesive: attaching explosive above water to all manner of surfaces (3)

Arson: methods of instruction in use of fire (6)

Aqua Vita: producing sterile water from contaminated sources (51)

Aunt Jemima: mix of RDX or HMX and flour that has properties of PE (16)

Balsam: edible paper for easy destruction but resistant to humidity, on which pencil, pen or other writing can be made (43)

Barney: glass cloth cover for outboard motors (52)

Belcher: chemicals that make water undrinkable but not poisonous (44)

Bigot: adaptor for .45-inch automatic to fire grenades or other explosive charges for short distances by the spigot mortar principle (13)

Big Joe: rifle sized Penetrometer see below, (13)

Black Joe: explosive coal (30)

Blackout: high-explosive electric bulb fired when current switched on (20)

Brimstone: general problems with incendiary devices (6)

Bulls Eye: devices for specific targets (not numbered)

Burp: British urgent railway plan for derailing locomotives (10)

Bushmaster: three different simulators of rifle and machine-gun fire set off after time delays (33)

Camel: camouflage (30)

Canister Locator: device for reception parties to find containers easily after night drop (4)

Cannon: assassin's pistol (7)

Casey Jones: attacks on railways (10)

Cluck: a communications device to identify friends from enemies in dark or on a raid (4)

Cricket: compact radio developments (37)

Emily Post: poisons (18)

Facsimile: transmitting reproductions of pictures by wire (34)

Fantasia: psychological methods of frightening an enemy (26)

Fountain: shaped charges to destroy railway engine boiler as it passes over explosion (10)

Hedy: panicking crowds without breaking the Geneva Convention (10)

Honeymoon: work on methods of making time-delay fuses (23)

Hooter: underwater noise device for ships or submarines to be detected when homing in on a small craft in order to pick up raiders or others returning to an RV (4)

IFT and IFL: electromagnetic devices by which a man wearing an Induction Field Locator (IFL) can home in on an Induction Field Transceiver (4)

Joe Louis: methods of firing grenades or mortars by a large penetrometer described below (13)

Lacrima Tojo: liquid explosive disguised as lubricating oil (40)

Little Joe: smaller version of 'Joe Louis' (13)

Locust: sabotage of precision machine tools by small quantities of chemicals (39)

Lost Chord: homing devices for agents (4)

Lulu: dispersal of inflammable dust (31)

Matchhead: waterproofed igniter from celluloid or magnesium materials to set off incendiaries silently (6)

Maude Muller: destroying tropical folliage (45)

Moth: easily destroyed brief case and note books (47)

MWT: short range communications by micro-waves (4)

Nemo: attacks on submarines (38)

Odometer: distance fuse switches set off after a train travelled a pre-selected distance (10)

Paul Revere (PR): incendiary capable of igniting crude oil (6)

Penetrometer: silent and flashless weapon using rubber as a catapult, see 'Joe Louis' etc above and William Tell (13)

Postell: methods of using enemy-controlled telephone wires (22)

Pneumonia: causing sudden death without detectable reasons (12)

Rainbow: ultra-violet and infra-red communication systems (5)

Saint Michael: magnetic recorder, micro-phone and telephone line attachment (29)

Salex: a slow burning explosive of sulphur, aluminium powder and TNT (31)

Shell: use of cashew nut oil to sabotage motor vehicles (9)

Shortstop: sabotage of electrical equipment by means that are not obvious and therefore difficult to correct (25)

Simultaneous Events: a radio-controlled switch, safe from being accidentally triggered (2)

Sky Wave: ground antennae for radio signals (22 & 24)

Speedometer: a fuse activated by centrifugal force when fixed to the axle of a railway truck (10)

UWT: underwater device for communicating between 'Sleeping Beauty' canoes (4)

Varga: a charge shaped to split open and set fire to oil storage tanks (35)

Veritas: delayed action device for firing signal flares dropped from aircraft (41)

Vitamin Pills: chemical capsules dissolved in water but undetectable by normal analysis, yet capable of destroying electric storage batteries (38)

William Tell: the final model of the penetrometer

Wire: an alloy of aluminium with adequate electrical and mechanical properties, yet which rapidly dissolves in salt water (11)

Woodchuck: a device to wreck a train on a bridge (32)

Zephyr: silencing outboard motors (52)

APPENDIX 3
NOTES ON ORGANIZATION, EQUIPMENT SPECIFICATIONS AND OTHER DETAILS

1 Typical of the confusion for historians of secret service operations is the quote 'gentlemen do not read each other's mail'. This has been attributed to Secretary Stimson as if made in 1929, although it was in all probability made in 1947 to his biographer. Nevertheless, it summed up his view that US Military Intelligence's cipher bureau, the 'Black Chamber' of World War I, should not breach Ambassadors' trust in peacetime dealings with the US State Department.

2 SOE's need for secrecy in the early 1940s both inside and outside the organization, prevented any neat and tidy arrangement of aims and objectives for departments. Nevertheless the organization of Country Sections withstood the test of operations these staff organized, with few major disasters. From time to time the boundaries of a 'country' might be varied to suit operations and after 1940 several sections were grouped into regions. In Europe there were north-west, south-west, south-east and Scandinavian regions; the Americas formed another region, as did the Sections for countries in south-east Asia.

SOE also established overseas headquarters or missions which in Cairo included staffs from SIS Section D known as 'MO 4' and MI R's staff in Cairo. The latter were still known as

'G(R)' until 1942 when both staffs were specifically ordered to integrate their work that autumn. The title 'MO 4' then became synonomous with SOE. Other overseas headquarters included: a mission to Singapore, the Oriental Mission of 1941; the HQ at Algiers with its 'Massingham' base and training school, opened in November 1942; an HQ at Meerut, India in 1943 which moved to Ceylon in December 1944; and in April 1944 the HQ in Cairo for Special Operations in the Mediterranean moved to Bari in Italy. The Regions, and Country Sections not in Regions, were controlled by the head of operations known as 'M'. When Gubbins held this appointment he also controlled training and liaison with other services for transport. However from the Spring of 1943 'M' was only directly concerned with operations. The Air Liaison (AL) Section continued to work with the RAF. Training became a separate branch, as did the weapons research organization at Welwyn. These and other specialist sections were then co-ordinated through the Council.

The first Director of SOE (known as CD) worked with Gladwyn Jebb, (later Lord Gladwyn) a diplomat with ties to the Foreign Office. Jebb had the title of Chief Executive even though when both he and the Director were present at a meeting, Jebb took the chair. In 1940 CD had a deputy and officers heading propaganda as SO 1, operations as SO 2 and plannning as SO 3 which was intended to provide information for SO 2, but was disbanded after a couple of months. In the following years after SO 1 became PWE outside SOE, the remaining organization became more formal, although no overall head of administration was appointed until November 1943 when an additional deputy to CD was appointed to this post. By this date there had been a number of other changes, Jebb returning to the FO in February 1942 when the senior staff of this department of State were satisfied—as were their political masters—that SOE was not going to disrupt British foreign policy. This was partly because of his responsible and balanced guidance of the Council of SOE, which since late in 1941 had met regularly every Wednesday afternoon. It was comprised of 16 senior heads of regions and sections who proposed means of implementing policies laid down from time to time for the Executive by the Chiefs-of-Staff. From 1942, if not before then, it proved an able body of councillors for CD.

The political head of SOE throughout its existence was the Minister of Economic Warfare but his staff in this Ministry played no part in the control or administration of SOE.

3 By October 1941 the Co-ordinator of Information controlled a number of branches and sections as shown in an organization chart prepared by his Budget & Planning Section. In addition to COI's New York office there was also an office in London and other personnel were overseas from the 'Special Activities' Section. Other branches included:

Radio News with three divisions: news, picture publications and non-news (preparing summaries of other radio broadcasts). The divisions co-ordinated information from various sources.

Research & Analysis had five divisions: economics and statistics; central information; special information; geography and psychology. Central information was further subdivided into eight regional sections which were not unlike the Country Sections of SOE, in that staffs worked on information about specific territories.

Visual Presentation was the branch concerned with preparation of digests of intelligence and reports for the President among others; this branch also had a reference library.

The organization reflects the uses of published sources as much as clandestine reports received by COI. In addition to the usual executive officers for administration and a general counsellor for legal advice, there were specialist assistants to COI. He also had a technical consultant who headed a business advisory panel; a Defence Morale Analysis Unit; a Psycho-analytic Field Unit; and an Oral Intelligence Section. These were pointers, perhaps, to the use made by COI of military psychological and associated methods which were in their infancy in 1942.

4 On the creation of OSS from COI's staff there were two distinct and relatively large divisions, one for intelligence activities and one for psychological warfare. The first dealt with the gathering of secret intelligence, regarded by OSS official historian as 'a process rather than a system'. In this the Geographic Desks found suitable cover stories for their agents in the field along with other support and control they provided in the same way as SOE's Country Sections. X-2 Section dealt

with counter-intelligence covering foreign secret services abroad as the FBI covered such activities in America. The Foreign Nationalities Section with 50 regular staff by early 1943 and 100 volunteer helpers, kept in touch with 'foreign nationality groups in the United States to aid in the collection of essential information'. This was made available, after consultation with the State Department, to the appropriate personnel of the division for Special Operations which was essentially 'to effect physical subversion of the enemy'. This division had agents operating as did those in SOE to physically sabotage enemy activities and raise guerrilla forces which would be helped by its Operational Groups. The Division also had a Morale Operation department which like the British PWE dealt in 'black' propoganda. The department also covered such activities as: bribery; counterfeiting currency; abduction; manipulation of the black market; and all forms of morale subversion—to quote a list of subjects its chief officer considered appropriate to his department in April 1943.

Mission headquarters overseas included one in Cairo in the summer of 1942, one in Algiers from November 1942, in Italy (first at Bari), in Switzerland, in India, in China with both Nationalists and Communists, and Operational Groups by 1945 attached to the headquarters of American armies in Europe.

The breadth of the Special Operations' commitment can be judged from the following schedule of combat stores and weapons. These were provided for the forward base near Algiers in the spring of 1943, details kindly provided by William Cassidy Intelligence Studies Foundation.

Supplies and Equipment for Base Staff: Six months' standard rations for 80 men; field equipment for 80; office equipment for a headquarters, a radio station and a training school; 12 trucks; eight cars; and three high speed long range boats.

Supplies for a Guerrilla Force of 3,000: *Weapons with ammunition*—2,000 Thompson SMG with 1-million rounds; 1,000 .38 cal pistols with 50,000 rounds; 100 .45 cal pistols with 5,000 rounds; 12 Reising SMG with 12,000 rounds; 12 Garand rifles with 6,000 rounds; and 40,000 handgrenades. *Explosives and sabotage equipment*—500 land mines, 1,000 pressure release switches, 1,000 pull switches, 1,500 reels of friction tape, Primacord (instanteous fuse) and other stores for making up charges, 200 three-coil flashlights with 1,000 batteries. *Survival kit*—2,000 hunting knives; 1,100 jack knives; 1,500 standard portable compasses; 3,000 first aid kits and 500 special medical supply packs. *Rations and clothing*—3,000 'K' rations; 3,000 standard rations for three months plus 500 special supplements; 5,000 sets of boots, underclothes, shirts and slacks.

Intelligence Gathering and Associated Items: *Miniature cameras*, 10 with accessories; dark room equipment and supplies; *Optical aids*—12 field glasses (six prs with eight × magnification), four telescopes; *Map making equipment*—100 portable sets; 200 sets map reading equipment; various maps of Europe and Africa including charts, topographical and other special maps. *Surreptitious entry devices*—14 sets of wire tapping equipment; six ultra-violet desk lamps [for checking documents for secret writing or forgeries]; six flashlights with ultra-violet filters; 12 high-powered magnifying glasses; 50 sets of lock picking equipment.

Operational Groups' Weapons and Stores: *Weapons*—300 Martin 9mm SMG (details of ammo not listed as readily available from army sources); Two Winchester 12 gauge Riot Shotguns with 200 rounds; four Brens with 5,000 rounds; four .32 cal pistols with 800 rounds; four .22 cal Colts with 4,000 rounds; four Luger pistols with 800 rounds; 500 fighting knives; and 200 spring coshes. *Sabotage Stores*—30,000 packets (1.3 tonne) of PE; 1,000 magnets; 1,000 fog signals [railway track special switch fuses]; 1,000 universal switch fuses; 1,500 assorted time pencil fuses; 150 limpets; 200 clams; 1,000 magnesium incendiaries; 1,000 assorted pocket time delay incendiaries; 100 striker bands [for igniting slow fuses]; 5,000 boxes of safety matches; 500 No. 6 non-electric caps; 500 No. 8 electric blasting caps; 20,000ft of fine .014 gauge steel wire [this might be used for trip wires, and possibly for operating mechanical switch fuses from a safe distance]; vaseline in tubes [presumably for waterproofing joints in fuse circuits]; and assorted items for unit training. *Other items*—12 fully equipped rubber [inflatable] boats with like numbers of scaling ladders, wall hooks, warf hooks and knuckle dusters; 12 smatchets; 100 units of knockout drops; 1,200 units of L tablets; 75 square yards of rubber substitute fabric [possibly used when caching stores to keep these dry]; 30 pairs of gym shoes; and 600 Benzedrene tablets.

Communications: Equipment for two field radio stations and one temporary station, including 20 No. 35 portable radios and items for unit training.

Training School: 20 sets of charts for identification of uniforms, aeroplanes, ships and weapons of Allied and enemy nations; four sets of models of all weapons [no doubt 'all weapons' covered those which guerrilla forces were likely to come across]; 35mm film and slide projectors with sound; Signal Corps equipment to train classes of 25 students; 500 type 'A' parachutes for large personnel with 500 jump suits and associated clothing; 50 map boards and sets of map reading equipment, and 50 dummy grenades.

5 The varieties of plastic explosive were made with 'a cyclonite [nitroglycerine in PE '808'] mixed with a plasticizing medium'. Noble 808 or its equivalent PE-2A, generated such temperatures that it would—weight for weight—cut through thicker steel than any other available explosive. It was usually supplied in four-ounce paper-wrapped cartridges one and a half inches in diameter and three inches long. It could also be supplied in eight-ounce cartridges, five-pound blocks or as charges specially made up to cut railway lines. Should the agent have to shape his charge with bare hands, some of the PE would be absorbed through the skin and some inhaled, causing severe headaches and sickness. Noble developed an experimental '100' PE which was yellow in colour and packed in a distinctive, light coloured wrapping. '100' was similar to ICI's PE and neither of these gave any side effects when handled.

The American equivalent to the British plastic explosives was based on RDX manufactured from 1939 by Ajax Explosives of Canada. It was very malleable even at low temperatures and appears to have been used by both SOE and OSS. By 1944, however, OSS was also using C-3 , less powerful than RDX but which could be lit by a match when used as incendiary material. The American C4 which was equivalent to PE-2A, could be rolled into flat sheets using a beer bottle or rolling pin. These sheets might then be used in letter bombs exploded by a No. 8 detonator only one eighth inch (less than four milli-metres) in diameter, linked to a deaf-aid or similar small electric battery.

The German equivalent to C3 was Nipolit. This could be produced according to one report as flexible strips sewn into belts and raincoat linings etc, in order to smuggle it to a target.

Other explosives used by SOE and OSS included: Amatol—ammonium nitrate blended with TNT in suitable proportions; wet guncotton which detonated at 18,000ft per second compared to the 24,000ft per second of the dry guncotton in primers; and a range of commercial products including Dynamite and Blasting Gelignite. The instantaneous fuses were also commercial products—Cordtex (PETN) from British sources and Primacord from American. The commercial explosives usually had a nitroglycerine base and were more suited to major blasting operations in bringing down a length of railway embankment or hillside, than was PE.

6 A wide range of lapel knives was made in the 1940s, many of which were sold commercially to individual service personnel. Those of J and I Marshall of Glasgow, for example were displayed in military tailors and priced for sewing into various positions in a tailored battledress. The military tailors Gieves and Hawkes sold Wilkinson blades in sheaths with metal chaps inside these leather cases. The chaps did not then cause any telltale outline on a jacket but still prevented the point of a knife working its way through the cloth. Some blades were hollow ground to give a recess along the cutting edge which was therefore sharper. Rolls Razor made blades marked 'RR' to designs requested by any Commando officer in uniform who came to their factory. Many of these knives could be made in an hour and a half or less, by employees working in their own time—that is the claim although more likely the knife was made in company time with the foreman's approval. Rolls Razor also had stocks of standard lapel knives. These were in sheaths left flat with the welt 'outside' so that there was unlikely to be any telltale impression of the sheath appearing in a cloth lapel. As none of these knives was more than one eighth inch thick, they normally nestled easily in a sheath which replaced horsehair stiffening in a suit lapel.

SOE's lapel knives were purchased in bulk lots from manufacturers, including Marshalls, Rolls Razor and the cutlers William Rogers and Son of Sheffield. The designs varied with the Mark I blades including those with sand glued to tape for the grip. The Mark II version had one, or later two holes for attachment to an improvised handle. Some lapel knives were made in Ceylon for distribution to British forces in SEAC command. One of these unused blades has the wrapping marked 'Bhandari, K' a respected name in Ceylon. Most lapel knives were 'blue' finished or otherwise darkened to prevent the blade flashing in sunlight, or in other ways giving the intended victim the hint of an attack. An instructor's blade from Camp X has one edge blued and one polished steel, to demonstrate this point.

7 The examples of clandestine radios listed in the table were those distributed in quantity to agents and others for subversive warfare communications. Other sets were made for specific operations.

Examples of Radios for Clandestine Operations

Origin	Year	Type	Weight	Output	Frequencies	Dimensions	Power Source
Britain (for SIS)	1938	XV Transmitter XV Receiver }	20.0kg	15-20 watts	3.0-13Mc/s 3.0-13Mc/s }	22cm×16cm×12cm(?)	6-volt battery
Britain (for SIS)	1940(?)	Paraset Transmitter and Receiver }	1.5kg	5 watts	3.0-7.6Mc/s 3.0-6.6Mc/s }	22cm×14cm×11cm	Mains or battery
Britain (for SOE)	1942	A Mark II* Transceiver	9.0kg	5 watts	3.0-9.0Mc/s	Three cases, each 22.5cm×10cm×8cm	Mains or battery
Britain (for SOE)	1942	B Mark II (B2) Transmitter 3 Mk II } Receiver B Mk II	14.8kg	20 watts	(?)	One case, 43cm× 28cm×13cm(?)	Mains or battery
Britain (for SOE)	1943	III Mark II Transmitter Receiver	3.4kg 3.4kg	> 20 watts	3.0-16Mc/s 3.0-15.5Mc/s	24cm×16cm×12cm 24cm×11cm×12cm	Mains or battery
Britain (for SOE)	1943	53 Mark I Pocket Receiver	0.4kg		3.0-12Mc/s	11cm×9cm×3cm	Mains
Britain (for SOE)	1943	51/1 Transmitter	0.6kg	> 3 watts	3.0-10.5Mc/s	14cm×12cm×4cm	Mains
Britain (for SOE)	1943	MCR 1 'Biscuit' Receiver			2.5-4.5Mc/s plus alternatives to 15Mc/s	8.5cm×5.4cm× 2.24cm	Mains or battery
Britain (for SOE)	c.1944	A Mark IV Transceiver	4.0kg	5 watts	3.0-9.0Mc/s	23.5cm×29cm×8cm	Mains or battery
Poland	1943	BP 3 Transceiver	c.3.0kg	30 watts	2.0-8Mc/s	28cm×21cm×9.5cm	12-volt battery
Poland	1943	BP 4 Transceiver	4.0kg	8 watts	2.0-8Mc/s	28cm×21cm×9.5cm	Mains or battery
USA (for OSS)	1942	SSTR-1 Transceiver	4.1kg[1]	8-15 watts	3.0-14Mc/s	Two cases, each 2.5cm ×10cm×8.2cm	Battery
USA (for OSS)	c. 1942	SSTR-3 R/T			40.0Mc/s	Chest set	Battery
USA (for OSS)	1944(?)	SSTR-5 C/W Transceiver				Case with batteries 20cm×25cm×5cm	Battery
USA (for OSS)	1944(?)	SSTR-6 Joan Eleanor equipment					
USA (for MID)	1942(?)	AN/PRC-5[2]	6.8kg	16 watts	4.0-16Mc/s	c. 33cm×30cm×12cm	Mains

[1] Power packs weighed between 5kg and 16kg depending upon type. [2] Output was reduced to 10 watts when the frequency was twice that of the crystal. Weight including carrying case, spare parts and aerials was 12kg when packed in one case with the power-supply transformer. It operated on 110 or 220 volts.

8   The development of special weapons had many pitfalls, as exampled by the design and development of the 'Stinger'. This started as a design for a single-shot survival (SSS) weapon, the MAC SSS-1 'Scorpion'. It used a lead .22-cal bullet which contravened the Geneva Convention's rules of warfare. Donovan prohibited the use of such bullets by OSS, although some were used by guerrilla forces with Stingers before Bell Telephone Laboratories produced a nickle-jacketed bullet which met the rules. They also made one with a tungsten jacket for penetrating such light sheet metal as the sides of vehicles. They also produced a gold .22 bullet which was probably intended as a device to hide bullion carried by an agent, when coins might attract thieves. In November 1943 the name 'Scorpion' was changed to 'Stinger' to avoid confusion in ordnance stores with other items of similar name.

The first batch of Stingers produced by the Rite-Rite Manufacturing Company of Illinois to OSS designs, had a six per cent rate of misfire on test in the early summer of 1943. More seriously, the SAE 1120 steel rod, only .123 inches in diameter but enlarged at each end, proved faulty. This served as the breech-block, but could burst through the retainer at the rear of the weapon. There were also misfires when the trigger lever was not used absolutely correctly as it then failed to cleanly release the striker/firing pin. This was a major handicap in a weapon that would be distributed to guerrilla forces. By January 1944 these and other modifications required major redesign work and OSS passed the development work to the Ordnance Department's Small Arms Development Branch.

They tested 50 with the original breechblock retainers; 200 with retainers of drawn steel; 50 with brass retainers reinforced with steel bands; and 50 with a steel breech retainer and a hand finished, not sintered, steel striker. Several Stingers of each type burst on test, in part because the cartridge rim of the integrated round was pierced, as it was not adequately secured in the chamber and gases then forced back the breechblock. Further examination also revealed that the seamless tube barrel was of smaller diameter than the .22-cal bullet, among other design faults. These were corrected by the Ordnance Department which undertook the supervision of the manufacture of further batches with the first of 10,000 in the summer of 1944.

Although a reloadable version had apparently been made by OSS, this never went into production. The Stinger therefore remained a device, as opposed to a hand gun with all the military regulations and restrictions attaching to the distribution of guns.

9 The study of codes is a complex subject but the following simplified examples give an indication of the way SOE and OSS agents used these in the field. In 1940 SOE agents had to memorize a phrase such as 'Marion enjoyed holidays in Wichita', which set out in five-letter blocks appeared as follows, when no letter is repeated—MARIO | NE*J*Y*D | — the stars being letters not repeated (letters not appearing in our phrase are in this simplified version added in alphabetical sequence to complete the 25-letter grid), W being the same as X in covering the alphabet:

```
MARIO          note RIO
NEJKD               JYD
HLSWC
TBFGK
PQUVZ
```

To encode JOHN HAS MOUSE, these letters were broken into pairs as JO-HN-HA-SM-OU-SE and each pair encoded by using the opposite letters in their respective sections of the grid. JO then becomes DR, HN being in the same vertical line are by a convention of this code, taken as the letters to the right—LE. HA becomes LM and so on giving a coded message DR LE LM HR RZ LJ which can be transmitted in five-letter blocks using random letters to complete the signal DRLEL | MHRRZ | LJXYZ. This simplified version of the 'Playfair' code gives an indication of the way it worked, although in 1941 the full version as used by SOE was considered too easily decrypted and was replaced. Agents then used a code based on a random number known, or so it was hoped, only to the agent and the cypher clerks in SOE. For simplicity, say the number was 587936. The agent wrote the message in clear below this number, with the result that a message of 16 letters would give him six columns each of three letters:

```
5 8 7 9 3 6
R O C K E T
S I T E A T
M I T S O N
```

By taking these vertical trios of letters in the numerical sequence with those under column three as first, those under five next and so on in writing them horizontally the message becomes:

EAORS | MTTNC | TTOII | KESXYZ

This A-Z code could also be deciphered by German cryptographers, but like many simple or low grade codes, it might take the enemy sufficient time to decrypt for the message to be valueless to him. SOE and other clandestine agencies, however, needed a more secure code and therefore in 1943 SOE adopted the Destelle code. This was later replaced by the one-time pad code.

10 Examples of standard European loads for 'C' Type containers: A—6 Brens + 6,000 rounds .303 and 48 empty magazines; 36 No. 4 (British) rifles or American carbines with 5,400 rounds to suit; 27 Sten or Marlin SMG, 7,100 rounds ammo, 80 empty magazines and 16 magazine loading devices; 5 .38 cal pistols with 250 rounds; 40 Mills fragmentation grenades; 12 Gammon grenades; 52 detonators; 8 kg of PE with fuses and tape; reserves of ammunition in cartons – 6,600 9mm, 3,168 .303 or .300 cal – with 20 empty SMG and 20 empty Bren magazines; and 156 field dressings.
B—9 rifles with alternatives throughout in 'A', plus 1,350 rounds to suit; 11 SMG with 3,300 rounds; 55 empty magazines and 11 loading devices; 66 kg PE; ammunition in cartons – 13,200 9mm, 22,176 rounds for rifles or carbines, 140 empty Bren magazines, 40 empty SMG magazines (with loading devices). This was essentially a load of ammunition and other items to resupply a guerrilla force already armed from earlier container loads.
D—8 Brens with 8,000 rounds and 64 empty magazines; 4 Bazookas with 56 rockets; nine rifles or carbines with 1,350 rounds; 66kg PE with fuses and tape; 9,504 rounds of .303 or .300 cal ammunition; 40 Bazooka rockets as reserve ammunition; and 234 field dressings, in this load as in others these dressings also served as packing. Note: When more than fifteen type 'A' or 'B' containers were to be dropped at one time, additional quantities of ammunition replaced weapons in some containers in order to avoid a surplus of automatic weapons for which there were no trained guerrillas. Loads 'D' sometimes included 10 Gammon grenades or a PIAT with 20 bombs, in place of Bazookas, since the general rule was to drop weapons of an appropriate calibre and type to suit the army which was advancing into the guerrillas' area, with those on the line of American forces' advance receiving .300 cal ammunition and carbines.

11 Two to five Operational Groups were normally commanded by a major with a Field Service Headquarters (FSHQ) roughly compariable to the HQ of an army battalion, as the OSS Field Manual explains. At times an FSHQ was based outside occupied territory, until tactical conditions warranted the movement of the HQ into the area of operations. An FSHQ had 28 all ranks with a command structure as shown in the diagram.

An Area Headquarters (AHQ) as the Operational Groups' headquarters cell in an OSS forward base, was commanded by a lieutenant-colonel with an executive captain and a 1st Lieutenant as Operations Officer and five specialist NCOs. The AHQ provided the link between one or more FSHQs and the theatre organization of OSS, with the AHQ also responsible for storing weapons, demolition and other combat stores to be issued to FSHQs as required.

FIELD SERVICE HEADQUARTERS COMMAND STRUCTURE

FSHQ
28 all ranks
Major commanding
Captain – Medical Officer
1st Lt – Adjutant
First Sergeant
Technical Sergeant as casualty replacement

Communications
1st Lt
3 × Tec Sgts
6 × Cpl Radio Ops
6 × Cpl Code Clerks/Courriers

Supply and Transport
1st Lt
2 × Tec Sgts
Cpl Armourer[1]
2 × Cpl Automobile Mechanics[2]
2 × Cpl Clerks

Operational Group (OG)[3]
34 all ranks[4]
Captain commanding
1st Lt as 2 i/c
Cpl Code Clerk
Cpl Courrier

No. 1 Section
1st Lt as Leader
Staff Sgt as 2 i/c
Staff Sgt Medic

No. 2 Section
15 all ranks

Squad
six all ranks[5]

Squad
Staff Sgt
4 × Cpl Scouts
Cpl Radio Operator

NOTES

1. The complement allowed for only 16 corporals for 17 posts.
2. Motorcyles, trucks and trailers were to be supplied by Area HQ when needed for operations.
3. There were two or three additional OGs in some FSHQ Commands.
4. A signaller/radio operator and an additional corporal code clerk might be allocated from FSHQ to each OG as necessary.
5. Corporals in a squad might be replaced by technicians fifth grade.

12 Force 136—This Indian based mission of SOE was commanded from its inception as GSI(k) by Colin Mackenzie. His practice of keeping the senior military staffs informed of pending SOE operations, led to his mission being respected in India. In 1941 its roles were to prepare for the possible invasion of India by German advances through eastern Persia, through Afganistan or even by putting agents into India by way of Tibet; and for invasion from the east by the Japanese coming through Burma. After August 1942 these roles were redefined by London with a greater reliance on the guerrilla-raising techniques used in Europe than would prove practical in the Far East before the spring of 1945. The result was that '136' became more involved in gathering intelligence than in sabotage, but all the force's operations required the sanction of the Viceroy and C-in-C India before late 1943, and thereafter of P Division of Lord Mountbatten's headquarters of SEAC. The operations can be briefly summarized as follows:

Assam—as the Japanese neared the borders of India, a number of agents were trained with the intention of their joining road repair gangs. This might enable them to sabotage equipment, but they were not sent into occupied territory. '136's' main work here then involved administering and training V (Vee) Force, drawn largely from men of the Assam Rifles. Their deep penetration patrols in Burma and elsewhere often required great feats of endurance when making reconnaissances of several weeks' duration with a minimum of rations.

Burma—many if not most Burmese cultivating paddy fields and vegetable plots on the central plains, were looking forward to the end of British rule. On the other hand the hill tribes looked to the British for protection from the plainsmen. SOE therefore were able to recruit Karens from the hills on the south-east borders with Thailand, Chins from the mountain borders with India, and Kachins from the more northerly mountains spreading into China. Early attempts to establish guerrilla forces in these areas met with a number of setbacks but by January 1945 several effective guerrilla forces had been raised.

The complex politics of the plains were a confusion of cross-loyalties. The communist *Thakin* (Master) Party had links apparently with China's Communists; while the Burma Independence Army had been formed by the Japanese. They became concerned with its officers' political ambitions and the army was re-formed in June 1942 as the Burmese Defence Army with less political influence. In August 1943 it was renamed the Burma National Army (BNA). In the late summer of the following year various anti-Japanese factions came together as the Anti-Fascist Organization (AFO). About this time in the summer of 1944, SOE established that the *Thakin* Party were worth arming, and contacts were eventually established by parachuting in radio operators. In December one of the first of several 'Jedburgh' parties parachuted to AFO contacts. But not until May 1945 did Aung San, the commander of the BNA visit General Slim's Fourteenth Army HQ. He was considered a war criminal in some quarters but on Mountbatten's instructions he was treated as 'a friendly guerrilla commander'. Slim agreed to provide the BNA units with rations on the understanding that they would mount operations in support of the Fourteenth Army.

Late in May there was a force of some 50,000 Japanese in the Karen hills, organized with sufficient numbers of armoured vehicles to protect road convoys. From these their foraging parties were looting villages for food. The force fought the Karen levies, driving 33 ambush parties of the 'Hyena' mission into the hills. But in August 750 guerrillas held the Japanese at crossings of the Sitang river. This action enabled the RAF to bomb the concentrations of Japanese, before they could break eastward out of Burma. Other guerrillas had equally fierce engagements, the last a running battle from the end of July until 8 September. This fighting continued despite leaflets being dropped in August to tell the 3,000 Japanese that they had been ordered to surrender.

China—little was achieved here, apart from intelligence provided through the Nationalists' Institute of International Relations. Attempts to establish training teams for Chinese guerrillas, failed. Nor did 'Oblivion' get under way in 1943, when the American State Department objected to teams of Canadian Chinese having contacts with communists. But in November 1944 SOE officers from BAAG were joined by OSS teams in delaying a Japanese advance on the Kweilin airfield used by the 14th USAAF (the 'Flying Tigers'). The Canadians were sent to Malaya and all other plans for SOE operations in China were dropped. SOE, however, continued to buy silk-worm eggs despite their export being banned from China. The silk was required in India to make parachutes. The Americans were not told of these illegal deals but given to understand that all raw materials were being purchased by the very legal Ministry of Production. Such deceptions could only have contributed to misunderstandings and mistrust between the Allies.

IndoChina—French forces had remained loyal to Vichy, allowing 40,000 Japanese troops to be stationed in the colony by August 1941. Three Free French agents landed in July 1944 but British and American foreign policies prevented 1,200 Free French of the 5th Colonial Regiment being sent to IndoChina. By December, however, contact had been established with the army and other Frenchmen willing to form a guerrilla force. On 9 March, after the Japanese had invited many officers to various social functions, they murdered many men, women and children before taking over key installations in the colony. All 21 clandestine radio stations went off the air at this time. The French survivors fought off further Japanese attacks, as some 10,000 troops retreated towards the Chinese border. They also established contact with some 1,200 guerrillas supported in the north by SOE. Belatedly the Americans agreed to supply ammunition to the French—ironically the State Department had not wished to support colonial French forces in what became after 1954, Vietnam, Cambodia and Laos. The British sent in several 'Jedburgh' teams and SOE officers who in the last days of the war were joined by Ho Chi Minh. He claimed British approval of his role as a guerrilla leader. 5th Regiment did not land in IndoChina until three months after the war ended, on 4 November 1945.

Malaya—On 24 May 1943 John Davis returned by submarine to reach a formal agreement for SOE to train and supply communist regiments. Chang Hung who negotiated this agreement for the guerrillas was also working for the Japanese, which accounted for 'some of Davis' difficulties in establishing contact with India' before February 1945. 'Int' circuits had been set up since 1943 but with radio contact established, prompt reports from the 'Carpenter' circuit, for example, gave details of ship movements from Singapore; and in May 1945 19 Royal Marines brought in 8,000lb of stores to the circuit's main base on the east coast of South Johore. Soon afterwards, Chang Hung fled from Singapore taking the Communist Party's money.

One wireless game was played by SEAC's Deception Centre after one of SOE's Malayan teams became controlled by the Japanese. The game lasted from October 1944 until the end of the war, the agents at one time being flown by the Japanese from the east to the west coast when SEAC had decided to have them 'march' across Malaya. Forty-eight other clandestine radio stations were operating in the jungle. These enabled SOE to keep in contact with 5,000 communist guerrillas and bands of others also trained by SOE's 90 officers in the jungle. By the summer of 1945, these guerrillas were ready to support a British landing, but this did not take place until the September after the war was over.

Sumatra—this island, like other Dutch territories, was defended not only by Japanese but also by Indonesian forces armed by the Japanese. This was one reason, no doubt, why one reconnaissance by an SOE team and two by Dutch commandos produced no worthwhile contacts in 1942 and 1943. Nor did missions sent in the spring of 1944 have any success, but a permanent base was established by 28 June 1944 and two other teams were sent to provide coast-watching reports.

Thailand—the government continued to run the country after the Japanese landed in December 1941. OSS established contacts here as did SOE after some years of conflicting British and American foreign policies. By 1945 villagers were building jeep tracks, airstrips and making other preparations under the supervision of guerrilla officers trained by SOE and working with OSS agents in readiness for an Allied advance into the country from China. This was never made but the preparations had contributed to a SEAC deception which suggested that Thailand, and not Malaya, was the next country the Allies intended to liberate after Burma.

Other operations—SOE distributed 25,000 rifles and carbines, 60,000 grenades and 300 support weapons (light machine-guns, small mortars and PIATs), and nearly 30 tons of explosives to guerrilla forces in Burma, IndoChina and Malaya. SOE schools in India had trained 1,500 agents to use these weapons and other clandestine techniques. They, OSS, and uniformed special forces like the COPPs, V Force *et al* are estimated in the official history of SOE to have killed over 22,000 Japanese in the SEAC theatre. The casualties among European officers (excluding those of OSS) who fought with the guerrillas, were 53 killed, or who died on active service.

13 OSS in South-East Asia—after the arrival of OSS Force 101 staff in India in 1942, there were some delays before they could begin to establish a guerrilla force of Kachins. Then by December 1943, OSS teams like other clandestine forces in SEAC, required P Division's approval for missions, and were working to the command of the American general commanding the China-Burma-India theatre. The OSS advanced base at Kandy, 120km from Colombo in modern Sri Lanka, ran a five-week basic course followed by three weeks' jungle training for agents or other appropriate field training for

radio operators. By January 1945, 131 officers and 418 enlisted men were employed by SI and SO missions in Thailand, Burma, Malaya, Sumatra, IndoChina and the Andaman Islands, operating 47 clandestine radio stations, 25 of these provided weather reports from stations as far apart as Singapore and north-east Thailand. OSS also broadcast 'black' propaganda from Chittagong (in modern Bangladesh) and later from Rangoon in Burma. OSS main contribution in this theatre was in supplying 10,000 guerrillas who made their contribution to the deaths of 22,000 Japanese mentioned in note 12 above. Fifteen Americans and 184 guerrillas were killed in these operations.

14 The Motor Submersible Canoe (MSC) was the first surface-craft submersible of its type built for special operations, a number of craft being delivered to the Royal Marines in July 1943. When on the surface its low profile and half hp engine enabled it to approach a target area with much less chance of being seen, than a conventional canoe with paddles inevitably making some splash. The diver-pilot was able to submerge the canoe by pumping water into a small trim-tank in the bow. He then applied the hydroplanes linked to his joystick and moved the canoe gently forward under power. This lead to the ballast tanks filling to a pressure equal to that of the surrounding water, neutralizing the canoe's buoyancy. If the craft dived deeper than intended, as shown on the depth gauge, the pilot first used his hydrofoils. Their action could be supplemented if necessary by a little of the high pressure air the canoe carried to increase buoyancy in the ballast tanks. The air valves were controlled by a touch of the thumbs on two small tabs, to bring the canoe onto even keel some 10m below the surface. The pilot might porpoise the boat for a moment's glimpse of the target area as he approached it. A procedure in which the Marines of the RMBPD (the Cockleshell Heroes) were skilled, as they piloting their MSCs with such gentle movements that a seagull was unlikely to be disturbed when the canoe surfaced. A pilot was intended to enter an enemy harbour while submerged, negotiating any boom defence nets before coming under the hull of his target ship. He moored his craft—if that does not make the operation sound too simple—by using a magnetic clamp securing a line from the canoe to the ship's blige keel. He then left the canoe, his diving tanks supplying his air or oxygen while he placed his limpets on the enemy hull. He then returned to the canoe and edged it out of the harbour, with the boat remaining submerged until well clear of any coastwatching sentries or radar. There was always the risk that the canoe might be picked up on an enemy echo sounder, but its small size and tiny propeller probably made insufficient noise to attract Asdic searches of the 1940s. The pilot surfaced the canoe by gently raising the bow in response to the hydrofoils and 'blew' the tanks with a minimum of turbulence. The canoe then drained of water as she moved forward, using self bailers (these were two nozzles near the propeller which helped to suck water through the hollow keel, in turn connected to a special pumping-out valve). On the surface the pilot protected his cockpit with a canvas covering which sealed around his neck to keep the MSC cockpit dry. The canoe is said to have been named the 'Sleeping Beauty' after its inventor, who was seen by one of his staff in an early mock-up of the craft, his eyes closed as if asleep.

SELECT BIBLIOGRAPHY

Histories and Memoirs

ALVAR, Rutheral, *The Last Escape*. London, 1974

BROWN, A. C. (editor), *The Secret War Report of the OSS*. New York, 1976

BEESLEY, Patrick, *Very Special Intelligence*. London, 1977

BEEVOR, J. G., *SOE Recollections and Reflections*. London, 1981

BOWEN, J., *Undercover in the Jungle*. London, 1978

BURGESS, A., *Seven Men at Daybreak*. London, 1960

CHAPMAN, F. S., *The Jungle is Neutral*. London, 1979

COLBY, W. E., *Honourable Men*. New York, 1978

COWBURN, B., *No Cloak, No Dagger*. London, 1960

CRUICKSHANK, C., *SOE in the Far East*. Oxford, 1983

DRUMMOND, J., *But for these Men*. London, 1971

FARAGO, L., *The Game of Foxes*. New York, 1971

FOOT, M. R. D., *SOE in France*. London, 1979

— *Resistance*. London. 1976

— *SOE*. London, 1984

— and Langley J. M., *MI 9 Escape and Evasion 1939–45*. London, 1979

FOURCADE, M–M., *Noah's Ark*. London, 1973

GALLAGHER, T., *Assault in Norway*. London, 1975

GEORGE, W., *Surreptitious Entry*. San Francisco, 1946

GOLDSMITH, J., *Accidental Agent*. London, 1971

HAMPSHIRE, Cecil, *Secret Navies*. London, 1978

HAWES, S. *et al*, *Resistance in Europe 1939– 45*. London, 1973

HASWELL, J., *The Intelligence and Deceptions of the D-Day Landings*. London, 1979

HINSLEY, F. H., *British Intelligence in the Second World War*. London, 1979

HOWARTH, P., *Undercover*. London, 1980

IND, A., *Allied Intelligence Bureau*. New York, 1958

LADD, J. D., *Commandos and Rangers of World War II*. London, 1978

LORAIN, P., *Armemant Clandestin SOE France*. Paris, 1972

MACLEAN, F., *Eastern Approaches*. London, 1949

MARSHALL, B., *The White Rabbit*. London, 1952

MASTERMAN, *The Double-Cross System*. Yale, 1972

OLSEN, O. R., *Two Eggs on My Plate*. London, 1952

PAINE, L., *Mathilde Carre: Double Agent*. London, 1976

— *The Invisible World of Espionage*, London, 1976

PEARSON, M., *Tears of Glory*. London, 1978

POPOV, D., *Spy/Counter Spy*. London, 1974

PIEKALKIEWICZ, J., *Secret agents, Spies and Saboteurs*. Munich, 1969

SETH, R., *A Spy Has No Friends*. New York, 1972

SKIDMORE, I., *Marines Don't Tell*. London, 1981

SMITH, R. H., *OSS*. California, 1972

SOLA, R. de, *Microfilming*. New York, c 1942

STEVENSON, W., *A Man called Intrepid*. London, 1976

TICKELL, J., *Moon Squadron*. London, 1956

TOLLEY, K., *Cruise of the Laniki*. Anapolis, 1973

TROY, T. F., *Donovan and the CIA*. Aletheia, 1981

VERITY, H., *We Landed by Moonlight*. London, 1978

Articles and references

Britschem Sabotagematerial. Official German manual, 1942

BUERLEIN, R. A., *Allied Military Fighting Knives and the Men Who Made Them Famous*. Richmond Va, 1984

After the Battle. Nos 24, 25 and others. London, 1979

CIA Explosives for Sabotage. Official manual, late 1940s

Enemy Sabotage Equipment. Official manual. War Office, 1943

Englische Sabotageanweisungen. Official German manual, 1944

German Secret Services. Official manual, 1940–5

GLEESON, J., et al, *Midget Submarine*. New York, 1975

GUBBINS, C. McV., *Partisan Leaders Handbook*. Official manual, 1939

Journal of Camp X Society

MINNERY, J. B., *et al*, *American Tools of Intrigue*. Cornville, 1980

MINNERY, John, *How to Kill*. Privately published

OSS Special Weapons, Devices and Equipment. Official manual, 1945

OSS Weapons. Official manual, June 1944

MCLEAN, D. B., *The Plumbers Kitchen*, New York, 1975

OSS Sabotage and Demolition. Official manual, c 1944

STEPHENS, F. J., *Fighting Knives*. London, Melbourne, New York, Ontario, 1980

Technical Reviews for OSS. No 3

INDEX

(References to pages that include illustrations are in **bold** type.)